Instructor's Guide, Volume 2
(Chapters 6–12)

Statistics in Action

UNDERSTANDING A WORLD OF DATA

Ann E. Watkins
Richard L. Scheaffer
George W. Cobb

Key Curriculum Press
Innovators in Mathematics Education

Consulting Editors	Christian Aviles-Scott, Cindy Clements
Editors	Anna Werner, Mary Jo Cittadino
Project Administrator	Kristin Burke
Editorial Assistants	Heather Dever, Michael Hyett
Teacher Consultant	Jim Bohan, Manheim Township School District, Lancaster, Pennsylvania
Mathematics Reviewer	Mary Parker, Austin Community College, Austin, Texas
AP Instructor Reviewers	Angelo DeMattia, Columbia High School, Maplewood, New Jersey
	Beth Fox-McManus, formerly of Alan C. Pope High School, Marietta, Georgia
	Dan Johnson, Silver Creek High School, San Jose, California
Accuracy Checkers	Monica Johnston, Christopher Sollars
Editorial Production Manager	Deborah Cogan
Production Editor	Jacqueline Gamble
Production Director	Diana Jean Ray
Production Coordinator	Charice Silverman
Text Designer	Monotype Composition
Compositor	The Cowans
Art Editor	Laura Murray
Technical Artist	Matt Perry
Technical Art Consultant	Brett Garrett
Art and Design Coordinator	Kavitha Becker
Cover Designer	Greg Dundis
Cover Photo Credit	*top:* Strauss-Curtis/Corbis; *center left:* Hulton Deutsch Collection/Corbis; *center right:* Tom Nebbia/Corbis; *bottom:* Bettman/Corbis
Prepress and Printer	Data Reproductions
Executive Editor	Casey FitzSimons
Textbook Product Manager	Fred Duncan
Publisher	Steven Rasmussen

Key Curriculum Press
1150 65th Street
Emeryville, CA 94608
510-595-7000
editorial@keypress.com
http://www.keypress.com

Printed in the United States of America
10 9 8 7 6 5 4 3 2   07 06 05   ISBN: 1-55953-334-X

Acknowledgments

Statistics in Action: Understanding a World of Data is designed for an introductory statistics course—either an introductory college course or its high school equivalent, Advanced Placement Statistics—and includes all of the standard topics for that course. The authors have field-tested the ideas and activities of *Statistics in Action* in their own college courses since 1997 and have utilized this material since it developed into a workable manuscript.

Many statisticians and teachers have been actively involved in helping the introductory statistics course evolve into one that emphasizes activity-based learning of statistical concepts, while reflecting modern statistical practice. *Statistics in Action* is a product of what the authors have learned from these statisticians and teachers. This book is written in the spirit of the recommendations from the Mathematical Association of America's STATS project and Focus Group on Statistics, the American Statistical Association's Quantitative Literacy projects, the College Board's AP Statistics course, and these AP Statistics field testers:

Jim Bohan, Manheim Township School District, Lancaster, Pennsylvania

Monica Brogan, Gloucester High School, Gloucester, Virginia

Gretchen Davis, Santa Monica High School, Santa Monica, California

Sheila Davis, Alan C. Pope High School, Marietta, Georgia

Angelo DeMattia, Columbia High School, Maplewood, New Jersey

Beth Fox-McManus, formerly of Alan C. Pope High School, Marietta, Georgia

Katherine France, Niles North High School, Skokie, Illinois

Will Frazer, Buchholz High School, Gainesville, Florida

Richard Fulton, Deerfield Beach High School, Deerfield Beach, Florida

Alaine Gorfinkle, Ramaz Upper School, New York, New York

Michelle Greene, Lamar High School, Lamar, South Carolina

Jeanette Hart, Melbourne High School, Melbourne, Florida

Philip Hogarth, The Webb Schools, Claremont, California

Dan Johnson, Silver Creek High School, San Jose, California

Pat Johnson, New Trier High School, Winnetka, Illinois

Allan King, Andrew Hill High School, San Jose, California

Sia Lux, Coachella Valley High School, Thermal, California

Padma Maui, Andrew Hill High School, San Jose, California

Mark Mavis, Pleasant Valley High School, Chico, California

Leona Mirza, North Park University, Chicago, Illinois

Valerie Muller, Eastside High School, Taylors, South Carolina

Lauren Nobles, Conway High School, Conway, South Carolina

Jennifer North Morris, West Hills High School, Santee, California

Robert Palma, Columbia High School, Maplewood, New Jersey

Diane Pors, East Side Union High School, San Jose, California

Karen Riggs, Lake Region High School, Eagle Lake, Florida

Murray Siegel, J. L. Mann High School, Greenville, South Carolina

Frank Steinhart, North Park University, Chicago, Illinois

William Stevens, Summerville High School, Summerville, South Carolina

Kathleen Strange, West Hills High School, Santee, California

Josh Tabor, Wilson High School, Hacienda Heights, California

David Thiel, Green Valley High School, Henderson, Nevada

Chris Tsuji, Santa Teresa High School, San Jose, California

Mark Vosskamp, North Cross School, Roanoke, Virginia

Susan Wallis, Terry Parker High School, Jacksonville, Florida

Jack Welc, Mt. Pleasant High School, San Jose, California

Joy Williams, Riverside High School, Greer, South Carolina

Hyman Yip, Independence High School, San Jose, California

Contents

Teaching with *Statistics in Action*

Producing and analyzing data require action on the part of the statistician. *Statistics in Action: Understanding a World of Data* helps you, the teacher, bring that action into the classroom so that your students can learn the concepts and tools of statistics in much the same way that it is practiced in the field. *Statistics in Action* will help you turn your classroom into a statistics laboratory where students will "learn by doing." Together you will work to discover the fundamental logic of statistics and why it is essential to the quantitative thinking required in the modern world. As a by-product, your students will be well prepared if they are taking the Advanced Placement Statistics examination.

We've designed *Statistics in Action: Understanding a World of Data* to help you accomplish two objectives. Your students will

- learn the fundamental logic and tools of statistics
- learn about the actual practice of statistics in real-world situations

Statistics in Action is built around activities, discussion questions, practice problems, and exercises. Simply reading the textbook will not be sufficient. Most activities are to be done in class or in a lab period so that students will have the opportunity to think critically about how data is collected and analyzed, and to articulate issues about basic statistical concepts. Discussion questions foster further debate over important issues among the whole class. Your close guidance is indispensable—you'll help your students stay on track, add emphasis to their discoveries, and clarify, focus, and connect the ideas they accumulate.

You may find that you'll follow the textbook quite closely. We have designed *Statistics in Action* much like a protocol for analysis, if not exactly as a script for teaching class sessions. If you guide your class through the material sequentially, doing the activities and addressing discussion questions in order, you'll find that your students will learn the important concepts in ways that foster understanding. They will adopt a healthy skepticism concerning data analysis (much the way that professionals do), and cultivate an interest and self-motivation for further study. In short, they will get caught up in the action!

Here's how you might proceed through a section of *Statistics in Action.*

Preparation

This *Statistics in Action Instructor's Guide* consists of two volumes. Volume 1 includes Chapters 1 through 5; Chapters 6 through 12 appear in Volume 2. Each chapter of this *Instructor's Guide* opens with an overview that highlights the goals and content to be mastered. The overview is followed by suggested time schedules, a list of materials needed, and suggested classwork and homework assignments. At the beginning of each section more specific objectives are listed, along with a list of the important terms and concepts introduced in that section. The suggested class time for the section, materials needed (if any), and suggested assignments for the section follow. In addition, in each section you will find extensive teacher's notes giving you additional information about the topics presented in the student text. For example, in Chapter 2 (in the *Instructor's Guide,* Volume 1) you will find extensive notes on why we typically use the standard deviation as the measure of spread.

Introduction and Activity

After you introduce the lesson, typically you will begin each section with an activity in which students work with partners or in small groups. (A few activities can be assigned as individual homework with class discussion in the following class session.) Students work through the activity while you circulate around the room and elicit answers to all the questions it poses. As work on the activity concludes, you'll be checking with each group to make sure that the students have answered the questions correctly or sensibly. Finally, you might pose a general question to the whole class that elicits the concept the activity was designed to introduce.

Notes for the activities in this *Instructor's Guide* offer practical step-by-step guidelines for moving through the activity, and present clear and realistic answers supported by plots and computer-generated data. As with all the notes in this *Instructor's Guide*, the activity notes are designed to provide a unique, in-depth focus on the statistical language being explored and the complexities behind the vocabulary of the lesson. Doing the activities aligns both the AP Statistics course and the college course with the goal of active engagement of the students in their learning, and helps students develop a powerful quantitative perspective.

Text

The activity leads to expository material that you usually will present to the class, describing the concepts and techniques and working through examples. Occasionally, you'll assign students to read the material on their own—and we've made every effort to make it lively reading—but you'll want to be sure that they understand when a rule must be used, what its exceptions are, and how to tell when a computation or a logical step has likely gone wrong.

Increasingly, students have had to read in their mathematics and statistics classes. Because of this greater emphasis on independent reading and research, we have tried to engage the student with clear text and attractive graphics. Still, there is a great reliance on you, the instructor, to present, explain, and emphasize; in this *Instructor's Guide,* you will find many lesson notes to aid your own understanding of the subject matter.

However you decide to implement the expository material, you'll always want to structure your time so your students have the opportunity to work on all of the essential and recommended discussion and practice questions.

Discussion Questions

Discussion questions occur periodically after text material. Because they often are open-ended, with no clear-cut "best" answer, they are meant for whole-class discussion. Many questions probe quite deeply into the concepts underlying the topic being discussed. Your guidance will be necessary. It is in these group discussions that students develop their instincts, support their reasoning, field challenges, and offer creative ideas. Sometimes you can precede a whole-class discussion by small-group discussions that go on while you circulate among the groups, giving hints or posing stepwise queries to be sure all groups are on track.

You won't usually want students to write out the answers to discussion questions: That would become tedious for both you and your students, and it might impede the dynamic exchange of views and easy reevaluation of an individual's position on an issue. However, most students will want to take notes because the answers to discussion questions do not appear in the back of the student book. Occasionally, you can have students write out a summary of the discussion to be sure that they understand the idea discussed.

This *Instructor's Guide*, Volume 2, includes a full solution for each discussion question in Chapters 6 through 12.

Practice Problems

Practice problems occur at intervals in the text for you to check that each student understands the preceding material. Students typically should work the assigned practice questions independently, either as an assignment or in class, as they encounter them while reading. We have designed the questions to solidify student skills and boost student confidence. These questions do not introduce new material or rely on complex scenarios, but we consider them important nonetheless: They are an opportunity for students to "digest" what they have done or read, and to make sure they are ready before going on.

Brief answers to practice questions (but not full solutions or graphics) are in the back of the student book; complete solutions—including graphics—for all practice questions in Chapters 6 through 12 are provided in this *Instructor's Guide*, Volume 2.

Exercises

A set of exercises appears at the end of each section. Typically, exercises are done at home as individual assignments, although you can assign some of the more difficult questions as collaborative work. Brief answers to most odd exercises are in the back of the student book, while fully detailed solutions to exercises in Chapters 6 through 12 are provided in this *Instructor's Guide*, Volume 2.

Technology

Students should, at a minimum, have access to a graphing calculator with statistics capabilities in order to carry out routine computations, create graphical displays, and perform some analyses. Your students should also learn to read a standard computer printout. To help students acquire this ability, a variety of program printouts—including Fathom, Minitab, Data Desk, and JMP-IN—are explained in greater detail in the student book and detailed in this *Instructor's Guide*. However, be sure that students can set up and conduct small-scale simulations without the use of a calculator or computer.

Reviewing for Exams

The *Statistics in Action* student book includes many features to aid students in self-guided review. Important vocabulary is indicated in boldface type and important concepts and theorems appear in boxes. We have also given special attention to the appearance of examples, so that they are visually easy to follow, and conceptual steps are clearly linked. Margin notes direct students to key ideas for review, as well as help to retain their attention during a first reading. Summaries are comprehensive; every summary uses important terms in full sentences, linking them to prior learning and to concepts under development.

There are more review problems in the student book than you will want to assign. You can use the remaining ones as a review for the course final examination or for the AP Statistics exam. In this *Instructor's Guide* you will find a chart at the end of each section which suggests essential, recommended, and optional review exercises for students to use as practice before exams.

The Joy of Teaching Statistics

We hope that you enjoy teaching statistics as much as we do. You will never have to ask yourself, "Do my students really need to know this?" Much of the progress of the last century, both in basic scientific research and in applied fields like agriculture, medicine, and industry, was progress guided and propelled by statistical thinking. Your students will come to realize this as the course progresses. As one of our own students said, "After taking your statistics class, I will never see the world in quite the same way again. Now everywhere I look, I see chance and variation."

Ann E. Watkins
Richard L. Scheaffer
George W. Cobb

6

PROBABILITY MODELS

Overview

Samples must be selected randomly in order for a statistic, like a sample mean, to have a known sampling distribution of potential values. Randomness allows you to predict the future to some degree because randomness actually produces patterns in the long run. Statistical conclusions are based on whether or not a particular outcome of a survey or an experiment agrees with what randomness suggests the outcome should look like.

This chapter begins the development of a set of definitions and rules for calculating the probabilities of random events. The next chapter builds on these rules to describe some common probability distributions, including the binomial and geometric.

Goals

The primary goals of this chapter are to provide students with the ability

- to build a reasonable probability model for a simple situation based on either data or symmetry (equally likely) arguments
- to see how the Law of Large Numbers relates data to probability
- to understand the general Addition Rule for probability and how it simplifies when events are mutually exclusive
- to understand and calculate conditional probabilities for discrete events
- to understand the general Multiplication Rule for probability and how it simplifies when events are independent

Students must acquire some facility with the Addition and Multiplication Rules, but they need to know very little about counting rules.

Content Overview

The basic definitions and rules for calculating the probabilities of events made up with "ands" and "ors" are illustrated with simple discrete scenarios in which students can easily count outcomes. The emphasis is on understanding the probability, not on using clever counting rules. Simulation is an excellent tool to aid the student's understanding of this material, and most of the examples and exercises involve situations that can be simulated easily.

Many examples used in the chapter make use of sampling concepts introduced in Chapters 4 and 5, such as sampling with and without replacement and how the latter is essentially equivalent to the former if the population is large compared to the sample. Those concepts can be used to motivate probability, which in turn forms a bridge to the statistical inference topics that come later.

Reasonable probability models may be built using either observed data or symmetry (equally likely) arguments, or some combination of the two. The assumptions of "equally likely" and "independent" are often used in building probability models. These assumptions are used because they yield simple models that often fit real data reasonably well. However, the only way to determine whether the assumptions are reasonable is to compare actual data with predictions made by the model. In the final analysis, our probability models should tell us something useful about the world around us.

Time Required

Traditional Schedule			Block	4 x 4 Block
Section 6.1				
2 days	Day 1	Overview, fundamental facts about probability, sample spaces, data and symmetry	2 days	1 long, 1 short
	Day 2	Activity 6.1, Law of Large Numbers, Fundamental Principle of Counting, summary, exercises		
Section 6.2				
2 days	Day 1	Overview, Addition Rule for Disjoint Events	2 days	1 long, 1 short
	Day 2	Activity 6.2, Addition Rule (general), Activity 6.3, summary, exercises		
Section 6.3				
2–3 days	Day 1	Overview, conditional probability from the sample space	3 days	2 long, 1 short
	Day 2	Multiplication Rule, definition of conditional probability		
	Day 3	Conditional probability and medical tests, conditional probability and statistical inference, summary, exercises		
Section 6.4				
2–3 days	Day 1	Definition of independent events, Multiplication Rule for Independent Events	2 days	1 long, 1 short
	Day 2	Activity 6.4, independence with real data, Mendel		
	Day 3	Summary, exercises		
Review				
1 day			1 day	1 long

If students already have some experience with probability and have mastered Chapter 5, this chapter should proceed fairly smoothly and quickly. Covering the chapter should take about eight to ten class periods, perhaps two class periods for each of the four sections with the possibility of using three class periods on each of Sections 6.3 and 6.4. This timeframe includes covering most of the discussions in class and requiring students to work through the practice problems and a selection of the exercises on their own time.

Materials

Section 6.1: For Activity 6.1, one penny for each student

Section 6.2: For Activities 6.2 and 6.3, a pencil and a sheet of paper for each student

Section 6.3: None

Section 6.4: For Activity 6.4, one penny for each student

Suggested Assignments

Classwork			
Section	**Essential**	**Recommended**	**Optional**
6.1	D1–D8, D11, D12 P1–P3, P5–P7	Activity 6.1 D9, D10	P4
6.2	Activity 6.2, Activity 6.3 D14–D22 P8, P9, P11, P12	D13 P10	
6.3	D23–D27, D29 P13–P19	D30–D33 P20, P21	D28
6.4	Activity 6.4 D34–D36 P22–P24	D37, D38 P25	

Homework			
Section	**Essential**	**Recommended**	**Optional**
6.1	E1, E2, E4, E5, E8	E3, E6, E7, E9	E10
6.2	E11–E18	E19, E20	
6.3	E21–E30	E31, E32	E33, E34
6.4	E35–E40, E43, E45	E41, E44, E46	E42, E47
Review	E48–E51, E54, E55, E57, E64	E52, E53, E61	E56, E58–E60, E62, E63

6.1 Sample Spaces with Equally Likely Outcomes

Objectives

- to learn to build probability models by observing data, with justification provided by the Law of Large Numbers
- to learn to build probability models by constructing a sample space of equally likely outcomes (symmetry)

Important Terms and Concepts

- probability model
- probability distribution
- sample space
- complete outcomes in a sample space
- disjoint (mutually exclusive) outcomes in a sample space
- equally likely outcomes
- Law of Large Numbers
- Fundamental Principle of Counting

Lesson Planning

Class Time

Two days. For students with some experience in probability, the essentials could be covered in one class period.

Materials

For Activity 6.1, one penny for each student

Suggested Assignments

Classwork		
Essential	**Recommended**	**Optional**
D1–D8, D11, D12	Activity 6.1	P4
P1–P3, P5–P7	D9, D10	

Homework		
Essential	**Recommended**	**Optional**
E1, E2, E4, E5, E8	E3, E6, E7, E9	E10

Lesson Notes: Probability Distributions

Discussion

D1. Jack's probability distribution for $n = 2$:

Number Who Choose T	Probability
0	1/3
1	1/3
2	1/3

D2. The sum of the probabilities must be 1 because the distribution includes all possible outcomes for a random process.

D3. Jill is correct; Jack forgot to account for the fact that there are two ways that one T and one B can occur, namely TB and BT.

D4. You could simulate the situation by flipping two distinct coins, perhaps a penny and a nickel, with *heads* $= B$ and *tails* $= T$. Flip the two coins many times and count the outcomes, {BB, BT, TB, TT}. Decide whether the proportions of times the outcomes occur are closer to Jack's or closer to Jill's.

Lesson Notes: Where Do Probabilities Come From?

There Is No Such Thing As an Unfair Flipped Coin

In Activity 6.1, students learn that a coin that is spun doesn't have equal probabilities of landing heads and tails. That is, spinning a coin isn't a "fair" process.

In other places, for pedagogical purposes, the idea of an unfair flipped coin is used. See, for example, page 334 in the student text, where a flipped coin is said to have a probability of .4 of coming up heads. In fact, if a coin is flipped so that it spins many times in the air and is caught at a random spot, the probability of heads is always .5, no matter how you try to weight the coin. That is, it is impossible to weight a coin so that when you flip it and catch it at a random spot in the air, the probability it comes up heads is different from $\frac{1}{2}$. You can change the coin's center of gravity, but according to the Law of Conservation of Angular Momentum, a coin spins at a nearly constant rate about the new center of gravity, slowing down slightly only because of air resistance. That means that as a thin coin spins in the air, half of the time heads are up and half of the time tails are up. The following article gives excellent ideas for classroom activities that illustrate this principle.

Andrew Gelman and Deborah Nolan, "You Can Load a Die, But You Can't Bias a Coin," *The American Statistician* 56, no. 4 (November 2002): 308–311.

Practice

P1. Listing of all possible outcomes:

First Person	Second Person	Third Person	Fourth Person	Number of T's
T	T	T	T	4
T	T	T	B	3
T	T	B	T	3
T	B	T	T	3
B	T	T	T	3
T	T	B	B	2
T	B	T	B	2
T	B	B	T	2
B	T	T	B	2
B	T	B	T	2
B	B	T	T	2
T	B	B	B	1
B	T	B	B	1
B	B	T	B	1
B	B	B	T	1
B	B	B	B	0

Probability distribution of the number who chose T:

Number Who Choose T	Probability
0	1/16
1	4/16
2	6/16
3	4/16
4	1/16

There is only a $\frac{1}{16} = .0625$ chance of everyone choosing correctly by guessing. Therefore, this outcome is not very likely to happen by chance, but Jack still may want a larger sample size to be more sure of protecting the image of Downhill Research.

Lesson Notes: Sample Spaces

Discussion

D5. The outcomes are complete and disjoint. They are not equally likely because the event *first flip is tails* occurs more often than either of the other two in a sequence of two coin flips.

D6. The list {has at least one English book, has at least one math book, has at least one other type of book, has no books} is complete but not disjoint because some students will fall into more than one category.

The set {has at least one math book, has no books} is disjoint but probably not complete because students carry other kinds of books.

Practice

P2. The list is complete but not disjoint because *heads on second flip* and *heads on first flip* can happen in the same pair of flips. No, the event *heads on second flip* has the same probability $\left(\frac{1}{2}\right)$ as *heads on first flip*, but both are more likely than *heads on neither flip*, which has probability $\frac{1}{4}$.

No. The probability of getting at least one head is $\frac{3}{4}$, but d'Alembert's sample space gives $\frac{2}{3}$.

P3. The 10 disjoint outcomes are {(28, 35), (28, 41), (28, 47), (28, 55), (35, 41), (35, 47), (35, 55), (41, 47), (41, 55), (47, 55)}. The probability that the two youngest people are the ones laid off is $\frac{1}{10}$.

P4. This problem is like P1. The list of outcomes:

First Flip	Second Flip	Third Flip	Fourth Flip	Number of Heads
H	H	H	H	4
H	H	H	T	3
H	H	T	H	3
H	T	H	H	3
T	H	H	H	3
H	H	T	T	2
H	T	H	T	2
H	T	T	H	2
T	H	H	T	2
T	H	T	H	2
T	T	H	H	2
H	T	T	T	1
T	H	T	T	1

(continued)

(continued)

First Flip	Second Flip	Third Flip	Fourth Flip	Number of Heads
T	T	H	T	1
T	T	T	H	1
T	T	T	T	0

The probability distribution of the number of heads:

Number of Heads	Probability
0	1/16
1	4/16
2	6/16
3	4/16
4	1/16

The probability of getting exactly two heads is $\frac{6}{16}$.

P5. The 36 outcomes for the roll of two dice:

		Second Roll					
		1	2	3	4	5	6
	1	1, 1	1, 2	1, 3	1, 4	1, 5	1, 6
	2	2, 1	2, 2	2, 3	2, 4	2, 5	2, 6
First	3	3, 1	3, 2	3, 3	3, 4	3, 5	3, 6
Roll	4	4, 1	4, 2	4, 3	4, 4	4, 5	4, 6
	5	5, 1	5, 2	5, 3	5, 4	5, 5	5, 6
	6	6, 1	6, 2	6, 3	6, 4	6, 5	6, 6

The probability distribution for the sum of two dice:

Sum of Two Dice	Probability
2	1/36
3	2/36
4	3/36
5	4/36
6	5/36
7	6/36
8	5/36
9	4/36
10	3/36
11	2/36
12	1/36

The probability of obtaining a sum of 7 is $\frac{6}{36}$, or $\frac{1}{6}$.

Lesson Notes: Data and Symmetry

Activity 6.1: Spinning Pennies

This activity is highly recommended because it demonstrates to the student the need for data when the "equally likely" principle lets them down. When pennies are spun rather than flipped, the data often support a model that has something other than $\frac{1}{2}$ for the probability of heads. The probability of getting a head by spinning seems to be related to the year in which the pennies were minted. For example, 1990 pennies have a probability of around .4 for heads, whereas 1961 pennies have a probability of only about .1 for heads. So, in step 2 the proportion of heads will largely depend on the ages of your classes' collection of pennies. However, most likely, the proportion of heads will be less than .5, which is not what the students expect. Whether your students will reject the model that spinning a penny is fair will largely depend on how far the proportion is from .5. (Students will learn a formal test for rejection in Chapter 8.)

Discussion

D7. **a.** There are eight possible outcomes. (The sample space would look like Jack's eight outcomes on page 330 in the student text.)
b. If the probability of a head is different from .5, then the outcomes are not equally likely. If the probability of getting a head is less than .5, then three tails would be most likely and three heads would be least likely.

D8. The sample space would look like the 16 outcomes in P4, with H representing being right-handed and T representing being left-handed. You can not determine the probability without additional information about the percentage of students in the school who are right-handed.

Lesson Notes: The Law of Large Numbers

Sample Paths in Random Sampling

The following display shows ten different sample paths for the same situation described on page 334 in the student text. Each path plots the cumulative proportion of successes as the sample size increases from 1 to 150. The sample paths are widely spread out when there have been few flips, but all but one lie close to .4 as the number of flips approaches 150.

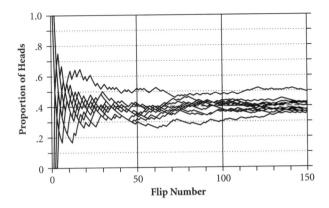

Misinterpreting the Law of Large Numbers

If the probability model is correct, the Law of Large Numbers guarantees that the sample relative frequencies will converge to the probabilities specified by the model as the sample size increases, so long as the trials are independent.

The Law of Large Numbers is often interpreted as a "law of small numbers" because people think that outcomes will "even out" after just a small number of trials. This way of thinking can be seen in statements like the following, which you may want to add to your class discussion:

- A baseball batter is "hitting 300," which means that he hits successfully about 30% of the times he comes to bat. An announcer remarks, "He has not had a hit in his last five trips to bat; he is due to get a hit this time."

- A student playing monopoly says, "I have not rolled doubles on the last six rolls; I am due for doubles."

The 300 hitter may eventually end up with about 30% hits, but it may not happen in any one game or series of games. The dice will eventually come up doubles, but the probability remains $\frac{1}{6}$ on each roll no matter what has happened before. Both people are ignoring the fact that any one particular random trial is just that—random.

Discussion

D9. The pollster is correct—but only if the sampling is done randomly. Then the Law of Large Numbers practically guarantees that in large samples the sample proportions will be close to the corresponding population proportions.

The casino operator is correct because the machines and games have a chance mechanism built in, and the probability of the house winning is always greater than .5. If many people play, the Law of Large Numbers takes over and the house is practically guaranteed to make money.

The manufacturer is wrong. Increasing the volume will increase the number of good products produced, as well as the number of defectives, but increasing the volume alone will not change the proportion of defectives (unless it results in sloppy workmanship by rushed workers). With machinery, the fraction of defectives should converge to a constant that represents the machine's true probability of producing a defective product.

D10. The plots at the bottom of the page show the cumulative counts and the cumulative proportions for five sets of 20 flips each. As the number of flips increases, the counts of heads diverge while the proportions of heads converge. (Convergence is not strongly apparent, however, for samples of only 20.) The fact that sample proportions (and sample means) converge to a constant makes them quite useful as estimators of population quantities.

Lesson Notes: The Fundamental Principle of Counting

The Fundamental Principle of Counting is used in counting the number of equally likely outcomes.

Discussion

D11. There are 4 · 4 · 4 · 4, or 256, possible outcomes (the first cola, the second cola, the third cola, can't tell). The equally likely model is not a good one in this case because there is no reason to believe that the four choices are equally likely.

D12. **a.** There are 2 · 2 · 2 · 2 · 2, or 32, possible outcomes.

b. There is only one way to get five heads, so the probability is $\frac{1}{32}$.

c. There are exactly five ways to get four heads and one tail (the tail could occur on any one of the five flips), so the probability is $\frac{5}{32}$.

Practice

P6.

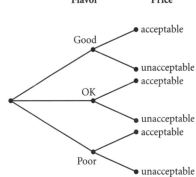

The equally likely outcome model is not reasonable because there is no reason to believe that the choices are equally likely for either flavor or price.

P7. There are 3 · 7, or 21, different pairs of dentists and dental hygienists that you could end up with. The probability of getting your

---

Lesson 6.1, D10

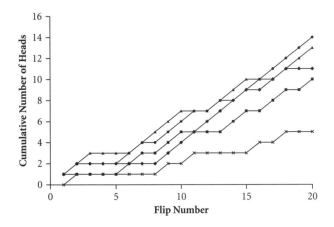

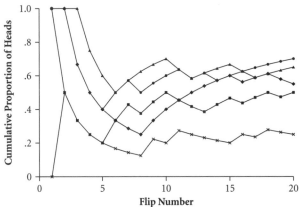

favorite pair is $\frac{1}{21}$. The following area model illustrates this situation.

Dentist

	A	B	C
a	aA	aB	aC
b	bA	bB	bC
c	cA	cB	cC
d	dA	dB	dC
e	eA	eB	eC
f	fA	fB	fC
g	gA	gB	gC

Hygienist (label to the left of rows a–g)

Exercises

E1.

Number of Heads	Probability
0	1/32
1	5/32
2	10/32
3	10/32
4	5/32
5	1/32

E2.   **a.** $\frac{30}{36}$ **b.** $\frac{4}{36}$
   c. $\frac{8}{36}$ **d.** $\frac{6}{36}$
   e. $\frac{11}{36}$ **f.** $\frac{1}{36}$
   g. $\frac{9}{36}$ **h.** $\frac{3}{36}$
   i. $\frac{2}{36}$; these outcomes are $(6, 1)$ and $(1, 6)$.

E3.   **a.**   Yes, there is. If both foods are the same, then the taste testers are choosing essentially at random. That implies that the chance of preferring food A to food B should be .5. As you will see later, this model forms the basis for deciding whether or not the data from a preference test supports the hypothesis that there is no difference in taste. (This assumes the foods are offered in random order and presented identically.)
   b.   No, there is not. Just because there are two possible outcomes does not mean they are equally likely. (Consider, for example, the two outcomes *wins the lottery* and *doesn't win the lottery*.) If you do not know from data what percentage of math majors are women, there is no way to argue that it is .5.

E4.   **a.**   There are 2^6, or 64, equally likely outcomes; the probability of getting heads all six times is $\frac{1}{64}$.

b.   There are $6 \cdot 6 \cdot 6 \cdot 6 \cdot 6 \cdot 6$, or 46,656, equally likely outcomes; the probability of getting a 3 all six times is $\frac{1}{46,656}$.
c.   No. There are two choices for each person (school, no school) and so 2^6, or 64, possible outcomes. They are not equally likely (far fewer people are in school than are out of school), so you cannot find the probability without further information.

E5.   **a.**   Six different backgrounds and four different types give $6 \cdot 4$, or 24, possible treatments.

b.

Back-ground	Type			
	Brown	**Black**	**Navy**	**Gray**
Blue	Blue, Brown	Blue, Black	Blue, Navy	Blue, Gray
Green	Green, Brown	Green, Black	Green, Navy	Green, Gray
Red	Red, Brown	Red, Black	Red, Navy	Red, Gray
Yellow	Yellow, Brown	Yellow, Black	Yellow, Navy	Yellow, Gray
White	White, Brown	White, Black	White, Navy	White, Gray
Beige	Beige, Brown	Beige, Black	Beige, Navy	Beige, Gray

c. With two levels of brightness added, the number of possible treatments is now 6 · 4 · 2, or 48.

d.

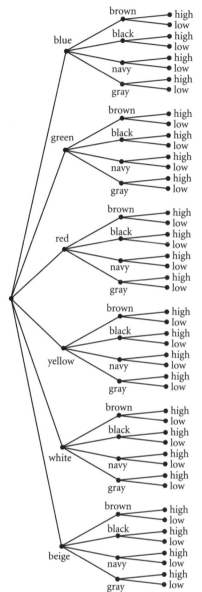

E6. The probability of getting exactly 3 heads is $\frac{4}{16}$.

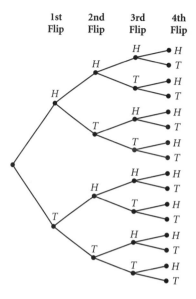

E7. **a.** 6 · 4, or 24

b. See the table at the bottom of page.

c. $P(a\ white\ shirt) = \frac{8}{24}, \frac{2}{6}$ or $\frac{1}{3}$
$P(the\ gray\ pants) = \frac{6}{24}$, or $\frac{1}{4}$
$P(a\ white\ shirt$ and $the\ gray\ pants) = \frac{2}{24}$, or $\frac{1}{12}$
$P(a\ white\ shirt$ or $the\ gray\ pants) = \frac{12}{24}$, or $\frac{1}{2}$

E8. **a.** 4 · 4, or 16

b.

		Second Roll			
		1	**2**	**3**	**4**
First Roll	**1**	1, 1	1, 2	1, 3	1, 4
	2	2, 1	2, 2	2, 3	2, 4
	3	3, 1	3, 2	3, 3	3, 4
	4	4, 1	4, 2	4, 3	4, 4

Lesson 6.1, E7b

		Shirts					
		Blue	**Green**	**Red**	**Yellow**	**White (Long)**	**White (Short)**
Pants	**Brown**	Brown, Blue	Brown, Green	Brown, Red	Brown, Yellow	Brown, White (Long)	Brown, White (Short)
	Black	Black, Blue	Black, Green	Black, Red	Black, Yellow	Black, White (Long)	Black, White (Short)
	Blue	Blue, Blue	Blue, Green	Blue, Red	Blue, Yellow	Blue, White (Long)	Blue, White (Short)
	Gray	Gray, Blue	Gray, Green	Gray, Red	Gray, Yellow	Gray, White (Long)	Gray, White (Short)

c. $\frac{4}{16}$ **d.** $\frac{1}{16}$ **e.** $\frac{3}{16}$

f. $\frac{5}{16}$ **g.** $\frac{4}{16}$ **h.** $\frac{7}{16}$

E9. a. Disjoint and complete; the probabilities for 0, 1, and 2 fours are $\frac{9}{16}$, $\frac{6}{16}$, and $\frac{1}{16}$, respectively.

b. Not disjoint but complete; *the first roll is a four* and *the second roll is a four* can occur on the same pair of rolls.

c. Disjoint but not complete; only outcomes with fours are included.

d. Disjoint but not complete; *the sum equal to 2* is not included.

e. Disjoint but not complete; *the second die is a four* is not included.

E10. The number of three-digit numbers is $3 \cdot 3 \cdot 3$, or 27. The number of outcomes less than 250 include all those that start with 1 and all those that start with 21 and 22. If the number starts with 1, there are 3 numbers to pick from for the second digit and 3 for the third digit, so there are $3 \cdot 3$, or 9, three-digit numbers that start with 1. If the number starts with 21 it can end with 1, 2, or 7. The same is true if the number starts with 22. So there are 6 three-digit numbers that start with 21 or 22. Therefore, the probability is $\frac{15}{27}$.

6.2 The Addition Rule and Disjoint Events

Objectives

- to learn that "or" has a special and specific meaning in probability, always carrying the connotation of "one or the other or both"
- to learn how to write events as collections of disjoint events connected by "or"
- to learn how to use the Addition Rule for Disjoint Events
- to learn how to use the general Addition Rule for any two events

Important Terms and Concepts

- disjoint events
- Addition Rule for Disjoint Events
- general Addition Rule

Time Required

Class Time

Two days. Students experienced with probability may require one day.

Materials

For Activities 6.2 and 6.3, a pencil and a sheet of paper for each student

Suggested Assignments

Classwork		
Essential	**Recommended**	**Optional**
Activity 6.2, Activity 6.3	D13	
D14–D22	P10	
P8, P9, P11, P12		

Homework		
Essential	**Recommended**	**Optional**
E11–E18	E19, E20	

Lesson Notes: *A or B*

Discussion

D13. The categories are complete for all types of fishing because they cover all possible fishing sites, but they are not disjoint. Some people fish in both salt water and freshwater, and some fish in both the Great Lakes and in other freshwater outside of the Great Lakes.

D14. Freshwater or salt water covers all the categories, so the probability must be 1. There are $(31,041 + 8,885) - 35,578$, or 4,348 thousands of people who fish in both freshwater and salt water. They are the people counted twice when you add people who fish in freshwater and people who fish in salt water.

Here is how the table breaks down:

Total Fishing in thousands (given)	35,578
Fresh and salt water: $(31,041 + 8,885) - 35,578$	4,348
Freshwater alone: $31,041 - 4,348$	26,693
Salt water alone: $8,885 - 4,348$	4,537

Total Freshwater in thousands (given)	31,041
Great Lakes and other: $(30,186 + 2,552) - 31,041$	1,697
Other than Great Lakes alone: $31,041 - 2,552$	28,489
Great Lakes alone: $31,041 - 30,186$	855

D15. First, the categories of *all freshwater fishing* and *saltwater fishing* overlap and should be divided into disjoint categories. Second, within freshwater fishing the categories should be recast into groups that are disjoint. (See the preceding table.) Now, the probability questions can be answered.

a. $P(freshwater \ alone \ or \ salt \ water \ alone) = \frac{26,693 + 4,537}{35,578} \approx .88$

Alternatively, $1 - \frac{4,348}{35,578} \approx .88$.

b. The probability that a freshwater fisherman fishes in the Great Lakes alone or only in freshwater outside the Great Lakes is $\frac{855 + 28,489}{31,041} \approx .95$.

Practice

P8. **a.** All categories are complete but not disjoint. The main categories of *supposed to receive payments in 1991* and *not supposed*

to receive payments in 1991 are disjoint and complete. The other three categories are disjoint subsets of *supposed to receive payments in 1991*.

b. The complete disjoint categories are the last four: *received full amount, received partial amount, did not receive payments,* and *not supposed to receive payments in 1991.*

c. Because the categories *received full amount* and *received partial amount* are disjoint, we can add cases to obtain

$$P(full \ amount \ or \ partial \ amount) = \frac{2552 + 1176}{9919}$$

$$\approx .38$$

Lesson Notes: The Addition Rule for Disjoint Events

Activity 6.2: Exploring "or"

This important activity helps students see why you can't always add $P(A)$ and $P(B)$ to get $P(A \ or \ B)$.

1–2. The categories are disjoint. All the essential information can be found from the separate counts of answers to the two questions.

3–4. The categories overlap; it is not unlikely that some females will select blue as their favorite color. You need to know how many are female *and* select blue as their favorite color in order to answer the "or" question.

Discussion

D16. Only the events in parts c and e must be disjoint.

D17. Answers will vary, depending on the actual proportions in the class.

D18. No, although $P(getting \ the \ disease \ with \ three \ exposures) = P(getting \ the \ disease \ on \ the \ first \ exposure$ or *getting the disease on the second exposure* or *getting the disease on the third exposure*), it is not true that this is equal to $P(getting \ the \ disease \ on \ the \ first \ exposure)$ + $P(getting \ the \ disease \ on \ the \ second \ exposure)$ + $P(getting \ the \ disease \ on \ the \ third \ exposure)$. That's because the three events are not disjoint. Presumably you could be infected each time you are exposed. To help students understand this, ask whether it is necessarily true that they would get the disease if they were exposed 5 times or 10 times.

Practice

P9. Only the pairs listed in parts b and c are mutually exclusive.

Lesson Notes: The Addition Rule

Activity 6.3: More on "or"

This activity shows practical ways to extend the Addition Rule to compute $P(A \text{ or } B)$ when A and B are not disjoint.

1–2. Yes, this can be determined.

$P(\text{female}) + P(\text{favorite color is blue})$
$\qquad - P(\text{female and favorite color is blue})$

3. The two-way table should be sorted by gender and whether blue is their favorite color. Here is an example:

<table>
<tr><td></td><td></td><td colspan="3">Favorite
Color Blue?</td></tr>
<tr><td></td><td></td><td>Yes</td><td>No</td><td>Total</td></tr>
<tr><td rowspan="3">Female?</td><td>Yes</td><td>6</td><td>4</td><td>10</td></tr>
<tr><td>No</td><td>8</td><td>7</td><td>15</td></tr>
<tr><td>Total</td><td>14</td><td>11</td><td>25</td></tr>
</table>

Make sure that each student sees that he or she fits into exactly one of the four cells in the interior of the table.

4. The probability for the sample table in step 3 above is shown at the bottom of the page.

$P(\text{male}) = P(\text{not female}) = \frac{15}{25}$

Discussion

D19. To simplify writing general solutions to these questions, let F denote female, M male, B that blue is the favorite color, and O that something other than blue is the favorite color. The respective totals are TF, TM, TFB (for total female and blue), and so on.

a. F or $B = TF + TB - TFB$. For the sample table, $18 = 10 + 14 - 6$.

b. F or $B = TFB + TFO + TMB$. For the sample table, $18 = 6 + 4 + 8$.

D20. To get the probabilities, take each side of the equations in D19 that give the counts and divide by the total number of students, n, in the data set. So,

$$P(F \text{ or } B) = P(F) + P(B) - P(F \text{ and } B)$$

and

$$P(F \text{ or } B) = P(F \text{ and } B) + P(F \text{ and } O)$$
$$+ P(M \text{ and } B)$$

Discussion

D21. $P(\text{not doubles or sum of } 8) = P(\text{not doubles}) + P(\text{sum of } 8) - P(\text{not doubles and sum of } 8) = \frac{30}{36} + \frac{5}{36} - \frac{4}{36} = \frac{31}{36}$

D22. If A and B are mutually exclusive, then $P(A \text{ and } B) = 0$, so the general form of the Addition Rule reduces to the Addition Rule for Mutually Exclusive Events.

Practice

P10.

<table>
<tr><td></td><td></td><td colspan="3">Fish in
Great Lakes?</td></tr>
<tr><td></td><td></td><td>Yes</td><td>No</td><td>Total</td></tr>
<tr><td rowspan="3">Fish in
Other
Freshwater?</td><td>Yes</td><td>1,697</td><td>28,489</td><td>30,186</td></tr>
<tr><td>No</td><td>855</td><td>—</td><td>855</td></tr>
<tr><td>Total</td><td>2,552</td><td>28,489</td><td>31,041</td></tr>
</table>

$P(\text{Great Lakes and other freshwater}) = \frac{1,697}{31,041} \approx .055$

P11. **a.** $P(\text{doubles or sum of } 4) = P(\text{doubles}) + P(\text{sum of } 4) - P(\text{doubles and sum of } 4)$

$$= \frac{6}{36} + \frac{3}{36} - \frac{1}{36}$$

$$= \frac{8}{36}$$

b. $P(\text{doubles or sum of } 7) = P(\text{doubles}) + P(\text{sum of } 7) - P(\text{doubles and sum of } 7)$

$$= \frac{6}{36} + \frac{6}{36} - \frac{0}{36}$$

$$= \frac{12}{36}$$

c. $P(5 \text{ on first die or } 5 \text{ on second die}) = P(5 \text{ on first die}) + P(5 \text{ on second die}) - P(5 \text{ on first die and } 5 \text{ on second die})$

$$= \frac{6}{36} + \frac{6}{36} - \frac{1}{36}$$

$$= \frac{11}{36}$$

Lesson 6.2, Activity 6.3, step 4

$$P(\text{female or blue}) = P(\text{female}) + P(\text{blue}) - P(\text{female and blue})$$
$$= \frac{10}{25} + \frac{14}{25} - \frac{6}{25} = \frac{18}{25}$$

P12. $P(2\ heads) = P(heads\ on\ first) +$
$P(heads\ on\ second) - P(heads\ on\ both)$

$$= \tfrac{1}{2} + \tfrac{1}{2} - \tfrac{1}{4}$$

$$= \tfrac{3}{4}$$

Exercises

E11. a and c

E12. a. $P(white) = \dfrac{221{,}334}{267{,}636} \approx .827$

$P(white\ and \geq age\ 40) = \dfrac{95{,}600}{267{,}636} \approx 0.357$

b. The six cells in the upper right of the table give the numbers of nonwhites under age 10, which sum to 8144. Thus, (see the equations at the bottom of the page)

c. $P(< age\ 10) = \dfrac{19{,}150 + 19{,}738}{267{,}636} \approx .145$

$P(< age\ 10\ and\ black) = \dfrac{6{,}039}{267{,}636} \approx .023$

d. See the equations at the bottom of the page.

E13.

Owns a Beeper?

		Yes	No	Total
Has a Dog?	Yes	26	46	72
	No	112	32	144
	Total	138	78	216

The probability a randomly selected student does not have a dog or does not own a beeper is $\dfrac{(46 + 112 + 32)}{216} \approx .88$.

14. a.

Whistle?

		Yes	No	Total
Swim?	Yes	55	25	80
	No	15	5	20
	Total	70	30	100

$P(swim\ or\ whistle) = .55 + .25 + .15 = .95$

b. $P(S\ or\ W) = P(S) + P(W) -$
$P(S\ and\ W) = .80 + .70 - .55 = .95$

E15. See table below.

$P(master's\ or\ doctorate) = \dfrac{19{,}200}{21{,}844} \approx .88$

E16. Letting D denote Democrat, R Republican, and A approve,

$$P(R\ or\ A) = P(R) + P(A) - P(R\ and\ A)$$

$$= \frac{640}{1500} + \frac{937}{1500} - \frac{449}{1500}$$

$$= \frac{1128}{1500}$$

$$= .752$$

Lesson 6.3, E12b

$$P(nonwhite\ and < age\ 10) = \frac{8{,}144}{267{,}636} \approx .030$$

$$P(nonwhite\ or < age\ 10) = \frac{15{,}184 + 15{,}560 + 33{,}947 + 2{,}322 + 10{,}033}{267{,}636} \approx .288$$

Lesson 6.3, E12d

$$P(black) = \frac{33{,}947}{267{,}636} \approx .127$$

$$P(black\ or < age\ 10) = \frac{19{,}150 + 19{,}738 + 33{,}947 - 2{,}892 - 3{,}147}{267{,}636} \approx .250$$

Lesson 6.3, E15

Highest Degree

		Bachelor's	Master's	Doctorate	Total
Type of Faculty	Full-Time	76	6,214	1,288	7,578
	Part-Time	2,568	10,699	999	14,266
	Total	2,644	16,913	2,287	21,844

	Democrat	Republican	Total
Approve	488	449	937
Not Approve	372	191	563
Total	860	640	1500

$$P(R \text{ or } A) = \frac{(488 + 449 + 191)}{1500}$$

$$= \frac{1128}{1500}$$

$$= .752$$

E17. Jill has not computed correctly because it is not true that these two events are mutually exclusive. It is common to use the language that "two events are mutually exclusive if they can not happen at the same time." As students can see from this example, that language can be misleading. These two events are not mutually exclusive even though they can not happen at the same instance in time. However, they can happen in the same situation. The first flip can be a head and the second flip can be a head, or *HH*, so the two events are not mutually exclusive.

E18. Jill has computed correctly using the right definition of mutually exclusive. *HT* and *TH* are mutually exclusive because one event involves getting a head on the first flip of the coin and the other event involves getting a tail. These cannot both happen in the same situation.

E19. All four of the following statements must be true in order for $P(A \text{ or } B \text{ or } C) = P(A) + P(B) + P(C)$:

$P(A \text{ and } B) = 0$ $\quad$ $P(B \text{ and } C) = 0$

$P(A \text{ and } C) = 0$ $\quad$ $P(A \text{ and } B \text{ and } C) = 0$

To understand why this is true, examine this Venn diagram.

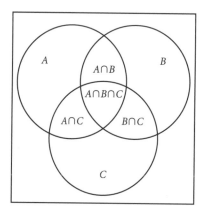

E20. This table shows this situation, with the given information in italic.

	Backpack	No Backpack	Total
Wallet	10	*30*	40
No Wallet	*40*	20	60
Total	50	50	100

Because 80% carry a backpack or a wallet, 10% must carry both. Or,

$$P(B \text{ or } W) = P(\text{just } B) + P(\text{just } W) + P(B \text{ and } W)$$

$$.8 = .4 + .3 + P(B \text{ and } W)$$

$$.1 = P(B \text{ and } W)$$

6.3 Conditional Probability

Objectives

- to understand the meaning of conditional probability, $P(A \mid B)$
- to learn the general Multiplication Rule: $P(A \text{ and } B) = P(A) \cdot P(B \mid A)$

Important Terms and Concepts

- conditional probability
- Multiplication Rule
- sampling with replacement versus sampling without replacement
- complement (see E34)

Lesson Planning

Class Time

Two to three days

Materials

None

Suggested Assignments

Classwork		
Essential	**Recommended**	**Optional**
D23–D27, D29	D30–D33	D28
P13–P19	P20, P21	

Homework		
Essential	**Recommended**	**Optional**
E21–E30	E31, E32	E33, E34

Lesson Notes: Conditional Probability

Discussion

D23. a. $P(F) = P(\text{the person was female}) = \frac{470}{2201}$
$P(F \mid S) = P(\text{the person was female given}$
that *the person survived*$) = \frac{344}{711}$

b. $P(\text{not } F) = P(\text{the person wasn't}$
female$) = \frac{1731}{2201}$
$P(\text{not } F \mid S) = P(\text{the person wasn't female}$
given that *the person survived*$) = \frac{367}{711}$
$P(S \mid \text{not } F) = P(\text{the person survived given}$
that *the person was not female*$) = \frac{367}{1731}$

D24. a. The conditional probability is $\frac{1}{3}$ without
replacement and $\frac{1}{2}$ with replacement. These
values are quite far apart.

b. The conditional probability is $\frac{49}{99}$ without
replacement and $\frac{1}{2}$ with replacement. These
values are quite close.

c. If the population size is large relative to the
sample size, sampling without replacement is
about the same as sampling with replacement.
If the population is small relative to the
sample size, sampling without replacement
can change the probabilities significantly.

Practice

P13. a. $P(\text{2nd draw is red} \mid \text{1st draw is red}) = \frac{2}{4} = \frac{1}{2}$
b. $P(\text{2nd draw is red} \mid \text{1st draw is blue}) = \frac{3}{4}$
c. $P(\text{3rd is blue} \mid \text{1st is red and 2nd is}$
blue$) = \frac{1}{3}$
d. $P(\text{3rd is red} \mid \text{1st is red and 2nd is red}) = \frac{1}{3}$

P14. a. $P(\text{club} \mid \text{black}) = \frac{\text{number of black clubs}}{\text{total number of black cards}} =$
$\frac{13}{26} = \frac{1}{2}$
b. $P(\text{jack} \mid \text{heart}) = \frac{\text{number of jack of hearts}}{\text{total number of black cards}} = \frac{1}{13}$

c. $P(\text{heart} \mid \text{jack}) = \frac{\text{number of jacks of hearts}}{\text{total number of jacks}} = \frac{1}{4}$

Lesson Notes: Computing P(A and B)

Discussion

D25. a.

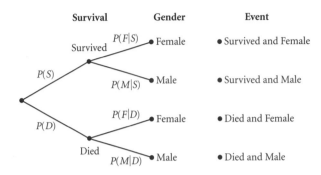

b. i. $P(S) = \frac{711}{2201}$
ii. $P(F \mid S) = \frac{344}{711}$
iii. $P(S \text{ and } F) = \frac{344}{2201}$
c. $P(S) \cdot P(F \mid S) = P(S \text{ and } F)$. This formula
matches the computation in the student text.
d. $P(M \text{ and } S) = P(M) \cdot P(S \mid M)$
$P(M \text{ and } S) = P(S) \cdot P(M \mid S)$

Lesson Notes: The Multiplication Rule

Discussion

D26. $P(M \text{ and } S) = P(M) \cdot P(S \mid M) =$
$\frac{1731}{2201} \cdot \frac{367}{1731} = \frac{367}{2201}$
$P(M \text{ and } D) = P(M) \cdot P(D \mid M) =$
$\frac{1731}{2201} \cdot \frac{1364}{1731} = \frac{1364}{2201}$

D27. $P(M \text{ and } S) = \frac{367}{2201} = \frac{711}{2201} \cdot \frac{367}{711} =$
$P(S) \cdot P(M \mid S)$
$P(M \text{ and } S) = \frac{367}{2201} = \frac{1731}{2201} \cdot \frac{367}{1731} =$
$P(M) \cdot P(S \mid M)$

D28. Let $n = c + d + e + f$.
Then, $P(A) \cdot P(B \mid A) = \frac{(c + e)}{n} \cdot \frac{c}{(c + e)} = \frac{c}{n} =$
$P(A \text{ and } B)$.
Also, $P(B) \cdot P(A \mid B) = \frac{(c + d)}{n} \cdot \frac{c}{(c + d)} = \frac{c}{n} =$
$P(A \text{ and } B)$.

Practice

P15. Without replacement, $P(HH) = \frac{13}{52} \cdot \frac{12}{51} = \frac{1}{17}$
With replacement, $P(HH) = \frac{13}{52} \cdot \frac{13}{52} = \frac{1}{16}$

P16. $P(W \text{ chosen 1st}) = \frac{2}{4}$
$P(W \text{ chosen 2nd} \mid W \text{ chosen 1st}) = \frac{1}{3}$
$P(WW) = P(W \text{ chosen 1st}) \cdot$
$P(W \text{ chosen 2nd} \mid W \text{ chosen 1st}) = \frac{2}{4} \cdot \frac{1}{3} = \frac{1}{6}$

P17. $P(\textit{sum of eight and doubles}) = P(\textit{doubles}) \cdot$
$P(\textit{sum of eight} \mid \textit{doubles}) = \frac{6}{36} \cdot \frac{1}{6} = \frac{1}{36}$
Note that this is not $P(\textit{sum of eight}) \cdot$
$P(\textit{doubles})$, which is $\frac{5}{36} \cdot \frac{6}{36} = \frac{5}{216}$.

Lesson Notes: The Definition of Conditional Probability

Discussion

D29.

Would Vote for Dole?

		Yes	No	Total
Gender	Male	4.2	55.8	60
	Female	6.4	33.6	40
	Total	10.6	89.4	100

$$P(F \mid D) = \frac{P(F \text{ and } D)}{P(D)} = \frac{6.4\%}{10.6\%} = .6038$$

Practice

P18.

	Right-Handed	Left-Handed	Total
Blue Eyes	8	2	10
Brown Eyes	16	4	20
Total	24	6	30

$$P(\textit{right-handed} \mid \textit{brown eyes}) = \frac{16}{20}$$

P19. For a typical set of 100 games, the won-lost record would look approximately like the following table. Note that the 36% is the conditional percentage of wins given that the team is facing a left-handed starting pitcher or $P(\textit{win} \mid \textit{left-handed pitcher})$.

	Right-Handed Pitcher	Left-Handed Pitcher	Total
Won	46.52	6.48	53
Lost	35.5	11.51	47
Total	82	18	100

The percentage of wins given a right-handed starting pitcher is $\frac{46.52}{82} \approx .57$, or 57%.

Lesson Notes: Interpreting Screening Tests

Discussion

D30. Here are the expected results for 20 contaminated samples:

Technician's Decision

		Positive	Negative	Total
Contamination	Present	18	2	20
	Absent	8	72	80
	Total	26	74	100

The false positive rate is $\frac{8}{26} \approx .31$.
The false negative rate is $\frac{2}{74} \approx .03$.
With 50 contaminated samples out of 100, the expected results change as shown here.

Test Result

		Positive	Negative	Total
Contamination	Present	45	5	50
	Absent	5	45	50
	Total	50	50	100

The false positive rate is $\frac{5}{50} = .10$.
The false negative rate is $\frac{5}{50} = .10$.
It is important to note that the false positive rate goes down when the population being tested has a higher proportion of contaminated cases.

D31. People interpreting test results begin by knowing they have a positive test result or a negative test result. They want to know the probability that the test is wrong. If, for example, someone has a positive test result, the false positive rate gives them some idea of the probability that they don't really have the disease even though the test is positive. On the other hand, sensitivity is the probability the test will be positive for a randomly selected person who has the disease. For an individual wondering whether they have the disease, knowing the sensitivity is not very helpful.

Practice

P20. False positive rate =
$P(\text{no disease} \mid \text{test positive}) = \frac{20}{80} = .25$

False negative rate =
$P(\text{disease} \mid \text{test negative}) = \frac{40}{50} = .80$

Sensitivity =
$P(\text{test positive} \mid \text{disease}) = \frac{60}{100} = .60$

Specificity =
$P(\text{test negative} \mid \text{no disease}) = \frac{10}{30} = .33$

The false negative rate is quite high because most of the population is actually inflicted with the disease. The test is neither very specific nor very sensitive. All things considered, it is not a very good screening test.

Lesson Notes: Conditional Probability and Statistical Inference

In a statistical context, most probabilities of interest are conditional. The dialogue between the statistician and the lawyer in the student text on pages 358–359 makes the point that $P(\text{data} \mid \text{model})$ can be calculated but $P(\text{model} \mid \text{data})$ generally cannot be.

In some situations, however, the investigator is able to place subjective probabilities on unknown parameters of the model so that probabilities conditioned on the data can be calculated. For example, in the scenario of the two coins (one with two heads) in D32 on page 359 of the student text, the probability of heads coming up on a flipped coin can be calculated once you know which coin is being flipped. That is, you can calculate $P(\text{heads} \mid \text{coin})$. To calculate $P(\text{coin} \mid \text{heads})$ you need to know the probability of Jill choosing each coin. Because these are not known, a subjective view taken from your experience with Jill would allow you to use your best guess for these probabilities, make the calculation, and state carefully that the result depends upon your *prior* probabilities for the coin choice. One person may model the coin choice as a random selection from the two as in E33 on page 363, whereas another might think that Jill has a trick up her sleeve and is highly likely to have chosen the two-headed coin. This latter way of thinking, where you adjust your probabilities to reflect your prior knowledge of the situation, is called Bayesian inference.

Discussion

D32. a. $\frac{1}{2}$

b. 1

c. We cannot tell because the probability depends on the probability model used for selecting the coin; either coin could have produced the observed head.

d. Same as c.

e. 1

f. 0

D33. In D32, the model would tell how the coin to be flipped was selected and the data are heads or tails—the outcome from Jill's one flip. It is possible to work out $P(\text{heads} \mid \text{model})$ but generally not possible to work out $P(\text{model} \mid \text{heads})$.

Practice

P21. False positive: $P(\text{actually not guilty} \mid \text{found guilty})$

False negative: $P(\text{actually guilty} \mid \text{found not guilty})$

The legal system is set up to keep the false positives to a minimum.

Exercises

E21. a. $P(\text{age} \geq 40 \mid \text{Asian or Pacific Islander}) = \frac{3,427}{10,033} = .34$

b. $P(\text{black} \mid \text{age} < 10) = \frac{2,892 + 3,147}{19,150 + 19,738} \approx .16$

c. $P(\text{age} < 10 \mid \text{white}) = \frac{15,184 + 15,560}{221,334} \approx .14$

d. $P(\text{black or} < 10 \mid \text{age} < 30) = \frac{50,001}{113,377} \approx .44$

E22.

		Carbolic Acid Used?		
		Yes	No	Total
Survived?	Yes	34	19	53
	No	6	16	22
	Total	40	35	75

a. $\frac{6}{40}$ **b.** $\frac{6}{22}$

c. $\frac{6}{75}$ **d.** $\frac{56}{75}$

E23. a. $\frac{3}{5}$ **b.** $\frac{2}{5}$ **c.** $\frac{1}{2}$

d. $\frac{1}{2}$ **e.** $\frac{3}{4}$ **f.** $\frac{1}{4}$

Tree diagram for drawing marbles:

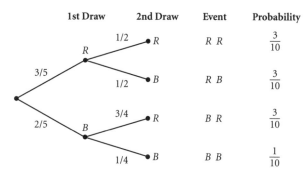

1st Draw	2nd Draw	Event	Probability
	1/2 → R	R R	$\frac{3}{10}$
3/5 R	1/2 → B	R B	$\frac{3}{10}$
2/5 B	3/4 → R	B R	$\frac{3}{10}$
	1/4 → B	B B	$\frac{1}{10}$

E24. This problem is easiest to understand if you first make a table.

Rain Predicted?

		Yes	No	Total
	Yes	6	18	24
Rain?	No	4	72	76
	Total	10	90	100%

a. 24%

b. First, pick a digit at random from 0 to 10. If the digit is a 1, then rain is predicted. In that case, pick another digit at random. If the digit is a 0, 1, 2, 3, 4, or 5, then it rains. If it's another digit, it doesn't rain.

If the first digit was not a 1, then no rain was predicted. In that case, pick another digit at random. If the digit is a 0 or 1, then it rains. If it's another digit, it doesn't rain.

Repeat this many times, and find the percentage of repetitions where it rains.

E25. Because

$(.36)(.62) = P(interested) \cdot P(< age\ 25 \mid interested)$
$= P(interested \text{ and } < age\ 25)$

the question is, if you select an adult at random from the United States, what is the probability that the person wants to go to Mars and is under 25 years old?

E26. No, you need one additional piece of (joint) information in order to complete the table. Information on any one cell will do the job.

Note: In Section 6.4, students will learn that if gender and survival were independent,

then you could fill in the table. (However, gender and survival are not independent.)

E27. a.

Gender

		Male	Female	Total
	Right	.44	.48	.92
Handedness	Left	.08	0	.08
	Total	.52	.48	1.00

b. $P(\text{left-handed} \mid \text{male}) = \frac{.08}{.52} \approx .15$

c. $P(\text{female and left-handed}) = 0$

E28. Note that the 47% is conditional information; of the remedial mathematics, 47% is taught by the part-timers or $.47 = P(\text{part-time} \mid \text{remedial})$.

Course Taught By

Type of Course	Full-Time	Part-Time	Total
Remedial	28%	25%	53%
Non-Remedial	34%	13%	47%
Total	62%	38%	100%

E29. a.

Test Result

Disease	Positive	Negative	Total
Yes	2.985	$.005 \cdot 3 = 0.015$	3
No	$.06 \cdot 97 = 5.82$	91.180	97
Total	8.805	91.195	100

b. .088

c. $\frac{.0582}{.088} \approx .66$

Note that the result in part c is the reason why many people do not believe that there should be universal, mandatory testing for the HIV virus, prostate cancer, and other such diseases. When the incidence of the disease is relatively low in the population, the number of false positives can be much larger than the number of cases of the disease.

E30. a. $\frac{4}{52} \cdot \frac{4}{52} \approx .0059$

b. $\frac{4}{52} \cdot \frac{3}{51} \approx .0045$

c. $\frac{4}{52} \cdot \frac{4}{52} \approx .0059$

d. $\frac{4}{52} \cdot \frac{4}{51} \approx .0060$

e. $1 \cdot \frac{12}{51} \approx .2353$

E31. Answers will vary. For example, consider the following table for a screening test that is 90% accurate (both sensitivity and specificity are .9).

Test Result

		Positive	Negative	Total
Disease	**Present**	72	8	80
	Absent	2	18	20
	Total	74	26	100

The false positive rate is $\frac{2}{74} \approx .03$.
The false negative rate is $\frac{8}{26} \approx .31$.

E32. **a.** For Officiousville, the table is

Test Result

		Positive	Negative	Total
Disease	**Present**	450	50	500
	Absent	50	450	500
	Total	500	500	1000

The false positive and false negative rates are both $\frac{50}{500} = \frac{1}{10}$.

b. For Mellowville, the table is

Test Result

		Positive	Negative	Total
Disease	**Present**	9	1	10
	Absent	99	891	990
	Total	108	892	1000

The false positive rate is $\frac{99}{108} \approx .92$, and the false negative rate is $\frac{1}{892} \approx .001$.

E33. A table (or a tree diagram) might help here.

Type of Coin

		Fair Coin	Two-Headed	Total
Flip Result	**Heads**	1/4	1/2	3/4
	Tails	1/4	0	1/4
	Total	1/2	1/2	1

a. $\frac{1}{2}$ **b.** 1 **c.** $\frac{1}{3}$
d. $\frac{2}{3}$ **e.** 1 **f.** 0

E34. The first statement is false, and the second is true. To see this, consider a two-way table such as this one.

	B	*Not B*	Total
A	72	8	80
Not A	2	18	20
Total	74	26	100

$P(A \mid B) + P(A \mid not\ B) = \frac{72}{74} + \frac{8}{26}$, which exceeds 1, so this can not be the probability of A.

It is true that $P(A\ and\ B) + P(A\ and\ not\ B) = \frac{72}{100} + \frac{8}{100} = \frac{80}{100} = P(A)$.

6.4 Independent Events

Objectives

- to understand the definition of independent events
- to know how to use the Multiplication Rule for Independent Events
- to understand that real data rarely meet the mathematical definition of independence
- to develop some insight into when an assumption of independence as part of the model is reasonable

Important Terms and Concepts

- dependent events
- independent events
- Multiplication Rule for Independent Events

Lesson Planning

Class Time

Two to three days

Materials

For Activity 6.4, one penny for each student

Suggested Assignments

Classwork		
Essential	**Recommended**	**Optional**
Activity 6.4	D37, D38	
D34–D36	P25	
P22–P24		

Homework		
Essential	**Recommended**	**Optional**
E35–E40, E43, E45	E41, E44, E46	E42, E47

Lesson Notes: Definition of Independent Events

One of the reasons independence is important in probability and statistics is that it simplifies the Multiplication Rule into a product of unconditional probabilities. Sometimes independence can be shown objectively, but most often independence is assumed in order to simplify a model. Students need to develop some insight into when an assumption of independence is reasonable and when it is not.

Discussion

D34. Let C denote the event *correctly identifies tap water,* B the event *drinks bottled water,* and M the event *is a male.* Then,

$$P(M \mid C) = \frac{21}{60} = .35 = P(M)$$

$$P(B \mid C) = \frac{24}{60} = .40 \neq \frac{30}{100} = P(B)$$

D35. Note that you are comparing $P(B \mid A)$ and $P(B)$.

a. Knowing A should decrease the probability of B.
b. Knowing A should increase the probability of B
c. Knowing A should not change the probability of B.
d. Knowing A decreases the probability of B to zero.

Practice

P22. $P(didn't\ survive) = \frac{1490}{2201} \approx .677$ is not equal to

$$P(didn't\ survive \mid male) = \frac{1364}{1731} \approx .788$$

so the events *didn't survive* and *male* aren't independent.

No two events described in this table are independent.

P23. Parts a and c give pairs of independent events, but part b does not.

a. $P(heart \mid jack) = \frac{1}{4} = \frac{13}{52} = P(heart)$
b. $P(heart \mid red\ card) = \frac{1}{2} \neq \frac{1}{4} = P(heart)$
c. $P(getting\ a\ 7 \mid heart) = \frac{1}{13} = \frac{4}{52} = P(getting\ a\ 7)$

Lesson Notes: Multiplication Rule for Independent Events

There is a seductive parallelism here that often snares even vigilant students. For mutually exclusive events, probabilities add. For independent events, probabilities multiply. Both phrases are unfamiliar, at least in their new context, and sound similar; both are polysyllabic and rhythmically parallel, with stresses on the next to last syllable. Worse yet, the informal meaning in each case is a variant of "one has nothing to do with the other." In fact, the meanings are quite different. For mutually exclusive events, the meaning of "nothing to do with the other" is "one rules out the other," whereas for independent events the meaning is "one has no influence or effect on the other." All the same, despite the substantive differences, there is a lot here that is superficially quite similar—a reliable recipe for confusion.

Discussion

D36. Let O denote the event that the person has type O blood and *not O* denote that the person does not have type O blood.

		Second Person		
		O	*Not O*	**Total**
First Person	*O*	.1764	.2436	**.4200**
	Not O	.2436	.3364	**.5800**
	Total	**.4200**	**.5800**	**1.0000**

$P(exactly\ one\ of\ the\ people\ has\ type\ O)$
$$= .2436 + .2436$$
$$= .4872$$

1st Person	2nd Person	Event	Probability
	.42 ● O	(O, O)	.1764
.42 O	.58 ● not O	(O, not O)	.2436
.58 not O	.42 ● O	(not O, O)	.2436
	.58 ● not O	(not O, not O)	.3364

Practice

P24. **a.** The probability that both students have graduated is (.8)(.8), or .64.

b. Letting *G* denote *graduated from high school* and *N* denote *did not graduate from high school*, the table is as follows:

		Second Person		
		G	*N*	Total
First Person	*G*	.64	.16	.80
	N	.16	.04	.20
	Total	.80	.20	1.00

The probability that exactly one student graduated is .16 + .16, or .32.

c. The tree diagram will have four paths. The two paths where one student graduates are *GN* and *NG*, each of which has probability (.8)(.2) = .16. Thus, *P*(*GN* or *NG*) = .32.

Lesson Notes: Independence with Real Data

Activity 6.4: Independence with Real Data

This activity demonstrates that samples often do not meet the mathematical definition of independence even when we have reason to believe that the events are independent. (A statistical test for independence is needed.) Sometimes, however, data can demonstrate that independence is not a reasonable assumption.

1. Eye dominance and hand dominance are associated, so a random sample should produce data that look dependent: *P*(*right-eyed* | *right-handed*) > *P*(*right-eyed*). One note of caution—the percentage of left-handers is rather small, so you may need a fairly large group of students in order to see any left-handed students.

2. Coin flips are independent, and the data should support this even though you are not likely to find

that *P*(*HH*) is exactly equal to *P*(*H on first flip*) · *P*(*heads on second flip*) in any set of sample data.

Lesson Notes: Probability and Genetics

Discussion

D37. The assumptions are

a. An offspring pea is equally likely to inherit a *tall* gene and a *short* gene from each parent.

b. The two genes are inherited independently of each other.

To understand the difference between these two assumptions, consider the following possibility. Suppose it were true that the female parent contributes a *T* or a *t* gene with equal probability but that the male parent must contribute a gene that matches that of the female parent. That is, if the female parent contributes a *T*, then the male parent must also contribute a *T*. If the female parent contributes a *t*, so must the male. Then assumption (a) is true. The probability is .5 that the offspring inherits a *T* from the female parent, and the probability is .5 that the offspring inherits a *T* from the male parent. The same is true of a *t* gene. However, the genes aren't inherited independently. If we know that the female parent contributed a *T*, then we know that the probability of the male parent contributing a *T* is 1.

It is not at all obvious *a priori* that genes from the two parents are transmitted independently of one another. Certainly it could not have been obvious in Mendel's day, when the mechanism of inheritance was not understood at all. But even today, although the idea of chromosomes inherited from both parents is common knowledge, the genetic principle of independent segregation is not an automatic consequence. Mendel's discovery relied heavily on observed data.

D38. The data fit very well. We expect that 75% of the peas will be tall, and Mendel got $\frac{787}{1064} \approx .740$. In fact, the results from many of Mendel's experiments fit so closely to his theory that, as soon as inferential statistics were invented, statisticians became suspicious. Mendel's results are *too* good, and therefore probably "doctored." For more about Mendel's data, see David Freedman,

Robert Pisani, and Roger Purves, *Statistics*, 1st, 2d, or 3d edition (New York: W. W. Norton, 1978, 1991, or 1997).

Practice

P25. The Punnett square follows. Each of the offspring will be heterozygous, and because *tall* is dominant, all of the offspring will be tall.

One Parent

		T	T
	t	tT	tT
Other Parent	t	tT	tT

Exercises

E35. **a.** These are not independent because $P(test\ positive\ |\ relative) > P(test\ positive)$.

b. These are independent because we would expect that $P(test\ is\ positive\ |\ last\ digit\ is\ a\ 3) = P(test\ is\ positive)$

c. These are not independent because the states where the highest elevation isn't very large tend to lie east of the Mississippi and so

$P(east\ of\ Miss.\ |\ over\ 8000\ feet) < P(east\ of\ Miss.)$ and

$P(over\ 8000\ feet\ |\ east\ of\ Miss.) < P(over\ 8000\ feet)$

In fact, both conditional probabilities are 0.

E36. **a.** $P(doubles) = \frac{1}{6}$; $P(doubles\ |\ sum\ of\ 8) = \frac{1}{5}$. Not independent.

b. $P(sum\ of\ 8) = \frac{5}{36}$; $P(sum\ of\ 8\ |\ 2\ on\ first) = \frac{1}{6}$. Not independent.

c. $P(sum\ of\ 7) = \frac{1}{6}$; $P(sum\ of\ 7\ |\ 1\ on\ first) = \frac{1}{6}$. Independent.

d. $P(doubles) = \frac{1}{6}$; $P(doubles\ |\ sum\ of\ 7) = 0$. Not independent.

e. $P(1\ on\ first) = \frac{1}{6}$; $P(1\ on\ first\ |\ 1\ on\ second) = \frac{1}{6}$. Independent.

E37. **a.** *BB, BG, GB,* and *GG*

b. two boys; two girls

c. (.51)(.51), or .2601, assuming births are independent

d. They may mean that their probability of getting a girl is higher than the population percentage for girls, and higher than the percentage for boys, if girls "run in the family." Under these conditions, *GG* would be the event with the highest probability.

E38.

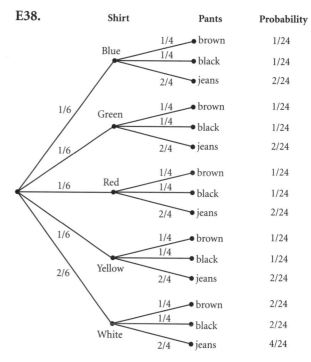

Shirt		Pants	Probability
Blue 1/6	1/4	brown	1/24
	1/4	black	1/24
	2/4	jeans	2/24
Green 1/6	1/4	brown	1/24
	1/4	black	1/24
	2/4	jeans	2/24
Red 1/6	1/4	brown	1/24
	1/4	black	1/24
	2/4	jeans	2/24
Yellow 1/6	1/4	brown	1/24
	1/4	black	1/24
	2/4	jeans	2/24
White 2/6	1/4	brown	2/24
	1/4	black	2/24
	2/4	jeans	4/24

To find the probability that she wears a white shirt with black pants, follow the white shirt to black pants branch of the tree and multiply the probabilities: $\frac{2}{6} \cdot \frac{1}{4}$, or $\frac{2}{24}$.

Alternatively, the tree could be made showing two branches for *white shirt* and two branches for *jeans*. Then there would be 24 equally likely paths through the tree. Two of them represent wearing a white shirt and wearing black pants.

E39. Jill's probability is for the event *4 on first* and *not 4 on the second*. She forgot to account for the event *not 4 on first* and *4 on second*. The correct probability is $\frac{10}{36}$.

E40. This involves sampling without replacement, and so the selections are dependent:

$$P(GG) = P(G\ first) \cdot P(G\ second\ |\ G\ first)$$
$$= \frac{2}{4} \cdot \frac{1}{3} = \frac{1}{6}$$

E41. Because roundness is dominant, the probability a seed will be round is $\frac{3}{4}$. Because yellowness also is dominant, the probability a seed will be yellow is $\frac{3}{4}$. If shape and color are independent, the probability a seed will be round and yellow is $\frac{3}{4} \cdot \frac{3}{4}$, or $\frac{9}{16}$. The probability a seed will be round and green is $\frac{3}{4} \cdot \frac{1}{4}$, or $\frac{3}{16}$. The assumption is independence of shape and color.

E42. a.

		Male Parent			
		TT	*Tt*	*tT*	*tt*
Female Parent	*TT*	*TT TT* / *TT TT*	*TT Tt* / *TT Tt*	*Tt TT* / *Tt TT*	*Tt Tt* / *Tt Tt*
	Tt	*TT TT* / *tT tT*	*TT Tt* / *tT tt*	*Tt TT* / *tt tT*	*Tt Tt* / *tt tt*
	tT	*tT tT* / *TT TT*	*tT tt* / *TT Tt*	*tt tT* / *Tt TT*	*tt tt* / *Tt Tt*
	tt	*tT tT* / *tT tT*	*tT tt* / *tT tt*	*tt tT* / *tt tT*	*tt tt* / *tt tt*

b. The total probability in each cell is $\frac{1}{16}$, and each of the entries in the cells is equally likely. Because tall is dominant, a pea plant will be tall unless *tt* occurs.

The sum of the probabilities of *tt* is

$$\frac{1}{4} \cdot \frac{1}{16} + \frac{1}{4} \cdot \frac{1}{16} + \frac{2}{4} \cdot \frac{1}{16} + \frac{1}{4} \cdot \frac{1}{16}$$

$$+ \frac{1}{4} \cdot \frac{1}{16} + \frac{2}{4} \cdot \frac{1}{16} + \frac{2}{4} \cdot \frac{1}{16}$$

$$+ \frac{2}{4} \cdot \frac{1}{16} + \frac{4}{4} \cdot \frac{1}{16}$$

$$= \frac{1}{4}$$

Thus, the probability that the grandchild pea plant is tall is $\frac{3}{4}$ (exactly what we would have hoped for).

E43.

	B	*Not B*	Total
A	1/8	1/8	1/4
Not A	3/16	9/16	3/4
Total	5/16	11/16	1

$P(B) = \frac{5}{16} \neq \frac{1}{2} = P(B \mid A)$; the events are not independent.

E44. a. Because these two events are independent, we can use the Multiplication Rule for Independent Events:

$P(\text{type O and } Rh+) = (.42)(.05) = .021$

b. See the equations at the bottom of the page.

c.

		Rh-Positive?		
		Yes	No	Total
Type O?	Yes	2.1	39.9	42
	No	2.9	55.1	58
	Total	5	95	100%

E45. The results of the surgeries must be assumed to be independent in order to find the probability both surgeries will fail, with the given information. This typically is not a reasonable assumption, because the two surgeries are to be performed on the same person at the same time. If the surgeries can be assumed to be independent, as perhaps with minor surgery performed on different parts of the body, $P(A \text{ fails}) = .15$ and $P(B \text{ fails}) = .10$ and the probability that they both fail is the product .015.

E46. Dave's arithmetic is not too bad. He is right that 2 percent means odds of 98 to 2, or 49 to 1, against an attack occurring on his rug if the dog selected a spot at random. However, if four attacks were to occur, each at a randomly selected spot in the house and each independent of the other, the probability all four would be on the rug is $(.02)^4 = \left(\frac{1}{50}\right)^4 = \frac{1}{6,250,000}$. This is one chance in about six million (or odds against of about 6,249,999 to 1), not one chance in five million. (Dave probably got one chance in five million by computing 49^4, or 5,764,801.)

However, Dave's logic is not too good because his computation assumed that the attacks were independent. Surely a sick dog would tend to be sick repeatedly in the same location rather than randomly wandering around the house.

E47. We are given that $P(A \text{ and } B) = P(A) \cdot P(B)$. From E34 on page 363,

$P(A \text{ and not } B) + P(A \text{ and } B) = P(A)$

Lesson 6.4, E44b

$$P(\text{type O or } Rh+) = P(\text{type O}) + P(Rh+) - P(\text{type O and } Rh+)$$

$$= .42 + .05 - .021$$

$$= .449$$

so

$$P(A \text{ and } not\ B) = P(A) - P(A \text{ and } B)$$
$$= P(A) - P(A) \cdot P(B)$$
$$= P(A) \cdot [1 - P(B)]$$
$$= P(A) \cdot P(not\ B)$$

Therefore, A and $not\ B$ are independent.

Review

Homework	
Essential	E48–E51, E54, E55, E57, E64
Recommended	E52, E53, E61
Optional	E56, E58–E60, E62, E63

Review Exercises

E48. **a.** $4 \cdot 6$, or 24

b.

Regular Die

		1	2	3	4	5	6
Tetrahedral Die	**1**	1, 1	1, 2	1, 3	1, 4	1, 5	1, 6
	2	2, 1	2, 2	2, 3	2, 4	2, 5	2, 6
	3	3, 1	3, 2	3, 3	3, 4	3, 5	3, 6
	4	4, 1	4, 2	4, 3	4, 4	4, 5	4, 6

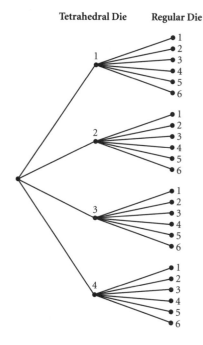

Tetrahedral Die   Regular Die

c. $\frac{4}{24}$

d. $\frac{2}{24}$

e. These events are not disjoint because you can roll (2, 2). These events are not independent events because $P(sum\ of\ 4) = \frac{3}{24}$, but $P(sum\ of\ 4 \mid doubles) = \frac{1}{4}$.

f. These events are not disjoint because you can roll (2, 5). These events are independent because $P(2\ on\ tetrahedral) = \frac{1}{4} = P(2\ on\ tetrahedral \mid 5\ on\ the\ regular\ die)$.

E49. Randomly select a digit from the set {1, 2, 3, 4, 5, 6, 7, 8, 9}. Repeat this process seven times (with replacement). See if the number 3 is among the seven digits selected. If so, the repetition was a "success." Repeat this process of seven selections many times. The theoretical probability is $1 - (\frac{8}{9})^7 \approx .56$.

E50. **a.** $p + q$

b. $\frac{q}{p + q}$

c. $\frac{p}{p + r}$

d. q

e. $p + q + s$ (or $1 - r$)

E51. **a.** It is easy to compute that $100\% - 15\% = 85\%$ have ridden one or the other or both. Nevertheless, students should still practice setting up the table.

		Merry-Go-Round?		
		Yes	No	Total
Roller Coaster?	Yes	40	5	45
	No	40	15	55
	Total	80	20	100%

b. We can quickly get the answer by computing $1 - .2 = .8$.

Here is the table.

		Merry-Go-Round?		
		Yes	No	Total
Roller Coaster?	Yes	5	45	50
	No	30	20	50
	Total	35	65	100%

The probability a randomly selected student has ridden one or the other is $P(not\ R \text{ and } M) + P(R \text{ and } M) + P(R \text{ and } not\ M) = .30 + .05 + .45 = .80$.

E52. **a.** The 15 outcomes in bold represent the rolls that enable you to hit your opponent. The probability of such a roll is 15/36.

$$(1, 1)\ (1, 2)\ (1, 3)\ \mathbf{(1, 4)}\ \mathbf{(1, 5)}\ (1, 6)$$
$$(2, 1)\ (2, 2)\ \mathbf{(2, 3)}\ (2, 4)\ \mathbf{(2, 5)}\ (2, 6)$$
$$(3, 1)\ \mathbf{(3, 2)}\ (3, 3)\ (3, 4)\ \mathbf{(3, 5)}\ (3, 6)$$
$$\mathbf{(4, 1)}\ (4, 2)\ (4, 3)\ (4, 4)\ \mathbf{(4, 5)}\ (4, 6)$$
$$\mathbf{(5, 1)}\ \mathbf{(5, 2)}\ \mathbf{(5, 3)}\ \mathbf{(5, 4)}\ \mathbf{(5, 5)}\ \mathbf{(5, 6)}$$
$$(6, 1)\ (6, 2)\ (6, 3)\ (6, 4)\ \mathbf{(6, 5)}\ (6, 6)$$

b. Yes, the events *sum of 5* and *5 on either die* are mutually exclusive:

$$P(\textit{sum of 5 or 5 on either die})$$
$$= P(\textit{sum of 5}) + P(\textit{5 on first die or 5 on second die})$$
$$= \frac{4}{36} + \frac{11}{36} = \frac{15}{36}$$

E53. Encourage students to tell an interesting story with only the calculations that are necessary. Students may make far more computations than they need to prove the important points, such as that although class mattered, being female was more important to survival. Some interesting probabilities to note are the following:

$$P(\textit{survived}) = \frac{499}{1316} \approx .379$$

$$P(\textit{survived} \mid \textit{3rd class}) = \frac{178}{706} \approx .252$$

$$P(\textit{survived} \mid \textit{1st class}) = \frac{203}{325} \approx .625$$

$$P(\textit{survived} \mid \textit{1st class female}) = \frac{141}{145} \approx .972$$

$$P(\textit{survived} \mid \textit{3rd class female}) = \frac{90}{196} \approx .459$$

$$P(\textit{survived} \mid \textit{1st class male}) = \frac{62}{180} = .344$$

E54. **a.** In this problem we will assume, as did Marilyn, that the probability of having a boy is $\frac{1}{2}$ with each birth and that births are independent. To represent two children, generate pairs of random digits from the set $\{0, 1\}$. The digit 0 will represent a girl, and the digit 1 will represent a boy. The first digit will be the first child, and the second digit will be the second child.

First, let's simulate the probability that the man has two boys. Generate pairs of random digits, ignoring any pair where the first digit is not a 1. Find the proportion of pairs where the first digit is a 1 and the second digit is also a 1.

Note: All pairs here should have a first digit of 1 because we are told that the man's older child is a boy.

To simulate the probability that the woman has two boys, generate pairs of random digits, ignoring any pairs that do not have a 1 as either digit. Find the proportion of pairs with at least one 1 that also has both 1's.

Note: All pairs here will have at least one 1 because we are told the woman has at least one boy.

b. Marilyn correctly gave the answer that the man has a larger chance of having two boys. All her readers agreed that the probability that the man has two boys is the same as the probability that the younger child is a boy: $\frac{1}{2}$. There are only two possible families for him, and each is equally likely: *BG* and *BB*. But Marilyn's readers disagreed on the probability that the woman has two boys. Many thought it also was $\frac{1}{2}$. However, the possible pairs for the woman are *GB*, *BG*, and *BB*. We are given no reason to doubt that these are equally likely. So the probability she has two boys is only $\frac{1}{3}$.

Some of Marilyn's readers got quite angry with her over this.

E55. **a.** This situation is not possible unless $P(A) = 0$ and $P(B) = 0$. If events A and B are disjoint, then $P(A \mid B) = 0$, and if they are independent, this implies $P(A) = 0$. Similarly, $P(B) = 0$.

b. This situation is possible. For example, when rolling two dice, a sum of 7 and a 1 on the first die are not disjoint events and are independent.

c. This is possible. For example, rolling a sum of 7 and rolling doubles are disjoint, dependent events.

d. This is possible. For example, rolling doubles and rolling a sum of 8 are not disjoint events and are dependent.

E56. Let's call these three conditions I, II, and III.

I: $P(A) = P(A \mid B)$
II: $P(B) = P(B \mid A)$
III: $P(A \text{ and } B) = P(A) \cdot P(B)$

The proof that I $\Rightarrow$ II is as follows:

Suppose $P(A \mid B) = P(A)$. Then by the definition of conditional probability,

$$P(B \mid A) = \frac{P(A \text{ and } B)}{P(A)}$$

$$= \frac{P(B) \cdot P(A \mid B)}{P(A)}$$

$$= \frac{P(B) \cdot P(A)}{P(A)}$$

$$= P(B)$$

By switching A and B, this proof also shows that II $\Rightarrow$ I. To show that I $\Rightarrow$ III, first write the definition of conditional probability:

$$P(A \mid B) = \frac{P(A \text{ and } B)}{P(B)}$$

Because I is assumed to be true, substitute $P(A)$ for $P(A \mid B)$ to get

$$P(A) = \frac{P(A \text{ and } B)}{P(B)}$$

Multiplying both sides by $P(B)$ gives

$$P(A) \cdot P(B) = P(A \text{ and } B)$$

which is III.

Now we need to prove that III $\Rightarrow$ I. Because III is true, we have

$$P(A \text{ and } B) = P(A) \cdot P(B)$$

Dividing both sides by $P(B)$ gives

$$P(A) = \frac{P(A \text{ and } B)}{P(B)}$$

But from the definition of conditional probability, we know that

$$P(A \mid B) = \frac{P(A \text{ and } B)}{P(B)}$$

Comparing the last two equations, we see that $P(A) = P(A \mid B)$. So I is true.

Because we have shown that II $\Leftrightarrow$ I and I $\Leftrightarrow$ III, we get by transitivity that II $\Leftrightarrow$ III, and the three conditions are equivalent.

E57. **a.** $P(two\ teachers) = \frac{2}{4} \cdot \frac{1}{3} = \frac{1}{6} \approx .167$

b. $P(two\ teachers) = \frac{5{,}000{,}000}{10{,}000{,}000} \cdot \frac{4{,}999{,}999}{9{,}999{,}999} = .249999975$

c. The draws in both parts a and b are technically dependent, but the large population size in part b makes independence a reasonable assumption. The probability is essentially $(.5)(.5) = .25$ for the large population.

E58. **a.** Think of a table with A and B intersecting. The symbol $\overline{A}$ denotes *not A*.

	B	$\overline{B}$
A		
$\overline{A}$		

From the table, $P(A) = P(B \text{ and } A) + P(\overline{B} \text{ and } A)$, which, using the Multiplication Rule, is equal to $P(B) \cdot P(A \mid B) + P(\overline{B}) \cdot P(A \mid \overline{B})$.

Using this to find $P(Dodgers\ win)$:

$$P(win) = P(win \mid day) \cdot P(day)$$
$$+ P(win \mid not\ day) \cdot P(not\ day)$$
$$= \frac{11}{21} \cdot \frac{21}{78} + \frac{30}{57} \cdot \frac{57}{78}$$
$$= \frac{41}{78}$$

b. $P(B \mid A) = \frac{P(A \text{ and } B)}{P(A)} = \frac{P(B) \cdot P(A \mid B)}{P(A)}$

But from part a, $P(A) = P(A \mid B) \cdot P(B) + P(A \mid \overline{B}) \cdot P(\overline{B})$. The Dodger probability is shown at the bottom of the page.

E59. **a.** Using I for *Test I is used*, II for *Test II is used*, and F for *false positive indicated*, the problem gives $P(F \mid I) = .10$, $P(F \mid II) = .05$, and $P(I) = .6$. These values can be used to complete the table.

	Test I	Test II	Total %
False Positives	6	2	8
Other Results	54	38	92
Total %	60	40	100%

Lesson 6.4, E58b

$$P(win \mid day) = \frac{P(day \mid win) \cdot P(win)}{P(day \mid win) \cdot P(win) + P(day \mid not\ win) \cdot P(not\ win)}$$

$$= \frac{\dfrac{11}{41} \cdot \dfrac{41}{78}}{\dfrac{11}{41} \cdot \dfrac{41}{78} + \dfrac{10}{37} \cdot \dfrac{37}{78}} = \frac{11}{21}$$

b. From the table, $P(I \mid F) = \frac{6}{8} = .75$

From the formula,

$$P(I \mid F) = \frac{P(F \mid I) \cdot P(I)}{P(F \mid I) \cdot P(I) + P(F \mid II) \cdot P(II)}$$

$$= \frac{(.1)(.6)}{(.1)(.6) + (.05)(.4)} = .75$$

E60. The table summarizing these results is as follows:

Would Vote for Dole?

	Yes	No	Total
Man	4.2	55.8	60
Woman	6.4	33.6	40
Total	10.6	89.4	100

Now, $P(Woman \mid Vote\ for\ Dole) = \frac{6.4}{10.6} \approx .604$.

By formula,

$$P(W \mid D) = \frac{P(D \mid W) \cdot P(W)}{P(D \mid W) \cdot P(W) + P(D \mid M) \cdot P(M)}$$

$$= \frac{(.16)(.4)}{(.16)(.4) + (.07)(.6)} = .604$$

E61. Call the four nucleotides *A*, *B*, *C*, and *D*. There are 4 different codons that have only one kind of nucleotide: *AAA*, *BBB*, and *CCC*. There are 12 different codons that have exactly two kinds of nucleotides: *AAB*, *AAC*, *AAD*, *BBA*, *BBC*, *BBD*, *CCA*, *CCB*, *CCD*, *DDA*, *DDB*, and *DDC*. (Order does not matter in a codon.) There are 4 different codons that have three kinds of nucleotides: *ABC*, *ABD*, *ACD*, and *BCD*. This is 20 in all, so

three nucleotides per codon is sufficient. To see whether we can get by with only two nucleotides per codon, we will list all possible codons of two nucleotides: *AA, BB, CC, DD, AB, AC, AD, BC, BD, CD*. There are only 10 of these, so two is not enough.

E62. Suppose the middle digit is a 0. Then there are 8 choices for the first digit and 10 choices for the last digit, giving 80 possible area codes.

Suppose the middle digit is a 1. Then there are 8 choices for the first digit and 9 choices for the last digit (we cannot use 1), giving 72 possible area codes.

Thus, there are $80 + 72 = 152$ possible area codes.

E63. **a.** There are 99,999 possible zip codes: 00001, 00002, . . . , 99999. The average number of people per zip code is $\frac{270,000,000}{99,999} \approx 2700$.

b. There are 99,999 possible zip codes and 9,999 possible plus 4 codes. Thus, there are $99,999 \cdot 9,999 = 999,890,001$ possible zip plus 4 codes. The average number of people per zip plus 4 code is $\frac{270,000,000}{999,890,001} \approx 0.27$. We each could have almost four zip plus 4 codes.

E64. The event *60 or more correct identifications of tap water* would occur only about 2.5% of the time if all of the tasters were guessing. Because this is so unlikely, it is the conclusion of Downhill Research that the tasters can distinguish between tap water and bottled water.

7

PROBABILITY DISTRIBUTIONS

Overview

A probability distribution describes the possible numerical outcomes of a chance process and allows you to find the probability of any set of possible outcomes. These numerical outcomes are called random variables because their values vary according to probabilities underlying the chance process being studied.

In previous chapters of the student text, several probability distributions were constructed by listing equally likely outcomes, such as Jack and Jill's distribution of the number of people who chose tap water and the distribution of the sum on the roll of two dice. The normal distribution, as an idealized model for many chance situations, is an example of a continuous probability distribution. In this chapter, we will use probability theory to develop two important discrete probability distributions—the binomial and the geometric distributions.

Like data distributions and sampling distributions, probability distributions are described by shape, center, and spread. The mean (now called the expected value) and the standard deviation are used almost exclusively for probability distributions because of their important role in basic statistical inference, which students will begin to study in the next chapter.

Goals

The primary goals of this chapter are to provide your students with the ability

- to use the terminology of probability distributions and to learn how to compute their expected values and standard deviations
- to use expected value to make decisions
- to recognize and apply the binomial probability model
- to recognize and apply the geometric probability model

Content Overview

We will construct the binomial and geometric probability distributions using the probability theory discussed in Chapter 6. However, if students are unable to design a correct simulation for a problem, it is likely that they do not understand the situation. Thus, on occasion, students will be asked to construct a simulation that can be used to estimate a probability.

Help your students build the connection between their theoretical models and what actually may be observed in practice by including a careful discussion of the assumptions underlying any model. This connection is one of the keys to understanding the statistics presented in the remaining chapters.

If students have mastered Chapters 5 and 6, this chapter should require considerably less time than either of these previous chapters.

The most mathematical topic is the derivation of the expected value of the geometric distribution, which you can skip if the result seems to make practical sense to your students.

Time Required

Traditional Schedule			Block	4 x 4 Block
Section 7.1				
2 days	Day 1	Probability distributions, expected value, variance, expected value in everyday situations	1 day	1 long, 1 short
	Day 2	Rules for means and variances, linear transformations of random variables, addition and subtraction rules, summary, exercises		
Section 7.2				
2 days	Day 1	Development of formula, Activity 7.1	1 day	1 long, 1 short
	Day 2	Shape, center, spread, summary, exercises		
Section 7.3				
2 days	Day 1	Development of formula, Activity 7.2	1 day	1 long, 1 short
	Day 2	Expected value and standard deviation, Activity 7.3, summary, exercises		
Review				
1 day			1 day	1 long

Materials

Section 7.1: None

Section 7.2: For Activity 7.1, about 40 identical paper or plastic cups, a container of bottled water, and a container of tap water

Section 7.3: For Activity 7.2, a device for generating random numbers. For Activity 7.3, graph paper.

Suggested Assignments

Classwork

Section	Essential	Recommended	Optional
7.1	D1, D3, D4 P1, P2, P4	P3	D2, D5
7.2	Activity 7.1 D6–D8, D11, D12 P5, P7, P8	D9, D10, D14 P6, P9	D13
7.3	Activity 7.2 D15, D17 P10, P11	D16, D18–D20 P12, P13	Activity 7.3 D21

Homework

Section	Essential	Recommended	Optional
7.1	E2–E4, E6	E1, E7	E5
7.2	E8–E12, E14	E13, E15, E17	E16, E18
7.3	E19–E21	E23, E24	E22, E25
Review	E26, E27, E37	E28, E30, E31, E33	E29, E32, E34–E36

7.1 Random Variables and Expected Value

Objectives

- to learn the terms *probability distribution, random variable,* and *expected value*
- to understand that different probability distributions may be constructed for the same chance process, depending on how you define the random variable
- to learn how to use the formulas for the expected value and standard deviation of a probability distribution
- to learn how to compute the expected value for situations such as lotteries and insurance and use the expected value appropriately to make decisions
- to compute the mean and standard deviation, when appropriate, for a linear transformation of a single variable and for a linear combination of several random variables

Important Terms and Concepts

- probability distribution
- random variable
- expected value and its formula
- expected value in everyday situations
- mean and variance of a linear transformation of X
- mean and variance (if appropriate) of a sum or difference of two random variables

Lesson Planning

Class Time

Two days

Materials

None

Suggested Assignments

Classwork		
Essential	**Recommended**	**Optional**
D1, D3, D4 P1, P2, P4	P3	D2, D5

Homework		
Essential	**Recommended**	**Optional**
E2–E4, E6	E1, E7	E5

Lesson Notes: Data Distribution, Sampling Distribution, and Probability Distribution

Your students have learned about three closely related types of distributions:

- a distribution of data (see pages 6–8 of Chapter 1, and Chapter 2)—a list of observations, along with the frequency or relative frequency (proportion) with which each observation occurs

- a sampling distribution (see page 288 of Chapter 5)—a list of all possible values, along with their relative frequencies, of a summary statistic, such as the mean, that can be computed from taking repeated samples from a population

- a probability distribution (see page 331 of Chapter 6)—a description of the possible numerical outcomes of a chance process that allows you to find the probability of any set of possible outcomes

All three types of distributions may be displayed on a histogram and described by the same three features: shape, center, and spread. Sometimes, a particular distribution can be classified as any one of the three types of distributions—data distribution, sampling distribution, or probability distribution. For example, consider the following distribution of the number of children in the families of 30 students in a statistics class:

Number of Children	Relative Frequency
1	10/30
2	12/30
3	5/30
4	2/30
5	1/30

This table could be considered a distribution of data because it shows 30 observations of students with the relative frequency of each observation. This table could also be considered a sampling distribution because it could indicate the mean number of children in all possible samples of size 1 from this class. Finally, if "Relative Frequency" was replaced by "Probability," the table could present a probability distribution. That is, if you select at random one student from this class, the table gives the probability of getting a student with a given number of children in his or her family.

Consider also the example in the student text for the number of CDs purchased by USC students on page 381. Because this example displays real-life observations, if we change the heading "Probability" to "Relative Frequency," it could be called a distribution of data instead of a probability distribution. It could also be thought of as a sampling distribution of the mean (or the median) of all samples of size 1 taken from this population.

So, as always in statistics, context matters. What kind of distribution you have may depend on how you plan to use it.

From Frequency to Relative Frequency to Probability

The algebra below shows the equivalence of the formulas for the mean of a frequency table, a relative frequency table, and a probability distribution table.

$$\mu_{frequency} = \frac{\sum x \cdot f}{n}$$

$$\mu_{relative\ frequency} = \sum x \cdot \frac{f}{n}$$

$$\mu_{probability} = \sum x \cdot p$$

Using a Graphing Calculator to Get the Expected Value (Mean) and Standard Deviation

To get the expected value (mean) and standard deviation on a TI-83, place the values of x in list L1 and the values of p in list L2. The command 1-Var Stats L1, L2 gives the mean, standard deviation, and other summary statistics. Enter the 1-Var Stats command by pressing [STAT] [CALC] 1:1-Var Stats.

Why Are Some x's Capitalized and Some Not?

Typically, capital letters are used for the random variable in general, and lowercase notation is used for a specific value of the random variable. For example, we can let X stand for the number of heads if you flip a coin 3 times. Then if we want to denote the probability of getting exactly 1 head, we could write $P(X = 1)$. If we want to denote the probability of getting exactly x heads, we could write $P(X = x)$, or using k for the specific value, as in the student text, $P(X = k)$. Also, we write $E(X)$ for the expected value because X, here, stands for the random value in general, not a specific value. But then we write

$$E(X) = \mu_X = \sum x_i \cdot p_i$$

with lowercase x's inside the summation because these x's are the individual values that X can take on.

Discussion

D1. Students may choose a random variable such as the absolute value of the difference of the two numbers, the smaller number, or the product of the two numbers. The probability distribution of the absolute value of the difference is shown in the following table. The expected value and standard deviation are $E(X) = 1.944$ and $\sigma_X = 1.433$.

Absolute Value of the Difference of Two Dice	Probability
0	6/36
1	10/36
2	8/36
3	6/36
4	4/36
5	2/36
Total	36/36

D2. The student would have sympathy with this quote. He or she would not like the idea of having 2.2 children per female "because you can not have part of a person." Of course, having an average of 2.2 children is possible even though no individual can have 2.2 children.

Practice

P1. The distribution of the sum is triangular. The distribution of the larger number is increasing at a constant rate. The expected value of the distribution of the sum is 7 with a standard deviation of 2.415. The expected value of the distribution of the larger number is 4.472 with a standard deviation of 1.404.

To find, for example, the expected value and standard deviation of the probability distribution for the larger number when two dice are rolled, the calculation can be done easily by extending the table as shown here.

Larger Number, x_i	Probability, p_i	$x_i \cdot p_i$	$(x_i - \mu_X)^2 \cdot p_i$
1	1/36	1/36	0.3349
2	3/36	6/36	0.5093
3	5/36	15/36	0.3010
4	7/36	28/36	0.0434
5	9/36	45/36	0.0696
6	11/36	66/36	0.7132
Total	1	161/36	1.9714

$\mu_X = \frac{161}{36} \approx 4.472$, and $\mu_X \approx \sqrt{1.9715} \approx 1.404$. We expect the larger number to be approximately 4.472, with a standard deviation of approximately 1.404.

Discussion

D3. **a.** For game B:

Value of Prize	Probability of Winning
0.69	1/4
0	3/4

$\mu_X = \$0.1725$, or 17.25 cents

For game C:

Value of Prize	Probability of Winning
1.44	1/8
0	7/8

$\mu_X = \$0.18$, or 18 cents

For game D:

Value of Prize	Probability of Winning
1.99	1/16
0	15/16

$\mu_X = \$0.124375$, or about 12.4 cents

The game with the highest expected value is game A.

b. Some people might not want the drink. Also, some people want to win a bigger prize and are willing to sacrifice the best expected value for the possibility of doing so.

Practice

P2. **a.** $\mu_X = 600 \cdot \frac{1}{500} + 0 \cdot \frac{499}{500} = \$1.20$

b. $\mu_X = 1000 \cdot \frac{1}{500} + 400 \cdot \frac{2}{500} + 0 \cdot \frac{497}{500} = \$3.60$

P3.

Outcome	Payout	Probability
No burglary	$0	.9728
Burglary	$5000	.0272

The expected payout per policy is $0(.9728) + 5000(.0272) = \$136$, so you should charge $136 to break even.

Discussion

D4. The total number of hours you expect to spend is $10 + 15 = 25$ hours. The variance of the total is $2^2 + 3^2 = 13$, so the standard deviation is about 3.61 hours. However, it is not reasonable to use the rule for adding variances in this case because the two times undoubtedly are not independent. There are only so many hours in the week, so if you work a lot, you must spend less time studying.

D5. **a.** The nine possible totals are 300, 450, 900, 325, 475, 925, 700, 850, and 1300. The standard deviation is 313.803, and the variance is 98,472.22. (You must compute all variances in this question by dividing by n, not $n - 1$.)

b. The variance of List A is 33,472.22 and of List B is 65,000. The variance of List A plus the variance of List B exactly equals the variance of the nine totals computed in part a.

c. The standard deviation of List A is 182.95 and of List B is 254.95. The standard deviation of List A plus the standard deviation of List B (437.9) does *not* equal the standard deviation of the nine totals computed in part a!

d. Yes: $341.67 + 350 = 691.67$.

e. No: $225 + 250$ doesn't equal 700, the median of the totals.

Practice

P4. You expect to save $52(20.40) = \$1060.80$, with a standard deviation of $\sqrt{52}(14.78) = \$106.58$, assuming savings from week to week are independent.

Exercises

E1. **a.** \$204.50 profit if there is no burglary; $5000 - 204.50$, or \$4795.50 loss if there is a burglary.

b. $\$204.50 + \frac{5000}{1000}$, or \$209.50

c. Examples include whether there is a burglar alarm; whether there are good locks on the doors; whether the house contains expensive items; what proportion of the time someone is at home.

E2. **a.**

Sum of Two Tetrahedral Dice	Probability
2	1/16
3	2/16
4	3/16
5	4/16
6	3/16
7	2/16
8	1/16
Total	16/16 = 1

The probability that the sum is 3 is $\frac{2}{16}$.

b.

Absolute Value of Difference of Two Tetrahedral Dice	Probability
0	4/16
1	6/16
2	4/16
3	2/16
Total	16/16 = 1

The probability that the difference is 3 is $\frac{2}{16}$.

c. $\mu_{|diff|} = 1.25$

E3. **a.** $\mu_X = \$0.185$

b. $1{,}000{,}000(0.50 - 0.185)$, or \$315,000! Alternatively, the state would take in \$500,000 for 1,000,000 tickets and would pay out prizes worth \$185,000 for a profit of \$315,000.

c. 37% of the income was returned in prizes.

E4. $\$0(.9784) + \$10{,}676(.0216) = \$230.6016$

E5. **a.** \$148,861,425

b. The value of all of the nonfood prizes is \$5,781,425, and $\frac{1}{10}$ of this, or \$578,142.50, is expected to be paid out. The value of the 196,000,000 cards with food prizes is \$143,080,000, and $\frac{1}{5}$ of this, or \$28,616,000, is expected to be paid out. Burger King expected to pay out a total of \$29,194,142.50, but almost all of this is in food.

c. The expected value of a card can be computed as $\frac{29{,}194{,}142.50}{196{,}011{,}489}$, or about \$0.149.

E6. **a.** Brand A: $950 + 0(.4) + 150(.3) + 300(.15) + 450(.1) + 600(.05) = \$1115$

Brand B: $1200

b. The advantage of Brand A is that you expect to pay less and there is a 70% chance you will pay less with Brand A than you will with Brand B, even with one repair. The advantage of buying Brand B is that the maximum you might spend is less. With Brand A you might be unlucky and spend $950 + 4(150) = \$1550$. The most you can spend with Brand B is $1200.

E7. The expected costs per month are

AT&T: $49.99 + 100(.1)(0.45) = \$54.49$

Verizon: $49.00 + 50(.3)(0.45) + 100(.2)(0.45) + 200(.1)(0.45) = \$73.75$

Voicestream: $39.99 + 50(.3)(0.25) + 100(.2)(0.25) + 200(.1)(0.25) = \$53.74$

Sprint PCS: $49.99 + 50(.3)(0.30) + 100(.2)(0.30) + 200(.1)(0.30) = \$66.49$

Voicestream is still the cheapest (but not by a lot), followed by AT&T, Sprint PCS, and Verizon.

7.2 The Binomial Distribution

Objectives

- to understand how the problems in this section relate to those in Section 5.4 on sampling distributions for proportions
- to use the binomial probability formula to compute probabilities and to understand why the formula works
- to compute the expected value and standard deviation of a binomial distribution
- to use the expected value to make decisions about the value of various courses of action

Important Terms and Concepts

- binomial distribution
- binomial probability formula

- expected value and standard deviation of a binomial distribution

Lesson Planning

Class Time

Two days

Materials

For Activity 7.1, about 40 identical paper or plastic cups (two cups for each student), a container of bottled water, and a container of tap water (both at the same temperature). Pepsi and Coke, or a diet soda and regular soda of the same brand may be used as substitutes for the different waters.

Suggested Assignments

Classwork		
Essential	**Recommended**	**Optional**
Activity 7.1 D6–D8, D11, D12 P5, P7, P8	D9, D10, D14 P6, P9	D13

Homework		
Essential	**Recommended**	**Optional**
E8–E12, E14	E13, E15, E17	E16, E18

Lesson Notes: Binomial Probabilities

Discussion

D6. Each outcome is made up of a series of four trials, each of which results in B or T with $P(B) = P(T) = \frac{1}{2}$. Thus, using the Multiplication Rule for Independent Events, the probability of any one of the 16 outcomes is $\frac{1}{2} \cdot \frac{1}{2} \cdot \frac{1}{2} \cdot \frac{1}{2} = \frac{1}{16}$.

D7.

Number of People Who Select Tap Water	Number of Outcomes	Probability
0	1	.015625
1	6	.09375
2	15	.234375
3	20	.3125
4	15	.234375
5	6	.09375
6	1	.015625

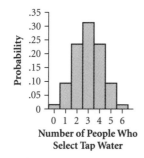

Practice

P5. Let X = number of heads from 8 flips of a coin.

$$P(X = 3) = \binom{8}{3}(.5)^8 = .21875$$

25% of 8 is 2 heads and

$$P(X = 2) = \binom{8}{2}(.5)^8 = .109375$$

$$P(X = 7 \text{ or } X = 8) = .03125 + .00391 \approx .03516$$

Lesson Notes: The Binomial Probability Formula

Why Both Independence and Fixed Probability?

In the box giving the binomial probability formula on page 394 of the student text, there are four conditions that a series of trials must meet before you can use the formula:

B: They are binomial—each trial must have one of two different outcomes, one called a "success" and the other a "failure."

I: Each trial is independent of the others. That is, the probability of a success doesn't change or depend on what has happened before.

N: There are a fixed number, n, of trials.

S: The probability, p, of a success is the same on each trial, $0 < p < 1$.

Your students may ask why both I and S are necessary. Aren't these saying the same thing?

Does a fixed value of p *indicate that trials are independent?*

No, it does not. For example, suppose Jack and Jill plan to go *together* up the hill to fetch a pail of water next Saturday, as long as it does not rain. If it rains, neither will go. The probability of rain is .2. Either each person will go up the hill (a success) or neither will go. There are a fixed number of trials (people): 2. The probability of a success on each trial is .8. That is, the probability that Jack goes up the hill is .8, and the probability that Jill goes up the hill is .8. However, the trials are not independent. If Jack goes, so will Jill, and vice versa.

Does the fact that the trials are independent indicate a fixed value of p?

Again, the answer is no. Suppose Jack and Jill each plan to flip a penny twice and count the number of heads in the two trials. They use different pennies, and Jill's is a two-headed penny. This means that the probability that she gets heads is higher than the probability that Jack gets heads. In this case, the trials are independent—what happens on Jack's flip does not affect the probability of Jill getting a head. But the probability of a success on the two flips is different.

Using the Calculator to Find Binomial Probabilities

You will have to decide how soon you want your students to go to the calculator when computing binomial probabilities as described next.

Calculating Binomial Probabilities with the TI-83

On the TI-83 the binomial probability distribution function is found by pressing [2nd] [DISTR] and selecting 0:binompdf(from the DISTR submenu. Upon selecting this function, the syntax is binompdf(n,p,x), where n is the number of trials, p is the probability of success on any one trial, and x is the number of successes or a list of numbers set in braces. If x is omitted, a list of probabilities for 0 to n is returned. Thus, binompdf(4,.2,3) gives the probability of exactly 3 successes out of 4 trials where the probability of success on any one trial is .2. The entry binompdf(4,.2)→L1 calculates the binomial probability distribution for $n = 4$, $p = .2$, and $x = 0, 1, 2, 3$, and 4 and stores the probabilities in list L1.

Calculating Binomial Probabilities with Minitab

To calculate binomial probabilities with Minitab, first enter into a column, say C1, the numbers of successes, x, for which probabilities are desired. Usually, this column will contain all possible values of x so that the entire distribution can be generated. Then, choose **Binomial** from the Calc | Probability Distributions menu. In the Binomial Distribution dialog box, select **Probability**, enter the Number of trials and the Probability of success, and enter C1 as the Input column. You can enter another column, say C2, into Optional storage. If no column is specified, the probabilities will be displayed in the session window.

Calculating Binomial Probabilities with Fathom

You have many options for calculating binomial probabilities in Fathom. One option—which is similar to using lists on a calculator or columns in Minitab—is to create a case table of probabilities. First, create a new case table and define two attributes: success and binomial. Enter into the success column the number of successes, x, for which probabilities are desired. Usually this column should contain all possible values of x so that the entire distribution can be generated. Then double-click the collection and define the binomial attribute by entering the formula binomialProbability(success, n, p), where n is the number of trials and p is the probability of success on any one trial. The formula will fill the attribute column with the binomial probabilities.

Another option is to follow the procedure above, but use sliders for n and p, so that the table is dynamic. A third option is to create a new graph, change it to a function plot, and plot a function in the form $y = $ binomialProbability(round(x), n, p). This creates a distribution plot for all values of x, but you should focus only on the integer values. A fourth option, also using a function plot, is to plot a value in the form binomialProbability(x, n, p),

where x is a particular number of successes. This shows the binomial probability for the particular value of x and graphs a vertical line at that value.

Discussion

D8.

Number of College Graduates	Probability
0	.133484
1	.311462
2	.311462
3	.173035
4	.057678
5	.011536
6	.001282
7	.000061

D9. $P(\textit{number of college grads} = k) = P(\textit{number not college grads} = 7 - k)$

Number of College Graduates	Number Who Aren't College Graduates	Probability
0	7	.133484
1	6	.311462
2	5	.311462
3	4	.173035
4	3	.057678
5	2	.011536
6	1	.001282
7	0	.000061

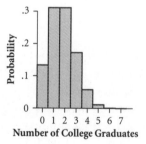
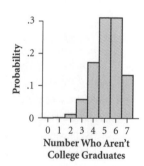

D10. Using the general Multiplication Rule, the probability that none will be chocoholics is

$$\frac{8}{12} \cdot \frac{7}{11} \cdot \frac{6}{10} \cdot \frac{5}{9} \cdot \frac{4}{8} \cdot \frac{3}{7} \cdot \frac{2}{6} \approx .010101$$

Using the binomial probability formula (inappropriately), where $p = \frac{4}{12} = \frac{1}{3}$, the probability is

$$P(X = k) = \binom{n}{k} p^k (1-p)^{n-k}$$

$$P(X = 0) = \binom{7}{0}\left(\frac{1}{3}\right)^0 \cdot \left(1 - \frac{1}{3}\right)^7 \approx .05853$$

Quite a difference!

D11. No. The binomial distribution will not be a good model in this scenario because the sampling is without replacement from a small population. Suppose the first person selected was a senior. Then the probability of selecting a senior on the second trial is $\frac{9}{19} \approx .47$, quite different from .5. An important assumption of the binomial distribution is that the trials are independent.

Practice

P6. **a.** $P(0) = (1 - .112)^5 \approx .5522$ or

$$\binom{5}{0}(.112)^0 (.888)^5 \approx .5522$$

b. $P(X \geq 1) = 1 - P(X = 0) \approx 1 - .5522 = .4478$

c.

Number of Dropouts	Probability
0	.552160
1	.348209
2	.087836
3	.011078
4	.000699
5	.000018

P7. Assign the triples 001 to 112 to represent the dropouts. The other triples 113 to 199 and 000 will represent non-dropouts. Start at a random spot in a random digit table, observe five triples, and count the number of triples representing dropouts. Record this number. Continuing where you left off in the table, repeat this process hundreds of times and make a frequency distribution of the number of dropouts in your hundreds of random samples. For the lines given, letting N denote the event that the person is not a dropout and letting D denote the event that the person is a dropout, you get the samples shown at the bottom of the page.

In the first sample of five, there are no dropouts. In the second, there is one dropout.

Activity 7.1: Can People Identify the Tap Water?

This activity is essential as an introduction to the use of the binomial distribution in significance testing.

You will need about 20 volunteers, which could be another classroom of students or the students in this class.

1. Characteristics of a good design include having the two types of water at the same temperature and poured at about the same time, randomizing which type of water is given first to each subject, and using identical cups for each type of water except for perhaps a small mark on the bottom for identification purposes.

2. For this distribution, $n = 20$ and $p = .5$.

Number Who Guess Correctly	Probability
0	.0000
1	.0000
2	.0002
3	.0011
4	.0046
5	.0148
6	.0370
7	.0739
8	.1201
9	.1602
10	.1762
11	.1602
12	.1201
13	.0739
14	.0370
15	.0148
16	.0046
17	.0011
18	.0002
19	.0000
20	.0000

Lesson 7.2, P7

892 | 54 9 | 953 | 8 18 | 315 | | 457 | 16 3 | 627 | 0 79 | 665 | |

  N   N   N   N   N | N   N   N   D   N

3. On the average, 10 people will select the tap water even if no one can tell the difference.

4. Student opinions will vary. The distribution shown in step 2 represents what would happen if people cannot tell the difference. It's not unusual for 13 or more people to be correct when no one can tell the difference, but it would be unusual for 17 or more to be correct. What is the cut-off so we would be convinced people aren't just guessing? It is standard to say that the result from the sample has to be in the upper 5% of the distribution. About 6% of the time, 14 or more people correctly select the tap water, if all 20 are guessing, and about 2% of the time, 15 or more select correctly. For your results to be in the upper 5%, 15 or more people would have to correctly select tap water.

5. It is common to find no convincing evidence that people can tell the bottled water from tap water.

Lesson Notes: Shape, Center, and Spread

Discussion

D12. *Shape.* For small values of p (close to 0) the binomial distributions are highly skewed toward the larger values of x. As p increases to .5, the distributions get more symmetric, with perfect symmetry achieved at $p = .5$. As p increases from .5 to 1, the distributions get increasingly skewed toward the smaller values of x.

As n increases, the skewness decreases for values of p different from .5 and the distributions tend to look more and more normal. For $p = .5$, the binomial distribution is symmetric and mound-shaped for any sample size.

Center. Because the mean is located at np, it increases with both n and p.

Spread. Again, the standard deviation increases with n. For a fixed n, the standard deviation is largest around $p = .5$ and gets smaller as p gets closer to 0 or 1.

D13.

Sample Size: n	Mean: np	SD: $\sqrt{np(1-p)}$
4	1	0.8660
10	2.5	1.3693
20	5	1.9365
40	10	2.7386

a. As students also saw in Section 5.4, for the counts or totals, the mean increases as the sample size increases. However, for a proportion, the mean stays constant, at p, for all sample sizes.

b. The standard deviation of the total number of college graduates in the samples increases as the sample size increases. This is quite different from the behavior of standard deviations of sample proportions, where the standard deviation decreases as the sample size increases.

D14. If X denotes the number of CD players that fail in the first month, X has a binomial distribution with $n = 10$ and $p = .08$.

Because the seller sells all 10 players for $100 each, the gain, G, is $G = 100(10) - 200X$. It follows that $E(G) = 100(10) - 200E(X) = 100(10) - 200(10)(.08) = 1000 - 160 = \$840$.

Practice

P8. **a.** Because the median income has half of the incomes below it and half above it, the chance of a randomly selected income exceeding the median is .5. So, we have a binomial distribution with $n = 5$ and $p = .5$. If X denotes the number of households with income exceeding the median, the probability distribution is the following:

Number of Households Whose Income Exceeds \$39,000	Probability
0	.03125
1	.15625
2	.31250
3	.31250
4	.15625
5	.03125

The probability of four or more households having incomes exceeding the median is .1875, the sum of the bottom two entries in the table. (In answering specific probability questions of this type, it is good to have students get into the habit of looking at the entire distribution.)

b. **i.** If X denotes the number of households with incomes below the median in a random sample of 16, then X has a binomial distribution with $n = 16$ and $p = .5$. Thus, $E(X) = np = 16(.5) = 8$.

ii. The standard deviation of X is given by $\sigma_X = \sqrt{np(1 - p)} = \sqrt{16(.5)(.5)} = 2$

iii. The exact binomial calculation gives $P(X \geq 10) \approx .227$.

c. This would be a very rare result, so you might suspect that the sample was not selected randomly. The sample selection method seems biased toward households with larger incomes.

P9. To get 60% correct, you have to get 3 or more on the 5-question quiz and 12 or more on the 20-question quiz. Looking at the graphs in Display 7.7 on page 396, the probability of getting 3 or more correct on a 5-question quiz is .5. On a 20-question quiz, the probability of getting 12 or more correct is about .25. It would be much better to have a 5-question quiz.

Exercises

E8. **a.** $\binom{5}{1}\left(\frac{6}{36}\right)^1\left(\frac{30}{36}\right)^4 \approx .4019$

b. $\binom{5}{3}\left(\frac{6}{36}\right)^3\left(\frac{30}{36}\right)^2 \approx .03215$

c. $P(\textit{at least one } 7) = 1 - P(\textit{no } 7) = 1 - \left(\frac{30}{36}\right)^5 \approx .5981$

d. $P(\textit{at most one } 7) = P(\textit{no } 7) + P(\textit{one } 7) =$

$\binom{5}{0}\left(\frac{6}{36}\right)^0\left(\frac{30}{36}\right)^5 + \binom{5}{1}\left(\frac{6}{36}\right)^1\left(\frac{30}{36}\right)^4 \approx .8038$

E9. **a.** $P(0, 1, 2, 3, \text{ or } 4 \textit{ doubles}) \approx .0202$. On the TI-83, you can get this in one step using the

binomial cumulative distribution function, binomcdf(60,1/6,4). The function is found by pressing 2nd [DISTR] and selecting A:binomcdf(from the DISTR submenu.

b. First, both $np = 60\left(\frac{1}{6}\right) = 10$ and $n(1 - p) = 60\left(\frac{5}{6}\right) = 50$ are at least 10, but the former just barely. Using the normal approximation from Section 5.4, $\mu_X = 60\left(\frac{1}{6}\right) = 10$, and $\sigma_X = \sqrt{60(1/6)(5/6)} \approx 2.8868$. So, $z = \frac{4 - 10}{2.8868} \approx -2.0784$.

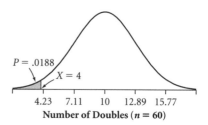

The probability is .01884, or .01883 if you do no rounding. This is reasonably close to the exact answer in part a.

E10. **a.** See the equation at the bottom of the page.

b. $\mu_X = 25(.127) = 3.175$, and $\sigma_X = \sqrt{25(.127)(.873)} \approx 1.6649$.

E11. **a.** $P(X \leq 10) = \text{binomcdf(100,.127,10)} \approx .2614$

b. First, both $np = 100(.127) = 12.7$ and $n(1 - p) = 100(.873) = 87.3$ are at least 10. So using the normal approximation, $\mu_X = 100(.127) = 12.7$ and $\sigma_X = \sqrt{100(.127)(.873)} \approx 3.3297$. Then, $z = \frac{10 - 12.7}{3.3297} = -.8109$.

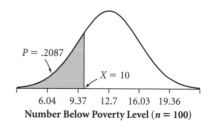

Lesson 7.2, E10a

$$P(X \geq 2) = 1 - P(X < 2) = 1 - P(X = 0) - P(X = 1)$$

$$= 1 - \binom{25}{0}(.127)^0(.873)^{25} - \binom{25}{1}(.127)^1(.873)^{24}$$

$$\approx .8446$$

The probability is .2087. This is fairly close to the answer in part a, which is exact.

E12. **a.** $E(earnings) = 15(.05)(10) - 15(1) = -\$7.50$

b. Because of the \$15 spent for the tickets, in order to gain \$10 or more, you must win \$25 or more. The only way you can do this is to win on 3 or more of the tickets: $P(3\ or\ more\ wins) = P(X \geq 3) = 1 - P(X \leq 2) \approx 1 - .9638 = .0362.$

E13. **a.** If the firm's gain is denoted by G and the number of wells that produce oil is denoted by X, then $G = 1{,}000{,}000X - 500{,}000$ because it costs \$50,000 to drill each of 10 wells. Then,

$$E(G) = 1{,}000{,}000 \cdot E(X) - 500{,}000$$
$$= 1{,}000{,}000(10)(.1) - 500{,}000$$
$$= \$500{,}000$$

b. $\sigma_G = 1{,}000{,}000\sigma_X = 1{,}000{,}000\sqrt{10(.1)(.9)} \approx 948{,}683.30$

c. For the firm to lose money, all 10 wells must be dry. The probability of this is $(.9)^{10} \approx .3487.$

d. For the firm to make \$1.5 million or more, 2 or more wells must produce oil. The probability of this is $1 - P(0\ or\ 1\ produces) \approx 1 - .7361 = .2639.$

E14. **a.** $P(at\ least\ one\ alarm\ sounds) = 1 - P(all\ alarms\ fail) = 1 - (.3)^3 = .973$

b. $P(X \geq 1) = 1 - P(X = 0) = 1 - (.3)^6 = .99927.$ No, the two probabilities are nearly the same.

c. Solving $1 - (.3)^n = .99$ gives $n = 3.825$, which rounds up to $n = 4$. This equation can be solved by trial and error or by logarithms.

E15. **a.** If X denotes the number of defective tapes in the sample, then $P(X\ is\ at\ least\ 1) = P(X \geq 1) = 1 - P(X = 0) = 1 - (1 - p)^n$, where p is the probability of observing a defective tape. This probability, $P(X \geq 1)$, is given as .5. With $p = .1$, the equation becomes $1 - (.9)^n = .5$ or $n \approx 6.5788$, which rounds up to $n = 7$.

b. With $p = .05$, the equation is $1 - (.95)^n = .5$ or $n \approx 13.513$, which rounds up to $n = 14$.

E16. If d is a constant, $E(dX) = dE(X)$, so $E\left(\frac{X}{n}\right) = \left(\frac{1}{n}\right)E(X) = \left(\frac{1}{n}\right)(np) = p.$

If d is a constant, $\sigma_{dX} = |\,d\,|\,\sigma_X$, so

$$\sigma_{(X/n)} = \frac{1}{n}\sigma_X = \frac{1}{n}\sqrt{np(1 - p)}$$
$$= \sqrt{\frac{np(1 - p)}{n^2}}$$
$$= \sqrt{\frac{p(1 - p)}{n}}$$

These are the same formulas as in Section 5.4.

E17. The expected value of 0.75 indicates the average number of college graduates that would appear in many random samples of size 3. Suppose 100 different polls each randomly selected three adults from the population and the total number of college graduates in all 100 polls was 75. Then these 100 samples average 0.75 college graduates per sample.

E18. **a.** The following table shows the distribution for $n = 2$ and probability of success p.

X	P(X)
0	$\binom{2}{0}p^0q^2 = q^2$
1	$\binom{2}{1}p^1q^1 = 2pq$
2	$\binom{2}{2}p^2q^0 = p^2$

The sum of the probabilities is $q^2 + 2qp + p^2 = (q + p)^2 = 1^2 = 1.$

b. This table shows the distribution for $n = 3$.

X	P(X)
0	$\binom{3}{0}p^0q^3 = q^3$
1	$\binom{3}{1}p^1q^2 = 3pq^2$
2	$\binom{3}{2}p^2q^1 = 3p^2q$
3	$\binom{3}{3}p^3q^0 = p^3$

The sum of the probabilities is $q^3 + 3pq^2 + 3p^2q + p^3 = (q + p)^3 = 1^3 = 1.$

c. Using the binomial theorem:

$$(q + p)^n = \binom{n}{n}q^n p^{n-n} + \binom{n}{n-1}q^{n-1}p^{n-(n-1)}$$

$$+ \binom{n}{n-2}q^{n-2}p^{n-(n-2)} + \cdots$$

$$+ \binom{n}{2}q^2 p^{n-2}$$

$$+ \binom{n}{1}q^1 p^{n-1} + \binom{n}{0}q^0 p^n$$

$$= P(X = 0) + P(X = 1)$$

$$+ P(X = 2) + \cdots + P(X = n - 2)$$

$$+ P(X = n - 1) + P(X = n)$$

So the terms in the expansion are the probabilities of a binomial distribution with n trials and probability of success p.

Note: We have shown at left that

$$P(X = 0) + P(X = 1) + \cdots + P(X = n - 1)$$

$$+ P(X = n) = (q + p)^n$$

$$= ((1 - p) + p)^n$$

$$= 1^n$$

$$= 1$$

So the sum of the probabilities is 1.

7.3 The Geometric Distribution

Objectives

- to recognize a situation that can be modeled by a geometric distribution
- to use the geometric probability formula to compute probabilities and understand why the formula works
- to compute the expected value and standard deviation of a geometric distribution

Important Terms and Concepts

- waiting-time problems
- geometric distribution
- geometric probability formula
- expected value and standard deviation of a geometric distribution

Lesson Planning

Class Time

Two days

Materials

For Activity 7.2, a device for generating random outcomes. For Activity 7.3, graph paper.

Suggested Assignments

Classwork		
Essential	**Recommended**	**Optional**
Activity 7.2	D16, D18–D20	Activity 7.3
D15, D17	P12, P13	D21
P10, P11		

Homework		
Essential	**Recommended**	**Optional**
E19–E21	E23, E24	E22, E25

Lesson Notes: Waiting-Time Situations

Activity 7.2: Waiting for Type A Blood

This activity is essential so that students can understand the nature of the geometric distribution. Activity 7.2 helps students understand what distinguishes a geometric distribution from other distributions. In addition, they will get practice in the use of the terms *at least* and *at most*.

1. Look at a single digit. You could let the digits 0–3 represent a donation that is type A and the other digits represent a donation that is another blood type.

2–4. Results will vary.

5. The following plot shows the frequencies for values of *x* obtained from 250 repetitions of the waiting time until the first success with $p = .4$. The mean of the 250 waiting times is 2.428, slightly smaller than the expected waiting time of 2.5. The estimated mean typically will be too small because a small simulation usually won't produce any of the large possible values for X.

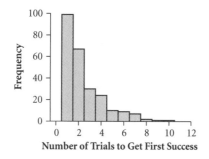

6. Answers will vary according to your students' simulation. The theoretical answers are (i) .24 (ii) .92224 (iii) .6 (iv) .8704.

7. The first checked donation is the most likely donation to be the first one that is type A. That probability is .4. Each subsequent checked donation has the same chance of being type A itself, but a number of failures have to occur before it even has the chance of being the first that is type A.

Discussion

D15. a. 1 trial is the shortest; there is no longest possible waiting time; 1 trial is most likely because there are no failures that have to occur beforehand.

b. The height of the first bar is .8 because that is the probability of getting a success on the first trial. To get the first success on the second trial, you must first fail and then succeed. Using the Multiplication Rule for Independent Events, this probability and the height of the second bar is (.2)(.8), or .16.

c. All four distributions show bars of decreasing height as the value of X increases, and all are skewed to the larger values. However, the rate at which the bars grow shorter increases as *p* increases. That is, the probabilities remain fairly constant between $X = 1$ and $X = 5$ when $p = .1$ but grow smaller very quickly in that same interval when $p = .8$.

The distributions are skewed toward the larger values in a very special way; the height of each bar is a fixed proportion $(1 - p)$ of the bar to its left. This is the property that makes the distribution "geometric." The plots differ in their spread; as *p* increases, the spread decreases.

D16. Examples include flipping a coin, counting the number of trials until you get a head, and counting randomly selected people until you see a male.

Practice

P10. a. The probability of getting a sum of 7 is $\frac{1}{6}$, so the probability of getting a sum of 7 for the first time on your first roll is $\frac{1}{6}$ and for the first time on your second roll is $\left(\frac{5}{6}\right)\left(\frac{1}{6}\right) = \frac{5}{36}$.

b. The graph should look like the following:

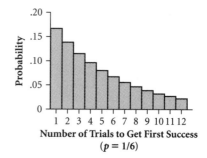

c. The sum of the heights of the bars (the probabilities) is less than 1. There are more possible values of X to the right of the last bar (in fact, an infinite number of possible values), but these values have very small probabilities.

Lesson Notes: The Formula for a Geometric Distribution

Geometric probabilities may be calculated with technology as shown in the following paragraphs.

Calculating Geometric Probabilities with the TI-83

On the TI-83 the geometric probability distribution function is found by pressing [2nd] [DISTR] and selecting D:geometpdf(from the DISTR submenu. Upon selecting this function, the syntax is geometpdf(p,x), where p is the probability of success and x is the number of trials until the first success or a list of numbers set in braces. For example, geometpdf(.1,{1,2,3,4,5}) gives the first five probabilities of the first plot in Display 7.8 on page 401 in the student text.

Calculating Geometric Probabilities with Minitab

The geometric distribution is easy to program into Minitab whenever such probabilities are needed. The following program sets the first 30 possible values of X into column C1, sets the variable K1 equal to the probability of success (.1 here), and calculates the geometric probabilities and stores them in column C2. To enter this program in Minitab, you must enable command language by clicking in the session window and choosing **Enable Command Language** from the Editor menu.

```
MTB > set C1
DATA > 1(1:30)
DATA > end
MTB > let K1=.1
MTB > let C2 = K1*(1-K1)**(C1-1)
```

Calculating Geometric Probabilities with Fathom

In Fathom, you calculate geometric probabilities with a formula or function in the form geometricProbability(x, p, 1, 1), where x is the number of trials until the first success and p is the probability of success. The 1s set the function's scale and minimum. As with the binomialProbability function (see page 43), you can use geometric Probability in a case table, with sliders to make a dynamic case table, in a function plot to create a distribution plot (use round(x) instead of x), or in a function plot to calculate the probability for a particular number of trials.

Solving "at least" Problems

Sometimes students will be asked to find the probability that it takes "at least" c trials to get the first success. That is, students are asked for the probability shown at the bottom of the page.

But there is another option. In general,

$$P(X \text{ is at least } c) = q^{c-1}p + q^c p + q^{c+1}p + \cdots$$
$$= p(q^{c-1} + q^c + q^{c+1} + \cdots)$$
$$= p\left(\frac{q^{c-1}}{1-q}\right)$$
$$= p\left(\frac{q^{c-1}}{p}\right) = q^{c-1}$$

The formula for the sum of an infinite geometric series was used in the next to last step. In short, the condition that X is at least c means that there must have been $c - 1$ failures up to this point but that anything can happen after that.

Discussion

D17. a. $(.9)(.9)(.1)$ or $(.9)^2(.1) = .081$

b. $P(X \le 3) = P(X = 1) + P(X = 2) + P(X = 3) = .1 + (.9)(.1) + (.9)^2(.1) = .271$; $P(X \ge 3) = 1 - P(X \le 2) = 1 - .1 - (.9)(.1) = .81$

c. .81. The same probability as in part b.

Lesson 7.3 Notes, Solving "at least" Problems

$$P(X \ge c) = P(X = c) + P(X = c + 1) + P(X = c + 2) + P(X = c + 3) + \cdots$$

This can be computed by finding

$$1 - P(X < c) = 1 - [P(X = 1) + P(X = 2) + \cdots + P(X = c - 1)]$$

d. Because each trial is independent of those that came before, the process does not remember that the technician has already been checking donations. You can compute the probability as though he had not yet checked any donations.

D18. The students should first make a table like the following:

Number of Flip	Theoretical Number of Flippers Left After Flip
0	200
1	100
2	50
3	25
4	12.5
5	6.25
6	3.125
7	1.5625
8	0.78125
9	0.390625
10	0.1953125

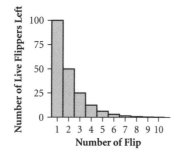

The plot should have roughly the same shape as the one from Activity 3.5. However, the heights of the bars will vary quite a bit between the two plots.

D19. Here, $p = \frac{1}{6}$. There are three ways of computing the probability of requiring 3 rolls or more:

I. $P(takes\ 3\ rolls) + P(takes\ 4\ rolls) + P(takes\ 5\ rolls) + \cdots$

$$\left(\frac{5}{6}\right)^2\left(\frac{1}{6}\right) + \left(\frac{5}{6}\right)^3\left(\frac{1}{6}\right) + \left(\frac{5}{6}\right)^4\left(\frac{1}{6}\right) + \cdots$$

$$= \frac{1}{6} \cdot \left[\left(\frac{5}{6}\right)^2 + \left(\frac{5}{6}\right)^3 + \left(\frac{5}{6}\right)^4 + \cdots\right]$$

$$= \frac{1}{6} \cdot \left[\frac{\left(\frac{5}{6}\right)^2}{\left(1 - \frac{5}{6}\right)}\right]$$

$$= \frac{1}{6} \cdot \frac{25}{6} = \frac{25}{36}$$

(See Exercise 24 for the formula for the sum of a geometric series: $a + ar + ar^2 + ar^3 + ar^4 + \cdots = \frac{a}{1-r}$ as long as $|r| < 1$)

II. $1 - P(2\ or\ fewer\ rolls) =$
$1 - \left[\left(\frac{1}{6}\right) + \left(\frac{5}{6}\right)\left(\frac{1}{6}\right)\right] = \frac{25}{36}$

III. $P(fail\ on\ first\ 2\ rolls) = \left(\frac{5}{6}\right)\left(\frac{5}{6}\right) = \frac{25}{26}$

Practice

P11. a. You are looking for nondefective engines. Therefore, $p = .91$. The probability of selecting the first nondefective engine on the third trial is $P(X = 3) = (.09)(.09)(.91) = .007371$.

b. $P(X < 4) = (.91) + (.09)(.91) + (.09)^2(.91) = .91 + .0819 + .007371 \approx .9993$. This value also can be computed as $P(X \le 3) = 1 - P(X > 3) = 1 - (.09)^3 \approx .9993$. The $(.09)^3$ is used because the first three trials must be failures but anything can happen after that.

P12. If the lines are busy 60% of the time, the chance of getting a call through is only $p = .4$. Thus,

a. $P(X = 1) = .4$

b. $P(X = 2) = .6(.4) = .24$

c. $P(X = 4) = (.6)^3(.4) = .0864$

d. You are assuming that whether you get through or not is independent of the outcome on any previous calls and that each call still has a probability of .4 of being completed. This condition might not be true if your calls are close together or placed at a particularly busy time of day. Ideally, for the geometric model to work well your calls should be placed at randomly selected times.

Activity 7.3: The Expected Value of a Geometric Distribution

Activity 7.3 is optional. In this activity students discover that the expected value of a geometric distribution is $\frac{1}{p}$.

1–2. The following table shows both the observed mean, or the expected value based on results for the values of X from 1 through 30, and the true expected value, based on theoretical results for all values of X. Students will have only the observed results.

p	Observed Mean	Expected Value
.1	8.3044	10
.2	4.9567	5
.3	3.3326	3.3333
.4	2.499993	2.5
.5	1.99999997	2
.6	1.6667	1.6667
.7	1.4286	1.4286
.8	1.2500	1.25
.9	1.1111	1.1111

3. Students' values will be slightly smaller because they used only the first 30 values in the distribution. After the first 3, the differences appear only past the fourth decimal place.

4. The following plot shows both theoretical means (dots) and observed means (**x**'s). Notice that they practically coincide, except for $p = .1$. Again, the students will have only the observed means. The theoretical points exactly follow a curved path that is symmetric with respect to the line $y = x$, and the observed points very closely follow the same path.

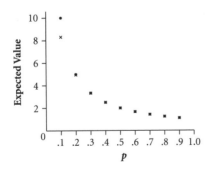

5. The plot of the theoretical means (dots) versus $\frac{1}{p}$ is linear, with slope 1. For the observed points (**x**'s), the slope of a line fit through these points is

close to 1, although the point at the extreme upper right is a little out of the pattern.

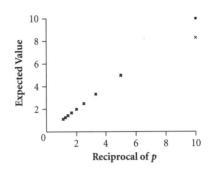

It looks as though $E(X) = \frac{1}{p}$ would be a good rule for the expected value of the geometric distribution with probability of success p.

Lesson Notes: Expected Value and Standard Deviation

Discussion

D20. **a.** $E(X) = \frac{1}{p} = \frac{1}{.4} = 2.5$
$\sigma_X = \sqrt{1 - p}/p = \sqrt{1 - .4}/.4 \approx 1.94$
b. It takes you, on average, 2.5 calls to get through the first time and then 2.5 more calls to get through the second time. So the expected total number of tries is $2(2.5) = 5$.
c. Neither of you has any advantage. There is no memory to the process, so it is as though both of you are starting from scratch.

D21. The expected value is cut in half because $E(X_{2p}) = \frac{1}{2p} = \frac{1}{2} \cdot \frac{1}{p} = \frac{1}{2} \cdot E(X_p)$. That is, when you double the probability of a success, on average it will take half as long to get the first success.

Practice

P13. **a.** $\mu_X = \frac{1}{.1} = 10$
b. $\sigma_X = \sqrt{1 - .1}/.1 \approx 9.487$
c. $2(10) = 20$; $3(10) = 30$. It takes an average of 10 donations to get the first that is type B, and then it takes an average of 10 more to get another that is type B, and so on.

Exercises

E19. **a.** $\frac{1}{4}$ because you have to answer just one question correctly.
b. $P(X > 3) = \left(\frac{1}{4}\right)^3 \approx \frac{1}{64}$ because you have to be successful on the first three questions.

c. $\frac{1}{.75} = \frac{4}{3}$

d. You expect $32\left(\frac{1}{4}\right) = 8$ to be left after the first round, $8\left(\frac{1}{4}\right) = 2$ to be left after the second round, and only $2\left(\frac{1}{4}\right) = 0.5$ to be left after the third round. On average, 0.5 people will be left after the third round if all are guessing on each question.

E20. a. If 12% have at least one defect, then 88% have no defects, so $p = .88$. Then, $E(X) = \frac{1}{.88} \approx 1.1364$. The expected number before the third defective engine is found is $3(1.1364) \approx 3.4092$.

b. $\sigma_X = \sqrt{.12}/.88 \approx .3936$

c. Letting cost be denoted by C, $C = 100X$ because it costs $100 to test each engine. Thus,

$$E(C) = 100 \cdot E(X) \approx 100(1.1364) \approx \$113.64$$

$$\sigma_C = 100 \cdot \sigma_X \approx 100(.3936) \approx \$39.36$$

d. The figure of $200 is about 2.2 standard deviations above the mean, and a point that far away from the mean will not be reached often.

E21. a. You are looking for a successful well, and $p = .1$. Thus, $E(X) = \frac{1}{.1} = 10$.

b. Because each well costs $50,000 to drill, the cost of drilling, C, is given by $C = 50,000X$. Thus,

$$E(C) = 50,000E(X) = 50,000(10) = \$500,000$$

and

$$\sigma_C = 50,000\sigma_X = 50,000\left(\frac{\sqrt{.9}}{.1}\right) \approx \$474,341.65$$

Notice that the standard deviation is almost as large as the expected cost. There is *great* variability in this process.

c. $P(X \text{ is at least } 5) = (.9)^4 = .6561$, and $P(X \text{ is at least } 15) = (.9)^{14} \approx .2288$

E22. If we assume that the testing stops as soon as the cracks are detected for the first time and

that the tests are independent of one another, then the number of tests until the first detection will have a geometric distribution. Thus, $P(X > 5) = (1 - p)^5 = .01$ must be solved for p. We take the fifth root of each side of the equation to get $1 - p \approx .398$ or $p \approx .602$.

E23. The probabilities for a geometric distribution follow exactly this same pattern: $p, qp, q^2p, q^3p, q^4p, q^5p, \ldots$

E24. To use this formula, the first term is $a = p$ and the common ratio is $r = q$ where $q = 1 - p$:

$$p + qp + q^2p + q^3p + q^4p + \cdots = \frac{p}{1-q} = \frac{p}{p} = 1$$

E25. a. Using the table in Display 7.9 on page 403 of the student text, $E(X) = 1p + 2pq + 3pq^2 + 4pq^3 + \cdots$

b. First, see the equations at the bottom of the page. Now note that the expressions in the parentheses correspond to the rows given in part b of the student text.

c. Ignoring the p for now, and using the formula for the sum of an infinite geometric series on each row (inside each set of parentheses), each of which has a common ratio of q but a different first term, you find the sums of the rows are, respectively, $\left(\frac{1}{p}\right), \left(\frac{q}{p}\right), \left(\frac{q^2}{p}\right),$ $\left(\frac{q^3}{p}\right), \ldots$.

(Note that you will have to use the fact that $1 - q = p$ in the denominator.)

d. Using the formula once again to sum these row totals, you get

$$E(X) = p\left(\left(\frac{1}{p}\right) + \left(\frac{q}{p}\right) + \left(\frac{q^2}{p}\right) + \left(\frac{q^3}{p}\right) + \cdots\right)$$

$$= p\left(\frac{1}{p}\right)(1 + q + q^2 + q^3 + \cdots)$$

$$= \frac{1}{1-q}$$

$$= \frac{1}{p}$$

Lesson 7.3, E25b

$$E(X) = 1p + 2pq + 3pq^2 + 4pq^3 + \cdots$$

$$= p(1 + 2q + 3q^2 + 4q^3 + \cdots)$$

$$= p(1 + q + q + q^2 + q^2 + q^2 + q^3 + q^3 + q^3 + q^3 + \cdots)$$

Reordering gives

$$p[(1 + q + q^2 + q^3 + \cdots) + (q + q^2 + q^3 + \cdots) + (q^2 + q^3 + \cdots) + (q^3 + \cdots) + \cdots]$$

Review

Review Exercises

E26.

Number of Heads	Probability
0	1/32
1	5/32
2	10/32
3	10/32
4	5/32
5	1/32

$\mu_X = 2.5$, and $\sigma_X \approx 1.118$.

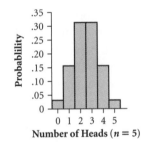

E27. **a.** $100,000\left(\frac{11}{1000}\right) = \$1100$
b. $10,000\left(\frac{31}{1000}\right) = \$310$
c. $x\left(\frac{0.1}{1000}\right) = 50$ or $x = \$500,000$

E28. **a.** The chance that at least one donation out of ten will be type B is

$$1 - (.9)^{10} \approx 1 - .349 = .651$$

You are assuming that the probability that the first donation checked is type B is .1, that the probability that any subsequent donation is type B is .1, and that the probability that a donation is type B is independent of the type of the donations previously checked.
b. Two ways of finding an answer to this problem have been presented in this text. The direct way is to use the binomial distribution with $n = 100$ and $p = .1$. A graphing calculator or computer can handle sample sizes this large. The exact calculation on a calculator is $1 -$ binomcdf(100,.1,9), which gives $P(X \text{ is 10 or more}) \approx .549$. An alternative method is to use the normal approximation

to the distribution of proportions. Both $np = 100(.1) = 10$ and $n(1 - p) = 100(.9) = 90$ are at least 10. The sample proportion for donations that are type B in a random sample of size 100 has approximately a normal distribution with a mean of .1. Because the normal distribution is symmetric with respect to its mean, the chance of seeing a sample proportion larger than or equal to .1 is approximately .5.
c. From direct binomial calculations, $1 -$ binomcdf(100,.1,15), $P(X \text{ is at least 16}) \approx .04$.

To use the normal approximation for sample proportions, the mean is .10 and the standard deviation is .03. (The conditions were checked in part b.) Thus, .16 is exactly two standard deviations above the mean of the distribution of sample proportions. Under the normal distribution, a randomly selected value lies more than two standard deviations above the mean with probability .025. This is not quite the same as the exact binomial value, but it is not a bad approximation to use in situations in which the technology to calculate the exact value may not be readily available. In either case, the blood bank does not have a good chance of getting the 16 type B donations out of a group of 100 donations. You should recommend a much larger sample size.
d. $P(X \geq 4) = (.9)^3 = .729$

E29. Using the binomial model for the number of students that apply out of $n = 120,000$, with $p = .1$, gives a mean of 12,000 and a standard deviation of about 104. But, the binomial model might not be a good model here, because these are not 120,000 independent decisions with $p = .1$ for the "success" of each one. Students tend to apply where their friends apply.

E30. **a.** Here, $p = .80$, and $P(X > 10) = 1 - P(X \leq 10) \approx 1 - .0026 = .9974$.
We are assuming that the region behaves like the country, with 80% of the girls wanting to do their best in all classes.
b. Here, $p = .65$, and $P(X > 10) = 1 - P(X \leq 10) \approx 1 - .1218 = .8782$.
Again, we are assuming that the region behaves like the country.
c. If you assume that half of the students in the population being sampled are girls, then

the probability that a randomly selected student will want to do his or her best in all classes is $p = .5(.80) + .5(.65) = .725$. With $n = 40$, $P(X > 20) = 1 - P(X \le 20) \approx 1 - .0021 = .9979$. Notice that even though the new p is midway between .80 and .65, the probability is not even close to being midway between the two probabilities in parts a and b.

E31. **a.** Here, $p = .86$, and $P(X > 430) \approx .480$. (Note that this probability is not .5 even though 430 is the expected number of successes.)

b. $C = 40X + 20(n - X)$
and
$E(C) = 40 \cdot E(X) + 20(n - E(X))$
$= 40(430) + 20(70) = \$18,600$
because $E(X) = np = 500(.86) = 430$.

c. Here, $p = .14$, and $E(number\ until\ first\ with\ no\ insurance) = \frac{1}{.14} \approx 7.143$. The expected number until two are found without health insurance is $2(7.143) = 14.286$.

E32. **a.** On a TI-83 calculator, enter the command binompdf(130,.9), press $\boxed{\text{STO}\rightarrow}$ $\boxed{\text{2nd}}$ $[\text{L1}]$ $\boxed{\text{ENTER}}$, which stores the probabilities of the different numbers of no shows in list L1, as shown in the following table. The first $P(X)$, .84793, is a cumulative probability.

Number of Passengers Who Show	Payout X	Probability P(X)
≤120	0	.84793
121	100	.06399
122	200	.04248
123	300	.02487
124	400	.01263
125	500	.00546
126	600	.00195
127	700	.00055
128	800	.00012
129	900	.00002
130	1000	.00000

$E(payout) = \sum x \cdot P(x) \approx \$31.804$

b. Let X denote the number of passengers who show up for the flight. We are given $p = .9$, where p is the probability a passenger shows up for the flight. Using the binomial model, which is okay if the passengers tend to make independent decisions, the task is to find n so that the binomial probability of $P(X > 120)$ is .05. Trial and error with the calculator or computer is good enough to see that n should be around 128. Notice that with 130 tickets sold, although the airline "expects" not to have to pay out for overbooked tickets, there is still a greater than 5% chance that they will.

E33. **a.** p

b. $1 - p$

c. The conditional probability of waiting more than $k + m$ trials for the first success, given that you have already waited more than m trials, is the same as starting all over and calculating the probability of waiting more than k trials as though you were starting fresh. Once you have waited m trials for the first success, the system has "forgotten" how long you waited and operates as though you are starting over. See the equation at the bottom of the page for a symbolic representation.

E34. **a.** The lot is accepted when there are no defective items in a random sample of size 5. The calculator command binompdf(5,p,0) gives the probability that there will be no defective items for each p. Alternatively, you can compute the probability that all five items will be good using $(1 - p)^5$. The probabilities are given in the following table.

p	$P(no\ defectives)$
0	1
.1	.59049
.3	.16807
.5	.03125

Lesson 7.3, E33c

$$P(X > k + m \mid X > m) = \frac{P(X > k + m)}{P(X > m)} = \frac{(1 - p)^{k+m}}{(1 - p)^m} = (1 - p)^k$$

b. The operating characteristic curve for the points in the table is shown in the first plot below. Notice that the probability of acceptance is high when the proportion of defective items in the lot is low and drops off rapidly as the proportion of defectives increases.

calculator the equation of the graph for $n = 5$ and $a = 1$ is $Y_1 = \text{binomcdf}(5,X,1)$.

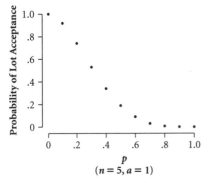

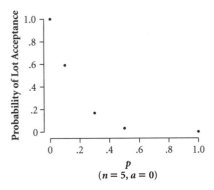

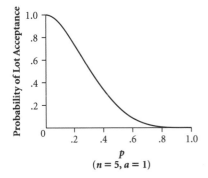

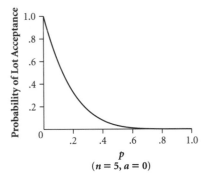

The second plot is the actual operating characteristic curve, which is a smooth continuous curve for *all* values of p, $0 \le p \le 1$. You can graph this curve on a calculator by defining $Y_1 = \text{binompdf}(5,X,0)$ in the $Y =$ menu and graphing Y_1 in an appropriate window. Here, X stands for the proportion of defective items, p.

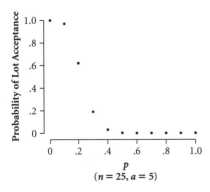

On a calculator, the equation of the graph for $n = 25$ and $a = 5$ is $Y_1 = \text{binomcdf}(25,X,5)$.

E35. **a.** To compute the probability of 1 or fewer defective items for a sample of size 5, use the calculator command $\text{binomcdf}(5,p,1)$. To compute the probability of 5 or fewer defective items for a sample of size 25, use $\text{binomcdf}(25,p,5)$.

The operating characteristic curves for the two plans are shown in the following plots. Again, these will be smooth continuous curves for *all* values of p, $0 \le p \le 1$, although students may plot discrete points. On a

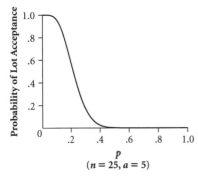

b. You would want a high probability of acceptance for p between 0 and .1. Both plans have high acceptance probabilities over this interval, but they are slightly higher for the plan ($n = 25$, $a = 5$).

c. At 30% defectives, the plan ($n = 5$, $a = 1$) has an acceptance probability around .5, which is quite high. (You would be accepting many bad lots.) The plan ($n = 25$, $a = 5$) has an acceptance probability of less than .20 when p is .30, and drops rapidly as p increases from there, which is what you are looking for.

E36. **a.** You are interested in one particular coupon out of five. Thus, your probability of success on any one purchase is $\frac{1}{5} = .2$, assuming the coupons are randomly distributed in equal numbers. You could sample random digits, counting the number of digits selected until the first 0 or 1 appears. This process should be repeated many times in order to generate a distribution of values for the number of coupons necessary to achieve success.

b. $P(purchase\ 4\ or\ fewer\ boxes) =$
$1 - P(desired\ coupon\ not\ in\ first\ 4\ boxes) =$
$1 - (.8)^4 = 1 - .4096 = .5904$

c. $E(number\ of\ boxes\ purchased) = \frac{1}{.2} = 5$

d. At the start, you have a chance of $\frac{2}{5}$ of getting a coupon you want, so you would expect to buy $\frac{5}{2}$ boxes to get one of the coupons. After one is found, you have a chance of $\frac{1}{5}$ of getting the remaining one on any one draw. So, you would expect to buy 5 more boxes to get this one. The expected number of boxes to get both coupons is, then, $\frac{5}{2} + 5 = 7.5$.

e. In the first stage, any coupon will denote success, and so the probability of success is 1. After you get one of these, the process starts over and any of the four remaining coupons will be a success, making the probability of success equal to $\frac{4}{5}$. After you find two coupons, the probability of success is reduced to $\frac{3}{5}$, and so on until you have all the coupons.

There are, then, five stages in the process. The expected waiting times until success are, respectively, 1, $\frac{5}{4}$, $\frac{5}{3}$, $\frac{5}{2}$, $\frac{5}{1}$. The overall expected waiting time is the sum of these, or about 11.4. If you are simulating by sampling random digits, continue until at least one digit from each group of pairs 0–1, 2–3, 4–5, 6–7, and 8–9 has been selected. It would be slightly easier to use a spinner with equal spaces numbered 1 to 5 or to draw (with replacement) slips of paper numbered 1 to 5 and to count how many trials it takes to hit every number from 1 to 5.

E37. **a.** Here we are asking, "On average, how many times do you expect to have to flip an individual copper flipper before it dies?" Students could carry out the actual experiment or use a random digit table, using, say, an odd digit to mean the flipper dies and an even digit to mean that it lives. The theoretical average length of time is 2 flips.

b. This question can be interpreted two ways by students: either "On average, how many *sets of flips* do you expect it will take for all 10 copper flippers to die?" or "On average, how many *individual* flips do you expect it will take for all 10 copper flippers to die?" Students could carry out the actual experiment or use a random digit table, beginning with a sequence of 10 digits with an even digit representing a penny that dies and an odd digit representing a penny that lives. The theoretical total number of flips is $2(10) = 20$ individual flips or, with the first interpretation, about 4.73 sets of flips.

c. Again, students can carry out the actual experiment or use a random digit table. On a given set of flips of 10 pennies, let X equal the number of pennies that die. Then $P(X \geq 1) = 1 - P(X = 0) = 1 - (.5)^{10} \approx .9990$, so the expected number of flips is approximately $\frac{1}{.9990} \approx 1.001$.

8

INFERENCE FOR PROPORTIONS

Overview

In this chapter, students begin their formal study of statistical inference. Statistical inference includes both confidence intervals and tests of significance (also called hypothesis tests).

Both confidence intervals and tests of significance are developed first graphically and then algebraically. In our experience, students have difficulty retaining the meaning of confidence intervals unless they first understand the geometry behind them, which is illustrated in Displays 8.3 and 8.4 and explained on pages 420–421 of the student text.

The logic behind confidence intervals and tests of significance is difficult for students, and the language is somewhat technical, but using that logic and language correctly is one of the main goals of an introductory statistics course, including Advanced Placement Statistics.

Goals

The primary goals of this chapter are to provide your students with the ability

- to understand the concept of a confidence interval for estimating the proportion of successes in a binomial population
- to construct such a confidence interval and interpret the results
- to use a test of significance to decide whether you should reject the claim that a sample was drawn from a binomial population with a specified proportion of successes
- to construct and interpret a confidence interval for the difference between the proportion of successes in one population and the proportion of successes in another population

- to use a test of significance to decide whether you should reject the claim that two samples were drawn from two binomial populations that have the same proportion of successes

Content Overview

In this chapter, students will use their understanding of sampling distributions, developed in Chapters 5 and 7 using simulation. The basic concept that students discovered for sampling distributions is used again and again for constructing confidence intervals and using tests of significance: If the sampling distribution can be considered approximately normal, 95% of all sample means will fall within two standard errors of the population mean. If students seem to lose this concept of a sampling distribution as you teach this chapter and Chapter 9, you may want to go back and construct a few sampling distributions by simulation and then assign D2 and P2 in Section 8.1 for review.

Sections 1 and 2 in this chapter are extremely important because they explain in detail the basics of inferential statistics: confidence intervals and significance tests.

Time Required

Traditional Schedule			Block	4 x 4 Block
Section 8.1				
4–5 days	Day 1	Overview, reasonably likely outcomes, Activity 8.1	4 days	2 long, 2 short
	Day 2	Meaning of a confidence interval, Activity 8.2		
	Day 3	From the chart to a formula, using the formula, Activity 8.3		
	Day 4	Capture rate, margin of error and sample size, opinion polls, sample size needed		
	Day 5	Summary, exercises		
Section 8.2				
4–5 days	Day 1	Overview, Activity 8.4, informal significance testing	4 days	2 long, 2 short
	Day 2	Statistical significance, the test statistic, critical values and level of significance		
	Day 3	Formal language of tests of significance		
	Day 4	Types of errors, minimizing the probability of an error, P-values, one- and two-sided tests		
	Day 5	Summary, exercises		
Section 8.3				
2–3 days	Day 1	Overview, sampling distribution for the difference of two proportions, Activity 8.5	2 days	2 long
	Day 2	Formula for the confidence interval, experiments to compare two treatments		
	Day 3	Summary, exercises		
Section 8.4				
3–4 days	Day 1	Overview, differences when there is no difference, Activity 8.6	3 days	2 long, 1 short
	Day 2	Theory of a significance test for the difference of two proportions		
	Day 3	Components of a significance test for the difference of two proportions		
	Day 4	Summary, exercises		
Review				
1 day			1 day	1 day

Materials

Section 8.1: For Activity 8.1, one $8\frac{1}{2}'' \times 11''$ sheet of paper for each student. For Activity 8.2, a transparent straightedge and a copy of "A Chart of Reasonably Likely Outcomes" for each student. (See Display 8.1 from the student text, reproduced as a blackline master at the end of Section 8.1.) For Activity 8.3, a calculator that generates random digits or a random digit table and a copy of "A Sample of 95% Confidence Intervals" for each student. (See Display 8.5 from the student text, reproduced as a blackline master at the end of Section 8.1.)

Section 8.2: For Activity 8.4, one penny for each student. Pennies from the 1960s are best because they tend to result in a low proportion of heads when spun.

Section 8.3: For Activity 8.5, a large bag of plain M&M's and a large bag of peanut M&M's. Colored beads may be substituted.

Section 8.4: For Activity 8.6, one sheet of graph paper for each student.

Suggested Assignments

Classwork

Section	Essential	Recommended	Optional
8.1	Activity 8.1, Activity 8.2, Activity 8.3 D1, D3–D6, D8, D9, D11–D16, D19 P1, P3–P11, P13, P14, P16	D7, D17, D18 P15	D2, D10 P2, P12
8.2	Activity 8.4 D20–D24, D26, D32, D34, D35, D37 P17–P19, P21–P25, P28, P29, P31	D25, D27, D29–D31, D33, D36, D38 P20, P26, P27, P30, P32	D28
8.3	Activity 8.5 D39–D41 P33, P34	D42–D44 P35, P36	
8.4	Activity 8.6 D45, D46, D48 P37, P38	D47, D49 P39	

Homework

Section	Essential	Recommended	Optional
8.1	E2, E3, E6, E8, E12	E1, E4, E5, E7, E9–E11	E13
8.2	E15, E16, E18	E14, E17, E21, E22	E19, E20
8.3	E23, E27	E24–E26, E28–E30	
8.4	E31, E33	E32, E34, E35, E37, E38	E36, E39–E41
Review	E42–E47, E50	E48, E51 (reading practice) or E52 (writing practice)	E49

8.1 Estimating a Proportion with Confidence

Objectives

- to find a confidence interval graphically
- to understand a confidence interval as consisting of those population proportions for which the result from the sample is reasonably likely
- to always check the three conditions before constructing a confidence interval
- to construct a confidence interval using the formula
- to interpret a confidence interval and the meaning of "confidence"
- to compute the required sample size for a given margin of error

Important Terms and Concepts

- reasonably likely outcome
- rare event
- confidence interval for a proportion
- level of confidence (capture rate)
- margin of error

Lesson Planning

Class Time

Four to five days

Materials

For Activity 8.1, one $8\frac{1}{2}'' \times 11''$ sheet of paper for each student. For Activity 8.2, a transparent straightedge and a copy of "A Chart of Reasonably Likely Outcomes" for each student.

For Activity 8.3, a calculator that generates random digits or a random digit table and a copy of "A Sample of 95% Confidence Intervals" for each student. (See Displays 8.1 and 8.5 from the student text, reproduced as blackline masters at the end of this section.)

Suggested Assignments

Classwork		
Essential	**Recommended**	**Optional**
Activities 8.1, 8.2, and 8.3	D7, D17, D18	D2, D10
D1, D3–D6, D8, D9, D11–D16, D19	P15	P2, P12
P1, P3–P11, P13, P14, P16		

Homework		
Essential	**Recommended**	**Optional**
E2, E3, E6, E8, E12	E1, E4, E5, E7, E9–E11	E13

Lesson Notes: Reasonably Likely Outcomes and Rare Events

This section begins with a review of Section 5.4, sampling distributions for a binomial proportion p. The definitions for reasonably likely outcomes and rare events are not in widespread use, but they give students an intuitive feel for the ideas that will come later.

Discussion

D1. **a.** The middle 95% of a sampling distribution for a binomial proportion p is cut off by the two points

$$p \pm 1.96 \sqrt{\frac{p(1 - p)}{n}}$$

which in this case equals

$$.35 \pm 1.96 \sqrt{\frac{.35(1 - .35)}{500}} \approx .35 \pm .042$$

So the two values are .308 and .392.

b. There are several ways to do the second part of this question. You could convert 145 out of 500 to the sample proportion .29 and note that because this proportion isn't in the interval in part a, it isn't reasonably likely to get 145 out of 500 when $p = .35$.

Alternatively, using the formula for reasonably likely numbers of successes at the bottom of the page, you get an interval from about 154.1 to 195.9. Because 145 doesn't fall within this interval, it is not a reasonably likely outcome.

D2. **a.** Using random digits, let 1 through 6 represent successes and the rest represent failures. Count the number of successes in many sets of 40 digits.

If students are using a TI-83 calculator, they can do this with the command randBin(40,.6). The calculator will return a single number, such as 23, to indicate that there were 23 successes out of a sample size of 40 with $p = .6$.

b. The TI-83 command randBin(40,.6,100) returns the number of successes in 100 different samples.

In Fathom, create a new collection and add 100 cases (**Analyze | New Cases**). Double-click the collection and define an attribute, *success*, by the formula randomBinomial(40,.6). You can view the number of successes in each of the 100 samples with a case table. You can recollect the 100 samples by selecting **Rerandomize** from the Analyze menu.

c. To generate a Minitab dot plot for 100 samples of size 40, use the menus or enter the commands

```
MTB > random 100 C1;
SUBC > binomial 40 0.6.
MTB > dotplot C1
```

(Remember that to enter commands, you must enable command language by clicking in the session window and choosing **Enable Command Language** from the Editor menu.)

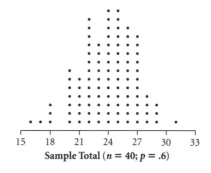
Sample Total ($n = 40$; $p = .6$)

Each dot in the plot gives the number of successes in a random sample of size 40 taken from a population with 60% successes.

A typical Fathom histogram created by dragging the success attribute from a case table to a graph follows.

Lesson 8.1, D1b

$$np \pm 1.96 \sqrt{np(1 - p)} = 500(.35) \pm 1.96 \sqrt{500(.35)(1 - .35)}$$
$$\approx 175 \pm 20.9$$

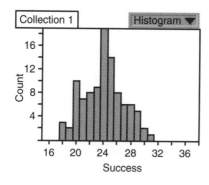

The most important concept to point out here (once again!) is that results from random samples vary. All of these results came from random samples of size 40 taken from a population with 60% successes.

d. Answers will vary according to the results from the simulation. For the dot plot in part c, around 2.5% of the time there were 17 successes or fewer (for a proportion of .425). Also around 2.5% of the time there were 30 successes or more (or .75). So it is reasonably likely to get any number of heads from 17 to 30. (The theoretical results are .448 to .752 or from about 18 successes to 30 successes, which is very close to the results from the simulation.)

Practice

P1. **a.** The middle 95% of the sampling distribution for $p = .4$ is bounded by the two points

$$p \pm 1.96 \sqrt{\frac{p(1-p)}{n}} = .4 \pm 1.96 \sqrt{\frac{.4(1-.4)}{50}}$$

$$\approx .4 \pm .136$$

or .264 and .536.

b. Getting 25 out of 50 is a sample proportion of .5. This is a reasonably likely outcome from a population with $p = .4$.

P2. You must repeatedly take samples of size 40 from a population with 30% successes. With random digits, let 1 through 3 represent successes and the rest represent failures. Count the number of successes in many sets of 40 digits. With a TI-83, you can do this with the command **randBin(40,.3)** and repeatedly pressing ENTER. Do this at least 100 times. Alternatively, the command

randBin(40,.3,100)→L1 stores numbers of successes for 100 samples in list L1. Sort the 100 results in ascending order with the command **SortA(L1)** and cut off the bottom 2.5% and the top 2.5%. Those cutoff points give the ends of the horizontal line segment for $p = .3$.

Activity 8.1: Determining Eye Dominance

Activity 8.1 is essential and requires only a couple of minutes.

Note: It is not necessary to use a piece of paper in Activity 8.1. As in Activity 6.4, students may hold their hands out at arms length, with hands and thumbs placed to make a triangular space or opening to see through. (A smaller space is better.) Through the space, students look at a small object at least 15 feet away. (See Activity 6.4 on page 369 of the student text.)

To use the paper, students can fold the paper in half, then in half the other way and tear out a small square in the folded corner. You should take results from exactly 40 students. Most classes will not have 40 students, so you may want to gather data beforehand from one of your other classes. If your class has more than 40 students, eliminate some students at random to get the total down to 40.

1. Make sure students understand that if they can not still see the object, the closed eye is the dominant eye.

2. The proportion of students who are right-eye dominant will vary. For a typical group of 40 students, about 25 to 30 will be right-eye dominant.

3. Answers will vary depending on the result from step 2. Probably, students won't think that 10% is plausible, but that 60% is. If, for example, 90% of the 40 students are right-eye dominant, students might be willing to make a statement such as, "We are pretty sure that more than half of all students are right-eye dominant." At this stage, student's responses probably won't be precise, although it would be great if they realized that with a sample of size 40, the value of $\hat{p}$ shouldn't be farther than about 15% from p:

$$1.96 \sqrt{\frac{p(1-p)}{n}} \approx 1.96 \sqrt{\frac{.5(1-.5)}{40}} \approx .15$$

Note that it may or may not be a reasonable assumption that your students are representative of all students with respect to eye dominance.

Lesson Notes: The Meaning of a Confidence Interval

Activity 8.2: Constructing a Chart of Reasonably Likely Outcomes

The following activity is essential for your students to get an intuitive understanding of confidence intervals.

To prepare for this activity, give each member of the class a transparent straightedge and a copy of "A Chart of Reasonably Likely Outcomes" (Display 8.1 in the student text, reproduced as a blackline master at the end of this section). You may want to make a transparency master of this chart as well.

1. The middle 95% of the sampling distribution for $p = .6$ is cut off by the two points

$$p \pm 1.96 \sqrt{\frac{p(1-p)}{n}} = .6 \pm 1.96 \sqrt{\frac{.6(1-.6)}{40}}$$

$$\approx .6 \pm .152$$

So the horizontal line segment at $p = .6$ should stretch from .448 to .752.

2–3. Answers will vary according to the results of Activity 8.1. If your class's sample proportion from that activity is between .448 and .752, then it is reasonable to assume that the true value of p might be .6. The reason is that if .6 is the true proportion of students who are right-eye dominant, then it is perfectly reasonable to get the result in a sample of size 40 that your class did. If your class's sample proportion from Activity 8.1 isn't between .448 and .752, then it isn't reasonable to assume that the true proportion is .6.

4–7. At this point divide the class so that there are about 10 groups, one for each of the population percentages 25%, 30%, 35%, 40%, 45%, 50%, 55%, 65%, 70%, and 75%. (60% was completed in step 1.) The line segments for the percentages 5%, 10%, 15%, 20% and 80%, 85%, 90%, 95% have already been placed on the chart because students shouldn't use the normal approximation for them as either np or $n(1-p)$ is less than 10.

Students will probably do step 4 using the formula they used in D1 and P1. If students use simulation, they can use the TI-83 command randBin(40,p,100)→L1, where p is their population proportion. This command stores 100 values in list L1.

If students use the formula, the middle 95% of a sampling distribution for a binomial proportion p is cut off approximately by the two points

$$p \pm 1.96 \sqrt{\frac{p(1-p)}{n}}$$

Have students come to the overhead projector and draw on the transparency master their horizontal line segments. If students used simulation, don't worry if the diagram looks rather ragged.

The following diagram, invented by Jim Swift, a high school teacher in British Columbia, is the key to understanding a confidence interval. Be sure students understand that the confidence intervals are read vertically and the reasonably likely outcomes are the horizontal line segments. Even after students have moved to the formula, continue to refer to the diagram to point out the meaning of a confidence interval. If you wish to give a copy of this completed diagram to your students, there is a blackline master of the completed chart at the end of this section.

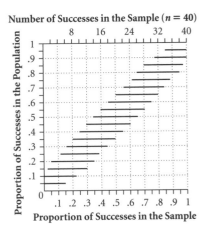

Lesson Notes: Confidence Intervals

The definition given on the bottom of page 418 in the student text is an important definition. The reason that you are only 95% confident is that there is a 5% chance that a rare event occurred in your sample. In this case, the population percentage would not fall within the confidence interval.

Symmetry and Length of Confidence Intervals

Students may notice that some of the confidence intervals in the chart in Display 8.2 aren't symmetric about $\hat{p}$. This happens when $\hat{p}$ is far from .5. For example, suppose you get a sample proportion of $\hat{p} = .75$, as in the example and Display 8.2 on page 418. The 95% confidence interval, from the chart, is 60% to 85%, which isn't centered at 75%. This is because when n is small, binomial distributions are quite skewed for small values of p or for large values of p. The binomial distribution is well approximated by the normal distribution only when $n\hat{p}$ and $n(1 - \hat{p})$ are both at least 10.

Note also that the longest line segment is at 50% and the line segments become shorter as the population percentages move farther away from 50%. You can see why from the formula for the standard error of the distribution of $\hat{p}$:

$$\sqrt{\frac{\hat{p}(1 - \hat{p})}{n}}$$

For a fixed sample size n, the value varies depending on how far $\hat{p}$ is from .5. The closer $\hat{p}$ is to .5, the larger the standard error. You may wish to have students graph

$$y = \sqrt{\frac{x(1 - x)}{40}}, 0 \leq x \leq 1$$

to see how y varies with x. This idea is explored in Exercise 13.)

Discussion

Note: The following answers are for the completed chart (Display 8.2 in the student text, reproduced as a blackline master at the end of this section).

D3. Students should look at the horizontal line segment they constructed in Activity 8.2 for $p = .6$. It stretches from proportions .448 to .752 or from about 18 successes to 30 successes. Because 27 successes out of 40 is included within this horizontal line segment or interval, then the answer is yes. Getting 27 people of Mexican origin out of 40 Hispanics is a reasonably likely outcome.

D4. No. The horizontal line segment at $p = .3$ goes from about .158 to .442, so a sample proportion of .6 isn't a reasonably likely result for a population with only 30% men. It may interest your students to know that, on the other hand, about 51% of people under age 5 are male. (*Source:* http://www.census.gov/prod/2001pubs/c2kbr01-9.pdf)

D5. As can be seen by drawing a vertical line downward from 34 out of 40 or upward from a sample proportion of .85, the confidence interval is about 70% to 95%. (If you

look closely, the vertical line just barely misses 70%, so students may say that the confidence interval is 75% to 95%.)

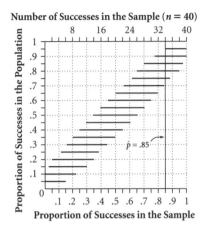

Number of Successes in the Sample ($n = 40$)

D6. As seen from the vertical line on the chart below, the populations for which a sample proportion of .5 is reasonably likely are 35% to 65%. This can be written as 50% $\pm$ 15%. (If you look closely, the vertical line just barely misses 35% and 65%; therefore students may say the confidence interval is 40% to 60% and the margin of error is 10%.)

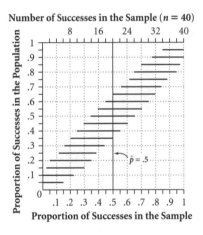

Number of Successes in the Sample ($n = 40$)

D7. We don't need a confidence interval for $\hat{p}$ because we already know exactly what that is from our sample and we know that it probably would have been different if we had taken a different sample. What we want is an interval that has a good chance of capturing the true but unknown proportion of successes p in the population from which our sample was taken.

Practice

Note: These are the theoretical answers. Because students are estimating from the chart, they probably won't get these numbers exactly.

P3. If the coin is fair, $p = .5$, so you are reasonably likely to get anywhere from 14 to 26 heads.

P4. Students should look at the horizontal line segment they constructed for $p = .6$ in Activity 8.2. It stretches from proportions .448 to .752 or from about 18 to 30 successes. Within this horizontal line segment, 32 successes out of 40 is not included, so the answer is no. When $p = .6$, getting 32 out of 40 still in school would be a rare event.

P5. From about 26 to 38 high school graduates. From .65 to .95.

P6. As can be seen from the vertical line on the following chart, the confidence interval is about 15% to 40%.

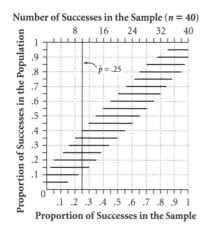

P7. The populations for which a sample proportion of .45 is reasonably likely are 30% to 60%. This can be written as 45% ± 15%. (The vertical line at $\hat{p} = .45$ just barely misses 30%, so students may say the confidence interval is 35% to 60%.)

Lesson Notes: Toward a Formula

Discussion

D8. **a.** See the chart that follows. The 95% confidence interval is 35% to 65%. (If you look closely, the vertical line just barely

misses 35% and 65%, so students may say the confidence interval is 40% to 60%.)

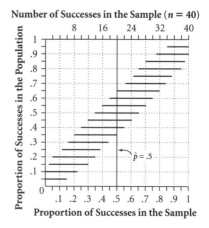

b.

c. The horizontal line segment shows all the sample proportions $\hat{p}$ that are reasonably likely for a population that has $p = 50\%$ successes. Those sample proportions are

$$.5 \pm 1.96 \sqrt{\frac{.5(1 - .5)}{40}} \approx .5 \pm .155$$

The endpoints of the horizontal line segment are then about .345 and .655.

d. The vertical line segment shows the population percentages that are in the confidence interval. That is, they are the populations for which a sample proportion of .5 is a reasonably likely result. Because it is about the same length as the horizontal line segment and is centered at the same point, the endpoints of the vertical line segment also are about .345 and .655.

e. The 95% confidence interval is about .345 to .655 or about 34.5% to 65.5%.

Practice

P8. **a.** Using the chart in Display 8.2, the 95% confidence interval is about 50% to 75% when the sample proportion is $\frac{25}{40}$, or .625.

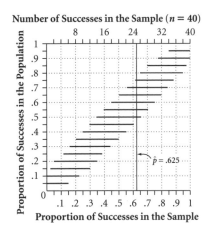

Number of Successes in the Sample ($n = 40$)

b. The confidence interval has endpoints at

$$.625 \pm 1.96 \sqrt{\frac{.625(1 - .625)}{40}} \approx .625 \pm .150$$

So the 95% confidence interval is about .475 to .775.

Lesson Notes: Using the Formula

Verifying the Conditions for a Confidence Interval

Students taking standardized exams such as the AP Statistics exam should *always* verify that the three conditions hold before calculating a confidence interval. (Sometimes students will be asked to "verify assumptions," but more typically it will be left for the student to remember that he or she must check the conditions before proceeding.) This applies both to confidence intervals and significance tests.

Your students may ask why the three conditions for a confidence interval are necessary.

- ***The sample was a simple random sample from a binomial population.*** This first condition is a statement of the type of situation being investigated: You have a random sample from a population with a fixed percentage of successes, *p*. The idea is to estimate the value of *p* from the proportion of successes in the sample $\hat{p}$. As your students learned in Chapter 4, if the sample isn't random, you can't make any inference about the population from which the sample comes.

- ***Both $n\hat{p}$ and $n(1 - \hat{p})$ are at least 10.*** From Chapter 5, your students know that if the sample size is large enough, the distribution of all possible values of $\hat{p}$ can be approximated by a normal distribution. The purpose of this second condition is to define "large enough": both $n\hat{p}$ and $n(1 - \hat{p})$ must be at least 10. Why do you need normality? One reason is so that you can use a *z*-score of 1.96 to compute the length of a 95% confidence interval.

  In recent AP Statistics readings, students were not given full credit for stating only that both $n\hat{p}$ and $n(1 - \hat{p})$ are at least 10 (even though that was fairly obvious in some cases). They actually had to substitute in the values of $\hat{p}$ and *n*.

- ***The size of the population is at least 10 times the size of the sample.*** The formula for a confidence interval is approximately correct as long as the sample size is small compared to the population size. The purpose of this condition is to warn you that if the sample size is large compared to the population size, then this confidence interval will be too conservative; that is, it will be longer than it needs to be. After all, if your sample was the entire population, the margin of error should be 0. In general, the larger the proportion of the population that you have in your sample, the closer $\hat{p}$ should be to *p*. So once the sample size gets to be more than about 10% of the size of the population, you should use a slightly different formula for the confidence interval:

$$\hat{p} \pm z^* \cdot \sqrt{\frac{\hat{p}(1 - \hat{p})}{n - 1}} \cdot \sqrt{\frac{N - n}{N}}$$

where *N* is the size of the population. However, if you have less than 10% of the population in your sample, it doesn't matter much whether you use this formula or the simpler one. The preceding formula won't be used at all in this textbook because surveys are almost always conducted with sample sizes that are small compared to the size of the population from which they come.

Interpreting a Confidence Interval

The example Safety Violations on pages 422–423 of the student text gives a 90% confidence interval of .47 to .73 for the proportion of all buses that have a safety violation. Students should understand that each time they compute a confidence interval or are asked to interpret a confidence interval, they should include the answers to the first two of the following questions. If they are asked the meaning of *confidence*, they need to give an answer like the one provided for the third question. We recommend that you ask all three questions each time you discuss a confidence interval.

1. ***What is it that you are 90% sure is in the confidence interval?*** The proportion of all of the buses in this population, if we could check them all, that have safety violations.

2. ***What is the meaning (or interpretation) of the confidence interval of .47 to .73?*** We are 90% confident that if we could check all of the buses in this population, between 47% and 73% of them would have safety violations.

3. ***What is the meaning of 90% confidence?*** If we took 100 random samples of buses from this population and computed the 90% confidence interval from each sample, then we would expect that 90 of these intervals would contain the proportion of all buses in this population that have safety violations. In other words, we are using a method that captures the true population proportion 90% of the time.

A complete interpretation of the meaning of this confidence interval would include all three answers.

Discussion

D9. Yes. The sample is a simple random sample from a binomial (success/failure) population. Both $n\hat{p} = 24$ and $n(1 - \hat{p}) = 16$ are at least 10. Finally, in a large city the number of buses would be greater than $10(40) = 400$.

D10. The quantity $n\hat{p} = 24$ is the number of buses in the sample that have a safety violation, and the quantity $n(1 - \hat{p}) = 16$ is the number of buses in the sample that don't have a safety violation. In general, $n\hat{p}$ is the number of "successes" in the sample, and $n(1 - \hat{p})$ is the number of "failures."

Practice

P9. **a.** First, was the sample a simple random sample from a binomial population? This isn't stated in the problem, but because the survey was taken by a reputable polling company, it is reasonable to assume that this condition is met. (In fact, Gallup doesn't use a simple random sample but rather a multi-stage sample that gives them a slightly smaller margin of error.)

Second, both $n\hat{p} = 744(.82) = 610.08$ and $n(1 - \hat{p}) = 744(.18) = 133.92$ are at least 10.

Third, the number of U.S. teenagers is much more than 10 times the sample size of 744.

b. The 95% confidence interval is

$$.82 \pm 1.96 \sqrt{\frac{.82(1 - .82)}{744}} \approx .82 \pm .028$$

or 79.2% to 84.8%. The margin of error is 2.8%.

c. The 90% confidence interval is

$$.82 \pm 1.645 \sqrt{\frac{.82(1 - .82)}{744}} \approx .82 \pm .023$$

or 79.7% to 84.3%. The margin of error is 2.3%.

d. The 95% confidence interval is longer. For now, students should say that if we want to be 95% confident that the true value of p falls within the interval, we need a larger interval than if we want to be only 90% confident.

Lesson Notes: The Capture Rate

Activity 8.3: The Capture Rate

To prepare for this activity, make a transparency of the following diagram, which is given as a blackline master at the end of this section.

A variation on this activity is to give each student a bag of plain M&M's and have them count out 40 and get a confidence interval for the proportion of M&M's that are red. The true proportion of plain M&M's that are red is .20.

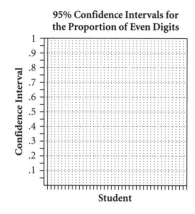

1–2. With a TI-83, students can get 40 random digits from 0 to 9 and place them in list L1 using the command randInt(0,9,40)→L1.

Students then can count the number of even digits in list L1 by using the command int(L1/2)=L1/2→L2. This tests whether the digit is even and, if so, stores a 1 in its position in list L2. If the digit is odd, the command stores a 0 in its position in list L2. Then students can count how many nonzero entries are in list L2 or they can sum up the number of even digits (represented now by 1's) by using the command sum(L2).

Be sure students have enough time to do this carefully. If they don't count accurately, you have another lesson. This lesson would be that the confidence interval doesn't have a 95% chance of capturing the true value of p if there are errors in the survey such as miscounting the number of successes in the sample.

3. Intervals will vary. Suppose a student's number of successes in step 2 is 21 or $\hat{p} = \frac{21}{40} = .525$. Then their confidence interval for the proportion of random digits that are even is

$$.525 \pm 1.96 \sqrt{\frac{(.525)(1 - .525)}{40}} \approx .525 \pm .155$$

or .37 to .68.

4. Continuing the example in step 3, if the student's confidence interval is .37 to .68, the student would choose one of the vertical grid lines in the chart and draw a vertical line segment on the chart from about three-quarters of the way between the horizontal lines for .3 and .4 to almost the horizontal line for .7. Point out that the centers of the intervals vary depending on the random digits in the sample, but they are almost the same length.

Note: As long as np and $n(1 - p)$ are at least 10, the interval lengths can range from the unlikely case of $\hat{p} = .25$ or $.75$ with interval length $2(.134) = .268$, to $\hat{p} = .5$ with interval length $2(.155) = .31$. Most students, however, will have interval lengths between $2(.148)$ and $2(.155)$.

It helps if you have many different colors of transparency pens so that students can readily recognize their own confidence intervals. The simulation below from Fathom shows typical results for 100 confidence intervals. Here, the parameter p shown by the dark vertical line is in 96 out of the 100 confidence intervals.

5. 50%

6. The percentage should be close to 95%, and may be 100% if you have a small class. So if your class is small, you may wish to have each student construct several confidence intervals. If you do a large number of confidence intervals, refer to the section "Other Formulas for Confidence Intervals" on page 72 of this section. Because the formula for a confidence interval uses several approximations,

the capture rate you get may be quite a bit less than 95%.

Confidence Interval

The Dialogue Between the Student and the Teacher: 95% Confidence in a 95% Confidence Interval

The reason that the formula gives a 95% confidence interval is not as obvious as it might seem. The term *95% confidence* means that the method of constructing the confidence interval captures the true value of the population proportion p 95% of the time. Here is the reasoning behind this assertion. We don't know the true population percentage, but let's say it is p on the diagram that follows. When is p in the confidence interval? It's in the confidence interval if the value of $\hat{p}$ falls along the horizontal line segment for p. How often does that happen? It happens 95% of the time, because that's how we constructed the horizontal line segment. This is true no matter what the value of p.

In other words, p is in the confidence interval if and only if $\hat{p}$ is a reasonably likely outcome for that value of p. Because the latter has a probability of .95, so does the former.

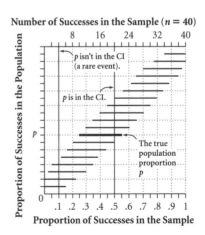

Note: We are defining the confidence interval as the set of population proportions p that have $\hat{p}$ as a reasonably likely outcome, and using the chart is accurate except for the fact that we don't have *all*

values of p. The formula we use for a confidence interval, $\hat{p} \pm z^* \cdot \sqrt{\hat{p}(1 - \hat{p})/n}$ is an approximation in two senses: The normal distribution is used to approximate the sampling distribution of $\hat{p}$, and the standard error of that sampling distribution is approximated by using the observed $\hat{p}$ to estimate p. For example, if $p = .5$, then the reasonably likely outcomes are in the interval $(.345, .65495)$; $\hat{p} = .35$ is in this interval, but barely. But using the formula, the confidence interval for the proportion of successes p in the population using the sample proportion $\hat{p} = .35$ is $(.202, .498)$, which doesn't contain .5. The confidence interval is a bit too small because using .35 in the formula for the standard error gives a smaller value than using .5.

Why Can't You Say That the Probability That p Is in the Confidence Interval Is .95?

You can, but only before the confidence interval is constructed. After the confidence interval is constructed, it is incorrect to say that there is a 95% "chance" or 95% "probability" that the parameter p is in the confidence interval. After the sample has been taken and the confidence interval computed, there is no randomness left. Either p is in the confidence interval or it isn't. This may seem like a small point, but students have not been given credit on the AP Statistics exam for interpreting a confidence interval correctly if they use the word *chance* or *probability* to refer to confidence after the sample has been taken. The correct interpretation is that the *method* gives us a confidence interval that contains p 95% of the time.

Other Formulas for Confidence Intervals

There are formulas other than the ones given in the text for a confidence interval for a proportion. The one we give has been standard for many years, but it is an approximation in several ways:

- The normal distribution is used as an approximation of the binomial distribution.

- The formula is symmetric around $\hat{p}$, but it shouldn't be because the distribution of $\hat{p}$ is slightly skewed for all $p \neq .5$.

- The sample proportion $\hat{p}$ is used in the formula for the standard error as an approximation of p.

As a result, the formula for a confidence interval gives a capture rate that tends to be less than the 95% advertised. Here are a histogram and boxplot of 1000 trials where each trial is made up of 100 confidence intervals. Each of these confidence

intervals was constructed following the steps in Activity 8.3. What was recorded and plotted was the proportion of the 100 confidence intervals that captured the true population proportion, $p = .5$. Note that the mean capture rate is closer to .92 than it is to the advertised rate of .95.

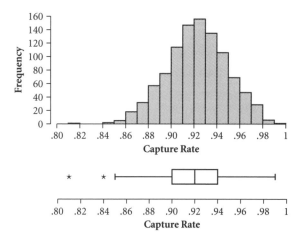

Several other methods for constructing confidence intervals have been proposed. One of these methods, adding 2 to both the number of successes and the number of failures in the sample before computing the confidence interval, seems to be gaining favor and may eventually make its way into introductory statistics books. (Note that this method makes $\hat{p}$ closer to .5.) For a discussion of these issues, see A. Agresti and B. A. Coull, "Approximate Is Better Than 'Exact' for Interval Estimation of Binomial Proportions," *The American Statistician 62* (1998): 119–126.

Discussion

D11. No, different numbers of even digits in the sample should give different confidence intervals.

D12. 90%. The method that we use to construct 90% confidence intervals captures the true population proportion 90% of the time. Thus, we would expect 90% of the 80 confidence intervals, or 72 confidence intervals, to contain the true population proportion of .60.

Lesson Notes: Margin of Error and Sample Size

Discussion

D13. Confidence intervals for samples of size 80 will be shorter because the horizontal line segments will be shorter. From Chapters 5 and 7, students should understand that the spread of a distribution of the proportion of successes decreases as the sample size n increases.

D14. a. The endpoints of the horizontal line segments for 99% confidence would be farther apart than the endpoints for 95% confidence. If we want to cover 99% of the possible values of $\hat{p}$, we have to have a longer interval: $2.576\sqrt{p(1-p)/40}$ rather than $1.96\sqrt{p(1-p)/40}$ for each value of p.
b. The interval would be longer for 99% confidence than for 95% confidence.

Practice

P10. For samples of size 100, the horizontal line segments will be shorter. Thus a confidence interval for a sample of size 100 will be shorter because a vertical line will cross fewer of the shorter horizontal line segments. Again, remind students that the spread of the sampling distribution of the proportion of successes decreases as the sample size n increases.

P11. You should use $z^* = 1.28$ because $z = \pm 1.28$ cuts off the outer 10% on either end of a normal distribution. The interval would be shorter for 80% confidence than for 95% confidence because $1.28\sqrt{p(1-p)/n}$ is smaller than $1.96\sqrt{p(1-p)/n}$.

In terms of the chart, the line segment that covers the middle 95% of all possible sample proportions has to be longer than the line segment that covers only the middle 80%.

P12. You should have used a sample size 9 times as big, or $9n$. The margin of error is given by the formula

$$z^* \cdot \sqrt{\frac{p(1-p)}{n}}$$

If you want this to be $\frac{1}{3}$ as large as it was before, you must solve for the new sample size, m, in the equation

$$\frac{1}{3} \cdot z^* \cdot \sqrt{\frac{p(1-p)}{n}} = z^* \cdot \sqrt{\frac{p(1-p)}{m}}$$

which will give the result $m = 9n$.

Lesson Notes: Back to the Opinion Polls

Discussion

D15. $1.96\sqrt{.51(1-.51)/1108} \approx .029 \approx .03$

D16. Yes. First, was the sample a simple random sample from a binomial population? This isn't stated in the text, but because the survey was taken by a reputable polling company, it is reasonable to assume that this condition is met. (In fact, Gallup doesn't use a simple random sample, but rather a multistage sample that gives them a slightly smaller margin of error.)

Second, both $n\hat{p} = 1108(.51) = 565.08$ and $n(1-\hat{p}) = 1108(.49) = 542.92$ are at least 10.

Third, the number of Americans is much more than 10 times the sample size of 1108.

D17. The term *error attributable to sampling* is the same as *sampling error* or *variation due to sampling*. It means that when we take random samples from a given population, the values of $\hat{p}$ do not turn out to be the same each time and usually aren't equal to p. However, these values do tend to cluster around p.

Practice

P13. a. The method of sampling is not given, so you can't verify that it was a simple random sample.

It is the case that both $n\hat{p} = 754(.71) = 535.34$ and $n(1-\hat{p}) = 754(.29) = 218.66$ are at least 10.

The total number of students aged 12 to 17 who have Internet access is at least 10 times the size of the sample, 754.

b. The 95% confidence interval is about 68% to 74%:

$$\hat{p} \pm z^* \cdot \sqrt{\frac{\hat{p}(1-\hat{p})}{n}} = .71 \pm 1.96\sqrt{\frac{.71(1-.71)}{754}}$$

$$\approx .71 \pm .032$$

c. The proportion of *all* students aged 12 to 17 with Internet access who would say they relied on the Internet the most in completing a project.

d. If we could ask all students aged 12 to 17 with Internet access whether they relied on the Internet the most in completing a project, we are 95% confident that the proportion who would say "yes" would be somewhere in the interval 68% to 74%.

e. Suppose we could take 100 random samples from this population and construct the 100 resulting confidence intervals. We'd expect that the true proportion of all students aged 12 to 17 with Internet access who would say they relied on the Internet the most in completing a project would be in 95 of these intervals.

P14. In addition to the variation in sampling that results from taking a random sample from a given population, general categories of sources of error include

- not getting a random sample in the first place (such as voluntary response surveys where people phone in to talk shows or write in to newspapers)

- errors in coding or recording the responses (a poll taker misunderstands what a person is saying)

- getting an invalid response from the people surveyed because they misunderstood the question or because they did not tell the truth about a controversial issue (in general, people want to appear knowledgeable and agreeable)

The formula for the margin of error takes into account only the variation that results from looking at a random sample and not at the entire population. It is generally impossible to predict the bias that may result from the three categories above.

Lesson Notes: What Sample Size Should You Use?

Discussion

D18. The sample size n appears in the denominator of the fraction in the formula for the margin of error. Thus, as n gets larger, that fraction, and so the margin of error, gets smaller.

D19. For $E = 10\%$, use

$$n = 1.96^2\left(\frac{.5(1 - .5)}{.1^2}\right) = 96.04$$

So you need a sample size of 97, which costs $97. (It is customary always to round up when computing sample size.)

For $E = 1\%$, use

$$n = 1.96^2\left(\frac{.5(1 - .5)}{.01^2}\right)$$
$$= 9604$$

which costs $9604.

For $E = .1\%$, use

$$n = 1.96^2\left(\frac{.5(1 - .5)}{.001^2}\right)$$
$$= 960,400$$

which costs $960,400.

Note that cutting the margin of error by $\frac{1}{10}$ requires multiplying the sample size, and the cost, by 100.

Practice

P15. Because you have no estimate for p, use $p = .5$. For $E = 2\%$ with 95% confidence, use

$$n = z^2\left(\frac{p(1 - p)}{E^2}\right)$$
$$= 1.96^2\left(\frac{.5(1 - .5)}{.02^2}\right)$$
$$= 2401$$

For $E = 1\%$ with 99% confidence, use

$$n = z^2\left(\frac{p(1 - p)}{E^2}\right)$$
$$= 2.576^2\left(\frac{.5(1 - .5)}{.01^2}\right)$$
$$= 16,589.44 \approx 16,590$$

For $E = 0.5\%$ with 90% confidence, use

$$n = z^2\left(\frac{p(1 - p)}{E^2}\right)$$
$$= 1.645^2\left(\frac{.5(1 - .5)}{.005^2}\right)$$
$$= 27,060.25 \text{ or } 27,061$$

P16. They should use a sample size of 897. (As usual, we round up.)

$$n = z^2\left(\frac{p(1 - p)}{E^2}\right)$$
$$= 1.96^2\left(\frac{.3(1 - .3)}{.03^2}\right)$$
$$\approx 896.37$$

Exercises

E1. **a.** No. A sample proportion of .9 isn't a reasonably likely result for a population with 75% successes.

b. Because 48% is close to 50%, we can estimate pretty well by using the line segment for the population of 50%. The largest is about .65 and the smallest about .35.

c. About 30% to 55%

E2. **a.** This is a multistage sampling plan with no apparent randomization. The Epilepsy Foundation selected 20 affiliates (assuming they have more than that), each of which selected schools, presumably in their local area. The surveys were passed out to (all, some?) of the students in these schools. We probably should consider this a nationwide convenience sample.

The results were "weighted" by age and region. This means that, for example, if 2% of the teens in their sample were 14-year-olds from the South, but 4% of the teens nationwide are 14-year-olds from the South, they would double-count the responses of each 14-year-old from the South in the sample.

b. No, there is no indication of a random sample. However, the other two conditions have been met.

c. Yes.

$$E = z^\star \cdot \sqrt{\frac{\hat{p}(1 - \hat{p})}{n}} = 1.96 \sqrt{\frac{.51(1 - .51)}{19{,}441}}$$
$$\approx .0070$$
$$\approx .01$$

d. The proportion of *all* U.S. teens who know that epilepsy isn't contagious.

e. We are 95% confident that the proportion of all U.S. teens who know that epilepsy isn't contagious is in the interval 50% to 52%.

f. Suppose we could take 100 random samples from this population and construct the 100 resulting confidence intervals. We'd expect that the actual proportion of all U.S. teens who know that epilepsy isn't contagious would be in 95 of these intervals.

E3. The text doesn't say whether or not this is a random sample of adults, but, given that it was done by *U.S. News & World Report*, it is likely some randomization was involved. Therefore, our formulas give a reasonable approximation to the margin of error. Both

$n\hat{p} = .81(1000) = 810$ and $n(1 - \hat{p}) = .19(1000) = 190$ are at least 10. Finally, the number of adults in the United States is greater than $10(1000)$.

We are 95% confident that if we were to ask *all* adults from the general public whether they thought TV contributed to a decline in family values, the percentage would be between 78.6% and 83.4%. The computations follow:

$$\hat{p} \pm z^\star \cdot \sqrt{\frac{\hat{p}(1 - \hat{p})}{n}} = .81 \pm 1.96 \sqrt{\frac{.81(1 - .81)}{1000}}$$
$$\approx .81 \pm .0243$$

E4. No. Because the return rate was only about 9.4%, it is unlikely that the group who returned the surveys were a random sample of Hollywood leaders. In general, those who feel strongly about issues tend to return surveys.

E5. Results will vary. Suppose for example, that 16 of the 40 students carry backpacks. For a 98% confidence interval students should use $z^\star = 2.33$. Students should state clearly that if they were to check *all* students on their campus, they are 98% confident that the proportion carrying backpacks would be in the confidence interval (.22, .58).

E6. **a.** About 65% to 90%

b. $.8 \pm 1.96 \sqrt{.8(1 - .8)/40} \approx .8 \pm .124$ or 67.6% to 92.4%

c. They are similar. There are several reasons for the slight difference in the confidence intervals from parts a and b. The chart would give the exact confidence interval but it doesn't include all possible values of p. Also, $n(1 - \hat{p}) = 40(1 - .8) = 8 < 10$, so the normal approximation to the binomial isn't very good.

E7. The 95% confidence interval is

$$\hat{p} \pm z^\star \cdot \sqrt{\frac{\hat{p}(1 - \hat{p})}{n}} = .6 \pm 1.96 \sqrt{\frac{.6(1 - .6)}{100}}$$
$$\approx .6 \pm .096$$

or .504 to .696.

Display 8.2 can not be used in this case because it applies only to samples of size 40.

E8. **a.** The sample size n appears in the denominator of the fraction in the formula for the margin of error. Thus as n gets larger, that fraction gets smaller, and so the length of the confidence interval gets smaller.

b. The length of the confidence interval increases. If you want to have more confidence that the interval captures the true population percentage p, you have to have a longer interval. This is seen in the formula, as z^* must be larger to have a larger probability of having $\hat{p}$ in the interval around p.

E9. The symbol p is used for the proportion of successes in the population from which we are drawing a sample. This is the unknown parameter—the value that we are trying to estimate. The symbol $\hat{p}$ is used for the proportion of successes in a sample drawn from the population with proportion of successes p. The value of $\hat{p}$ varies from sample to sample. When constructing a confidence interval, the value of $\hat{p}$ from the sample is at the center of the confidence interval and so is always in it. The value of p may or may not be in the confidence interval.

E10. By a factor of 16. Because quadrupling the sample size cuts the margin of error in half, quadrupling it again cuts it by one-fourth. To see this algebraically, suppose that a sample of size n gives a margin of error E. Then to get an error of $\frac{E}{4}$, the new sample size would have to be

$$z^2 \cdot \frac{p(1-p)}{(E/4)^2} = 16z^2 \cdot \frac{p(1-p)}{E^2}$$

$$= 16n$$

E11. a. The distribution of the values of $\hat{p}$ has mean p and can be approximated by a normal distribution with mean p provided both $n\hat{p}$ and $n(1-\hat{p})$ are at least 10. Of all values in a normal distribution, 95% lie within approximately two standard errors of the mean.

b. If 95% of all values lie within two standard errors of p, then there is a 95% chance that the proportion $\hat{p}$ from a random sample lies within two standard errors of p. Basically, parts a and b are saying the same thing.

c. If $\hat{p}$ is within two standard errors of p, then p is within two standard errors of $\hat{p}$.

d. This formula says in algebra exactly what part c said in words: There is a 95% chance that p is within two standard errors of $\hat{p}$.

Symbolically, the argument may be written as shown at the bottom of the page.

This is almost the formula for a confidence interval, except that we need to use p in the formula for the standard error and we don't know it. So we estimate p with $\hat{p}$.

E12. D

E13. a. Because $x(1-x)$ is of the form of $p(1-p)$, which we are trying to maximize. The domain of x is restricted because a probability can be at most 1 and must be at least 0.

b. The graph is the graph of the parabola $y = x - x^2$. This parabola opens down as shown here:

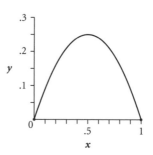

c. The maximum y-value occurs at the vertex. The vertex for a parabola $y = ax^2 + bx + c$ occurs at $x = \frac{-b}{(2a)}$. Here, $a = -1$ and $b = 1$, so the vertex is $x = \frac{-1}{2(-1)} = \frac{1}{2}$. The value of y at $x = \frac{1}{2}$ is $y = \frac{1}{2}(1 - \frac{1}{2}) = \frac{1}{4}$.

Lesson 8.1, E11d

From the Central Limit Theorem we know that when n is large enough,

$$P\left(p - 1.96\sqrt{\frac{p(1-p)}{n}} \le \hat{p} \le p + 1.96\sqrt{\frac{p(1-p)}{n}}\right) \approx .95$$

Solving for p in the inequality, this is equivalent to

$$P\left(\hat{p} - 1.96\sqrt{\frac{p(1-p)}{n}} \le p \le \hat{p} + 1.96\sqrt{\frac{p(1-p)}{n}}\right) \approx .95$$

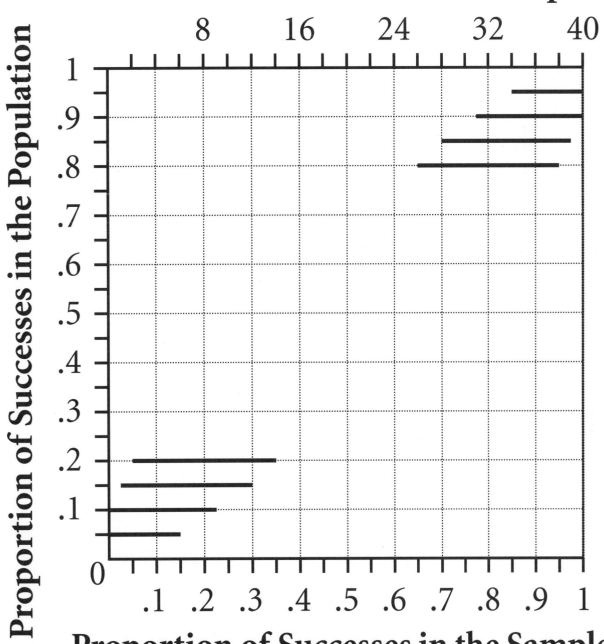

Number of Successes in the Sample

Proportion of Successes in the Population

Proportion of Successes in the Sample

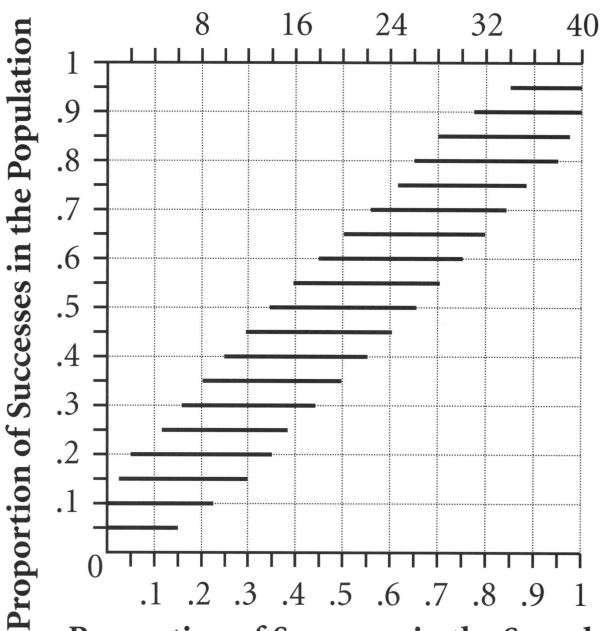

Number of Successes in the Sample

Proportion of Successes in the Population

Proportion of Successes in the Sample

95% Confidence Intervals for the Proportion of Even Digits

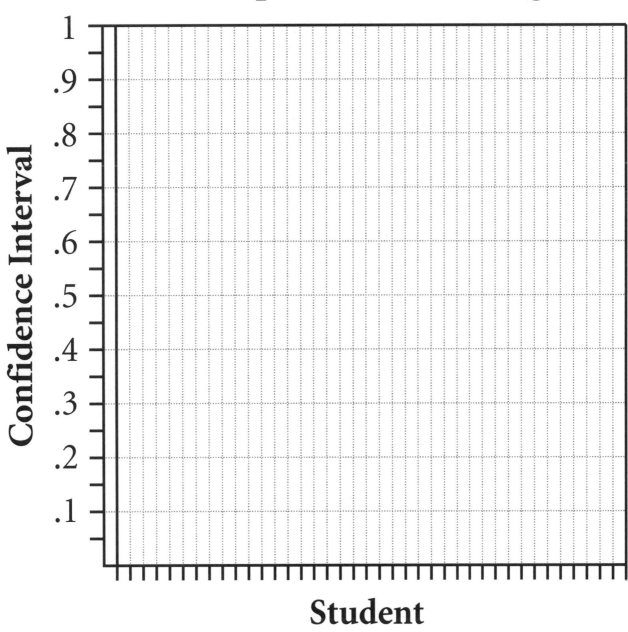

8.2 Testing a Proportion

Objectives

- to understand the logic of a significance test for a proportion
- to use a significance test (hypothesis test) to decide whether you should reject the claim that your sample has been drawn from a binomial population with a specified proportion of successes
- to understand the meaning of these terms: statistical significance, null hypothesis, alternate hypothesis, test statistic, level of significance, one-tailed test, and two-tailed test
- to compute and interpret a *P*-value
- to know the meanings of Type I and Type II errors and how to reduce their probability
- to know the meaning of the power of a test and how to increase it

In this section, students use the ideas they have learned about confidence intervals to learn about tests of significance (hypothesis testing).

Important Terms and Concepts

- significance test for a proportion
- variation in sampling
- statistical significance
- conditions (assumptions) for a test
- null hypothesis and alternate hypothesis
- test statistic
- critical values

- level of significance
- Type I error
- Type II error
- power of a test
- *P*-value
- one-tailed test and two-tailed test
- conclusion in context

Lesson Planning

Class Time

Four to five days

Materials

For Activity 8.4, one penny per student. Pennies from the 1960s are best because they tend to result in a low proportion of heads when spun.

Suggested Assignments

Classwork		
Essential	**Recommended**	**Optional**
Activity 8.4 D20–D24, D26, D32, D34, D35, D37 P17–P19, P21–P25, P28, P29, P31	D25, D27, D29–D31, D33, D36, D38 P20, P26, P27, P30, P32	D28

Homework		
Essential	**Recommended**	**Optional**
E15, E16, E18	E14, E17, E21, E22	E19, E20

Lesson Notes: Informal Significance Testing

Barn Swallows at Chernobyl

When students read the information about barn swallows at Chernobyl in the introduction to this section, you may wish to take the opportunity to discuss the crucial interplay of sample size and the difference between the standard p_0 and the sample proportion $\hat{p}$.

No sample size was given in the article. If, for example, the sample size was 1000, then $\frac{140}{1000} = 14\%$ would be convincing evidence that the proportion of barn swallows with mutations had increased from 2%. However, if the sample size was only 7, then $\frac{1}{7} \approx 14\%$, wouldn't be convincing.

However, $\frac{7}{7} = 100\%$ would be convincing evidence that the percentage has increased from 2%! So good evidence isn't simply a matter of sample size, but also of the difference between the standard p_0 and the sample proportion $\hat{p}$. The methods of statistical inference were designed to help us balance these in situations where our intuition doesn't lead us to a clear conclusion.

Activity 8.4: Spinning and Flipping Pennies

In Activity 8.4, your class will confront the difference between theory and reality. That is, your students may expect the probability of heads when a penny is spun to be .5. As they will learn in this introduction to hypothesis testing, that isn't the case—the probability is closer to .4 for newer pennies and much less for pennies from the 1960s. (Statistics teachers aren't sure why—this is one of the burning issues yet to be resolved—some speculate that the edges of pennies are slightly beveled to make it easier to handle a stack of coins or to make it easier to pop them out of a mold.)

Your class will need the results from 40 spins of a penny and 40 flips of a penny for D20 and P17. This can be done quite quickly in class because only a couple of flips and spins are needed per student. Make sure desks have nothing on them to interfere with the spin. If your class is small, or you don't want to use even a few minutes of class time, you can ask students to do the spinning and flipping of pennies at home.

Try to get a classroom set of relatively old pennies of about the same date. Pennies from the 1960s work well. You will need one set of 40 flips and one set of 40 spins from your class. For example, from one class, there were 26 heads out of 40 flips and 12 heads out of 40 spins.

1–2. Heads and tails are not equally likely when a penny is spun. However, from a single sample of 40 spins, it may be difficult to conclude that. One good strategy students may suggest is to construct a 95% confidence interval, based on their 40 spins, for the true proportion of heads when a penny is spun and see whether $p = .5$ is in that confidence interval.

Don't tell your students until you finish this section, but other classes have found that the probability of a head is about .4 when recently minted pennies are spun. However, for pennies from the 1960s, this probability can be much smaller.

3–4. Heads and tails are equally likely when a penny is flipped, so if your students construct a 95% confidence interval, it will have a 95% chance of capturing .5.

Discussion

D20. **a.** The process of spinning a penny results in heads half of the time. The process of spinning a penny doesn't result in heads half of the time.

b. Sample proportions will vary according to the results of the spins. If your class did not do Activity 8.4, give them these typical results: A class got 12 heads from spinning a penny 40 times. For this class, $\hat{p} = \frac{12}{40} = .3$.

c. Answers will vary according to the results of the spins. The reasonably likely sample proportions for $p = .5$ are in the interval .345 to .655. So, for the class with $\hat{p} = .3$, this value is not reasonably likely if $p = .5$.

d. Answers will vary according to the results of the spins. For the class with $\hat{p} = .3$, we conclude that the data do not support the standard. If the process of spinning a penny results in heads half of the time, it is unlikely to get 12 heads out of 40 spins.

Practice

P17. Answers will vary according to the results of the flips. Answers should follow the form of the four steps in D20. If your class did not do Activity 8.4, give them these typical results: A class got 26 heads from flipping a penny 40 times. In this case, $\hat{p} = \frac{26}{40}$, or .65. This sample proportion does lie in the interval .345 to .655 of reasonably likely outcomes for $p = .5$, so the data do support the standard. If the process of flipping a penny results in heads half of the time, it is likely to get 26 heads out of 40 flips.

Lesson Notes: Statistical Significance

Discussion

D21. **a.** Two-thirds (about 66.7%) of today's teens want to study more about medical research. Or, using symbols, $p = \frac{2}{3}$, where p is the proportion of today's teens who want to study more about medical research.

b. The percentage of today's teens who want to study more about medical research isn't $\frac{2}{3}$. Symbolically, $p \neq \frac{2}{3}$.

c. $\hat{p} = \frac{23}{40} = .575$

d. No, this result isn't statistically significant because .575 is a reasonably likely result when the proportion of successes in the population is between 65% and 70%. See the display that follows. We conclude that there is no evidence that the proportion has changed from two-thirds.

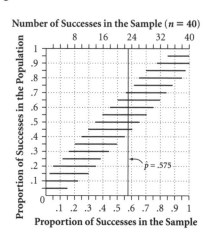

Number of Successes in the Sample ($n = 40$)

Practice

P18. **a.** The student is guessing, and so the probability the student gets a question right is .5. Or, using symbols, $p = .5$, where p is the probability a student gets a question right.

b. The student is not guessing, and so the probability he or she will get a question right is more than .5. Symbolically, $p > .5$. (This is a one-tailed test, which will be introduced formally toward the end of this section.)

c. The sample proportion is $\hat{p} = \frac{30}{40} = .75$.

d. The result is statistically significant. The vertical line leading from a sample proportion of $\hat{p} = .75$ does not intersect the middle 95% of the possible values of $\hat{p}$ when $p = .5$. Thus .75 is not a reasonably likely result if $p = .5$. We reject the hypothesis that the student was guessing. However, this does not prove beyond any doubt that the student was not guessing. The student may have been guessing and been extremely lucky to get a score this high.

Lesson Notes: The Test Statistic

The Test Statistic

Many students need considerable help in order to "see" why the z-statistic

$$z = \frac{\hat{p} - p_0}{\sqrt{\dfrac{p_0(1 - p_0)}{n}}}$$

is so reasonable as a test statistic.

Students should learn to understand algebraically why the following will make z larger:

- The observation from the sample, $\hat{p}$, is farther from the hypothesized value, p_0.
- The sample size increases.
- The hypothesized value, p_0, is farther from .5. (It is optional for students to understand this last statement.)

Finally, students should understand that a large z-statistic is evidence against the standard (null hypothesis).

You can work on these ideas with your students while doing D24.

Why Is p_0 in the Standard Error for the Test Statistic and not $\hat{p}$ as with a Confidence Interval?

In a test of significance, you begin by assuming that a standard is true: the proportion of successes p in the population is p_0. If the standard is true, the sampling distribution of the sample proportion $\hat{p}$ has mean p_0 and standard error

$$\sqrt{\frac{p_0(1 - p_0)}{n}}$$

Thus, p_0 is the right proportion to use in the formula for the standard error. When you were constructing a confidence interval, the sample proportion $\hat{p}$ was the only value you had and so you had to use it as an estimate of the proportion of successes in the population.

Actually, with large n, it makes little difference whether students use $\hat{p}$ or p_0, except perhaps in the grading of an exam! It is somewhat better to use p_0 because it reduces the amount of variation in the test statistic and improves its normality for moderate sample sizes. (This procedure should not be used at all for small sample sizes.)

Discussion

D22. The test statistic is

$$z = \frac{\hat{p} - p_0}{\sqrt{\dfrac{p_0(1 - p_0)}{n}}} = \frac{.425 - .5}{\sqrt{\dfrac{.5(1 - .5)}{40}}} = -0.949$$

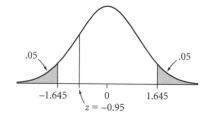

This value of z doesn't lie in the outer 10% of the standard normal distribution, so Jenny and Maya don't have evidence to reject the standard that spinning a penny is fair.

D23. **a.** 1%

b. For the test statistic z to fall in the outer 2% of the standard normal distribution, it must be less than -2.33 or greater than 2.33, so $z^* = \pm 2.33$.

D24. **a.** The test statistic z will increase. An increase in the sample size n makes the denominator of the test statistic smaller, which makes the test statistic larger. This means that we are more likely to have a statistically significant result.

b. The test statistic z will increase because its numerator will increase. This means that we are more likely to have a statistically significant result.

D25. Yes, they could be wrong. The inescapable fact about statistical inference is that, no matter what decision rule you use, you can never be certain whether you are right or wrong. However, enough statistics students have spun pennies and their teachers shared the results that it is virtually certain that Miguel and Kevin are not wrong.

Practice

P19. **a.** The test statistic will vary, depending on the results of the spins. If students' results are typical, with a sample size of 40 they will not be able to reject the standard that the proportion of heads is .5. In our example, where $\hat{p} = \frac{12}{40} = .3$, the test statistic is

$$z = \frac{.3 - .5}{\sqrt{\dfrac{.5(1 - .5)}{40}}} \approx -2.53$$

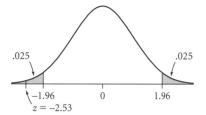

The test statistic is less than -1.96 and so falls in the outer 5% of the standard normal distribution. We would reject the standard that the proportion of heads when spinning a penny is .5.

b. The test statistic is

$$z = \frac{\hat{p} - p_0}{\sqrt{\dfrac{p_0(1 - p_0)}{n}}} = \frac{.388 - .5}{\sqrt{\dfrac{.5(1 - .5)}{500}}} \approx -5.01$$

A z-score of -5.01 is quite extreme and certainly more extreme than the critical value $z^\star = \pm 1.96$. So there is evidence to reject the standard of $p = .5$.

P20. **a.** The test statistic will depend on the results of the spins. Typically, students will not be able to reject the standard that $p = .5$. For our example, $\hat{p} = \frac{26}{40}$, or .65. The test statistic is

$$z = \frac{.65 - .5}{\sqrt{\dfrac{(.5)(1 - .5)}{40}}} \approx 1.897$$

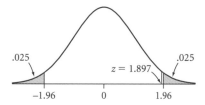

The test statistic is less than 1.96 and does not fall in the outer 5% of the standard normal distribution, so we can not reject the standard that the proportion of heads when flipping a penny is .5.

b. The test statistic is

$$z = \frac{\hat{p} - p_0}{\sqrt{\dfrac{p_0(1 - p_0)}{n}}} = \frac{.53 - .5}{\sqrt{\dfrac{.5(1 - .5)}{500}}} \approx 1.34$$

As in part a, the test statistic is not in the outer 5% of the distribution, so we do not have evidence to reject the standard of $p = .5$ that the proportion of heads when flipping a quarter is .5.

P21. **a.** About ± 1.55

b. $2(.0418) = .0836$

Lesson Notes: The Formal Language of Tests of Significance

Discussion

D26. *Check conditions.* Presumably we can assume that the quarters were spun carefully and independently so that we can consider the number of heads students got to be a binomial random variable. Both $np_0 = 40(.5) = 20$ and $n(1 - p_0) = 40(.5) = 20$ are at least 10. The population of all possible spins is infinitely large, so it is at least 10 times their sample size of 40. It is thus appropriate to do a significance test for a proportion.

State your hypotheses.

H_0: The probability of heads when a quarter is spun is .5.

H_a: The probability of heads when a quarter is spun is not .5.

Compute the test statistic and draw a sketch.
The test statistic is

$$z = \frac{\hat{p} - p_0}{\sqrt{\dfrac{p_0(1 - p_0)}{n}}} = \frac{.388 - .5}{\sqrt{\dfrac{.5(1 - .5)}{500}}} \approx -5.01$$

Because we weren't given a level of significance, we will use $\alpha = .05$, which has critical values of ± 1.96. The test statistic is outside these values.

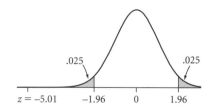

Write a conclusion in context. Because the test statistic is more extreme than the critical values of ±1.96, the result from this sample is unlikely to occur if spinning a quarter is fair. Therefore, we reject the hypothesis that spinning a quarter is a fair process that results in heads 50% of the time.

D27. The symbol p stands for the actual proportion of successes in the population from which the sample was drawn. The symbol p_0 stands for the hypothesized proportion of successes in the population from which the sample was drawn. The symbol $\hat{p}$ stands for the proportion of successes in the sample itself. The exact value of p is unknown and usually unknowable (it is estimated from the sample); p_0 is a value hypothesized in advance by the investigator; and $\hat{p}$ varies from sample to sample but is always known exactly for any particular sample.

D28. **a.** Probably not. To one set of parents, the probability that a baby will be a boy is essentially the same as the probability it will be a girl. Even if they have several children, the probabilities don't change much. For example, the probability that a family's four children will all be boys is $(.512)^4 \approx .069$, and the probability that a family's four children will all be girls is $(.488)^4 \approx .057$.

b. Across the United States, the difference in percentages amounts to quite a few more boy babies than girl babies. There are almost 4,000,000 births in the United States each year. So we would expect about 2,048,000 boys and 1,952,000 girls, or 96,000 more boys. People planning government or commercial services that might depend on gender, such as people who manufacture clothing or other items for children, would find this an important difference.

D29. **a.** About .025; about .05.

b. About .05; about .10.

c. If H_0 is true and n is sufficiently large, then the sampling distribution of the sample proportion $\hat{p}$ does indeed have an approximate normal distribution with mean p_0 and standard error $\sqrt{p_0(1 - p_0)/n}$. The probabilities in parts a and b are based on that normal distribution.

For example, for a fixed null hypothesis, the probability that z is larger than 1.96 depends on whether or not that null

hypothesis is true. If p is indeed equal to p_0, that probability is .025. But if p is much larger than p_0, then the difference between $\hat{p}$ and p_0 will tend to be quite large, making z quite large, and so the probability that z will be greater than 1.96 could be almost certain.

Practice

P22. *Check conditions.* We are told that the sample is random. Both $np_0 = 500(.5) = 250$ and $n(1 - p_0) = 500(.5) = 250$ are at least 10. The total number of bookstores in the United States is greater than $10(500) = 5000$.

State your hypotheses.

H_0: The proportion of all U.S. bookstores that sell CDs is .5.

H_a: The proportion is not .5.

Compute the test statistic and draw a sketch. The test statistic is

$$z = \frac{\hat{p} - p_0}{\sqrt{\dfrac{p_0(1 - p_0)}{n}}} = \frac{.53 - .5}{\sqrt{\dfrac{.5(1 - .5)}{500}}} \approx 1.34$$

We weren't given a level of significance, and so will use $\alpha = .05$, which has critical values of ±1.96. The test statistic is inside these values.

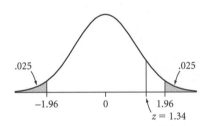

Write a conclusion in context. Because the value of the test statistic is $z = 1.34$, the result from this sample is reasonably likely to occur if half of all bookstores sell CDs. That is, the fact that we got 53% rather than a perfect 50%, reasonably can be attributed to chance alone. Therefore, we do not reject the hypothesis that half of all U.S. bookstores sell CDs.

P23. **a.** The student is guessing, and so the probability that he or she gets any one question correct is .2.

Or, $p = .2$, where p is the probability that the student gets any one question correct.

b. Half of all newscasters are men (or half are women).

Or, $p = .5$, where p is the proportion of newscasters who are men (or women).

c. Of the people who wash their car once a week, $\frac{1}{7}$ wash them on Saturday.

Or, $p = \frac{1}{7}$, where p is the proportion of people who wash their cars once a week who wash them on Saturday.

Note that the scenario in part c might make a good mini-project for students.

P24. B

Lesson Notes: Types of Errors

$P\ (\hat{p} \mid H_0)$ versus $P\ (H_0 \mid \hat{p})$

A test of significance tells you the probability of getting data like those observed in a sample given that H_0 is true. This conditional probability is not the one that you really want to know. It would be more useful to know the probability that H_0 is true given that you got data like those observed in a sample. Unfortunately, this latter conditional probability is unknowable in most situations. That is, using the standard methodology presented in this book, we can never make statements like, "The probability the null hypothesis is true is .95." All we can say are things like, "If the null hypothesis is true, the probability of getting the observed sample result or one that is even more extreme is .95."

More on Errors and Power

The significance level of a test, called α, is the probability of rejecting the null hypothesis if it is true. That is, α is the probability of making a Type I error. A Type II error is not rejecting a null hypothesis that is false. The probability of a Type II error is sometimes designated beta or β.

The power of a test is the probability of rejecting the null hypothesis. If the alternate hypothesis is true, then the power of the test is equal to $1 - \beta$. If the null hypothesis is true, then the power of the test is equal to the significance level, α, which is also the probability of a Type I error.

In practice, it is impossible to compute the power of a test because to do that you would have to know the value of p. However, for a fixed sample size, statisticians can compute the power of a test for all values of p they think are in the ballpark. This enables them to decide whether the sample size is large enough to reject a false null hypothesis with reasonably high probability.

Notice that decisions are always made with regard to the null hypothesis—we either reject it or do not reject it. "Do not reject" is not the same as "accept." Not rejecting a null hypothesis that $p = .5$, for example, makes .5 a plausible value for p. But there are many other plausible values (all of those inside a confidence interval, for example). So, we can not accept the statement that p is, in fact, .5 without a lot more evidence than a sample is going to provide.

This analogy might help: You want to determine whether a candidate for a job is male or female given the information (name, address, education, work experience, etc.) that you might find in an application. All of this data may lead you to a decision of not rejecting the possibility that the applicant is female. This is not the same as accepting the fact that the applicant is female. The fact of the matter is not going to be determined unquestionably by the data. (It will be determined when she shows up for an interview.)

Discussion

D30. **a.** Yes, it's possible for both to make a Type I error if they reject this true null hypothesis. Taline is more likely to do so because she has a larger value of α.

b. No, it isn't possible for either of them to fail to reject a false null hypothesis because the null hypothesis isn't false.

D31. **a.** No, it isn't possible for either of them to reject a true null hypothesis because the null hypothesis isn't true.

b. Yes, it's possible for both of them to make the Type II error of failing to reject this false null hypothesis. Jeffrey is more likely to make a Type II error because he has the smaller value of α. Jeffrey thus needs a larger difference between $\hat{p}$ and p_0 before he can reject the null hypothesis.

D32. About $2(.005) = .01$, because this is the area under the normal curve beyond the values ± 2.576. This is a Type I error because the null hypothesis is actually true and it has been rejected.

D33. Because there are too many situations in the world where the null hypothesis is actually false. If we use a large critical value, we will fail to reject the null hypothesis in many of these cases and so make many Type II errors.

Practice

P25. a. Because Hilda is using a significance level of $\alpha = .05$, she should reject the null hypothesis if her test statistic is larger than 1.96 or smaller than -1.96. The value of her test statistic is

$$z = \frac{\hat{p} - p_0}{\sqrt{\dfrac{p_0(1 - p_0)}{n}}} = \frac{.22 - (1/6)}{\sqrt{\dfrac{.167(1 - .167)}{100}}} \approx 1.43$$

Hilda does not reject the null hypothesis.

b. She has not made an error; she made the correct decision. The null hypothesis is true, and she did not reject it.

P26. a. Yes, it's possible for both to make a Type I error if they reject this true null hypothesis. They are equally likely to do so because they have the same value of α.

b. No, it isn't possible for them to fail to reject a false null hypothesis because the null hypothesis isn't false.

P27. a. No, it isn't possible for them to reject a true null hypothesis because the null hypothesis isn't true.

b. Yes, it's possible for both to make the Type II error of failing to reject this false null hypothesis. Jeffrey is more likely to do so because he has the smaller sample size.

Lesson Notes: *P*-Values

Using the Calculator

Calculators such as a TI-83 will conduct a significance test and draw a picture of the situation. For example, Jenny and Maya would press $\boxed{\text{STAT}}$, arrow to the TESTS menu, and select 5:1-PropZTest (a *z*-test for a single proportion). The value of p_0 is the proportion under the null hypothesis, .5. The variable x stands for the number of "successes" in their situation, 17. The variable n stands for the sample size, 40. Their choice in the next line is $prop \neq p_0$. (The other two choices will be explained shortly.)

Arrowing down to Calculate and pressing $\boxed{\text{ENTER}}$, they find the value of z is -0.949, the *P*-value is .343, the value of $\hat{p}$ is .425, and the sample size n is 40. The value of z, and hence the *P*-value, is slightly different from the ones we computed because the calculator carries many digits at all stages and that

gives a slightly more accurate answer than our method of rounding and then using the table or calculator.

Repeating the process but arrowing down to Draw, Jenny and Maya get a diagram similar to Display 8.11 on page 446 of the student text.

NOTE: Before using Draw, turn off any stat plots and any functions in the Y= screen. ∎

Discussion

D34. a. *Check conditions.* We were told that the sample is a random sample. Both $np_0 = 40(.5) = 20$ and $n(1 - p_0) = 40(1 - .5) = 20$ are at least 10. Finally, we need to check that the number of students in the school is at least $10(40) = 400$. If that is true, the conditions are satisfied for doing a significance test for a proportion.

b. *State your hypotheses.* The null hypothesis is that half of the students in the school carry backpacks to class. In symbols:

H_0: $p = .5$, where p is the proportion of students in the school who carry backpacks to class.

The alternate hypothesis is that the proportion of students in the school who carry backpacks to class is not .5. Symbolically:

H_a: $p \neq .5$, where p is the proportion of students in the school who carry backpacks to class.

c. *Compute the test statistic and draw a sketch.* Because $\hat{p} = .55$, the test statistic is

$$z = \frac{\hat{p} - p_0}{\sqrt{\dfrac{p_0(1 - p_0)}{n}}} = \frac{.55 - .50}{\sqrt{\dfrac{.50(1 - .50)}{40}}} \approx 0.632$$

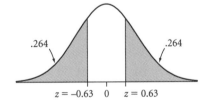

Using Table A, the *P*-value is $2(.2643) = .5286$. Doing the test on the calculator, $z \approx .6325$ and the *P*-value is .5271. If it is true that half of the students carry a backpack to class, the probability of getting 22 or more or 18 or fewer in a sample of size 40 is about .5286.

d. Write a conclusion in context. If it is true that half of the students carry a backpack to class, it is quite likely that the result will be like the one we got in our sample or will be even more extreme. Thus we have no evidence to reject the hypothesis that half of the students carry a backpack to class.

D35. B

Practice

P28. a. Check conditions. We were told that the sample is a random sample. Both $np_0 = 40(.5) = 20$ and $n(1 - p_0) = 40(1 - .5) = 20$ are at least 10. Finally, we need to check that the number of students in the school is at least $10(40) = 400$. If that is the case, it is reasonable to proceed with a test of significance for a proportion.

b. State your hypotheses. The null hypothesis is that half of the students in the school carry backpacks to class. Or, using symbols:

H_0: $p = .5$, where p is the proportion of students in the school who carry backpacks to class.

The alternate hypothesis is that the proportion of students in the school who carry backpacks to class is not .5. Symbolically:

H_a: $p \neq .5$, where p is the proportion of students in the school who carry backpacks to class.

c. Compute the test statistic and draw a sketch. Because $\hat{p} = \frac{28}{40} = .7$, the test statistic is

$$z = \frac{\hat{p} - p_0}{\sqrt{\frac{p_0(1 - p_0)}{n}}} = \frac{.7 - .50}{\sqrt{\frac{.50(1 - .50)}{40}}} \approx 2.530$$

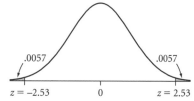

The P-value is $2(.0057) = .0114$. If it is true that half of the students carry a backpack to class, the probability of getting 28 or more or 12 or fewer in a sample of size 40 is only about .0114.

d. Write a conclusion in context. It would be a rare event to get a result as extreme as the one we got in our sample and we have evidence to reject the hypothesis that half of the students carry a backpack to class.

P29. From page 437 of the student text, the value of Miguel and Kevin's test statistic was -3.16. The probability of getting a test statistic of 3.16 or larger or -3.16 or smaller is approximately $2(.0007889) \approx .0016$. If it is true that spinning a penny is fair, there is only about a .0016 chance of getting 10 heads or fewer or 30 heads or more.

P30. Substituting into the formula for the test statistic, we get

$$z = \frac{.14 - .02}{\sqrt{\frac{.02(1 - .02)}{500}}} \approx 19.17$$

The P-value is almost 0. If the probability of a mutation were still .02, it would be almost impossible to get 14% mutations in a sample of 500 barn swallows. The researchers should report something like this: In the Chernobyl area, about 2% of the swallows had mutations before the accident. Ten years after the accident, we captured a sample of 500 barn swallows, which we believe are a random selection of the barn swallows in the area. Of these, 14% had mutations. There is almost no chance of this happening unless the percentage of barn swallows with mutations has increased.

Lesson Notes: One- and Two-Sided Tests

Discussion

D36. Because this result is in the opposite tail of the distribution from which the sample proportion was expected to go, we would not reject the null hypothesis with a one-tailed test.

D37. a. $\frac{2}{3}$. You can explain this in two ways. The first way is to have the first student sit down anywhere. Then the probability the second student sits corner-to-corner is $\frac{2}{3}$ because, of the three seats that are left, two are adjacent seats. The other explanation is to list all 12 of the ways two students, A and B, can sit in chairs 1, 2, 3, and 4.

b. The null hypothesis is that the proportion of pairs of students who are seated on adjacent sides of a table is $\frac{2}{3}$.

c. The alternate hypothesis is that the proportion of pairs is greater than $\frac{2}{3}$. (This indicates a preference for sitting on adjacent sides.)

d. Not quite. The problem is that this isn't a random sample from any population. Nevertheless, let's see whether the result can reasonably be attributed to chance.

e. The test statistic is

$$z = \frac{\hat{p} - p_0}{\sqrt{\dfrac{p_0(1 - p_0)}{n}}} = \frac{.70 - 2/3}{\sqrt{\dfrac{2/3(1 - 2/3)}{50}}} = 0.5$$

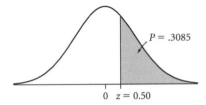

P = .3085

0   *z* = 0.50

f. The *P*-value for this one-sided test is about .3085. We don't reject the null hypothesis.

g. The probability that two students will sit on adjacent sides of a table just by chance is $\frac{2}{3}$. In the psychologist's sample of size 50, 70% of the students were sitting on adjacent sides. This is just about what you would expect from chance variation alone. There is no evidence that students prefer sitting on adjacent sides. To establish that, the psychologist would need a larger sample size or a sample proportion quite a bit higher than .7.

For extensions to D37, see the article referenced in the student text. For example, suppose that one side of each table is placed against a wall so that there are only three chairs. Now could the psychologist conclude that students have a preference for sitting on adjacent sides of a table?

D38. To reject a null hypothesis, you need a small *P*-value. It is easier to reject a false null hypothesis with a one-tailed test (if you have the right direction). For a given test statistic *z*, the *P*-value will be half that of a two-sided test.

Practice

P31. *Check conditions.* The conditions are met for doing a test of significance for a proportion because you have a random sample, both $np_0 = 169(.51) = 86.19$ and $n(1 - p_0) = 169(1 - .51) = 82.81$ are at least 10, and the number of teens in your community (probably) is at least $10(169) = 1690$. If this latter condition doesn't hold, the test will be conservative.

State your hypotheses. The null hypothesis is that 51% (or even fewer) of teens in your community know this fact. The alternate hypothesis is that the percentage is greater than 51%.

Compute the test statistic and draw a sketch. The test statistic is

$$z = \frac{\hat{p} - p_0}{\sqrt{\dfrac{p_0(1 - p_0)}{n}}} = \frac{.55 - .51}{\sqrt{\dfrac{.51(1 - .51)}{169}}} \approx 1.04$$

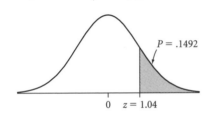

P = .1492

0   *z* = 1.04

The *P*-value from Table A is about .1492. Thus, .55 is much the sort of sample proportion you might get when taking a random sample of size 169 from a population with $p = .51$. Doing the test on the calculator, $z \approx 1.0479$ and the *P*-value is about .1473.

Write a conclusion in context. You should not reject the null hypothesis. If it is true that the percentage of teens in your community who know epilepsy is not contagious is only 51%, then it is reasonably likely to get 55% who know this in a sample of 169 teens.

P32. a. False. This is considered cheating because, for example, after looking at the data you could realize that if you switch to a one-sided test, you would get a smaller *P*-value and then could reject H_0.

b. False. The *P*-value for a one-sided test is half that for the two-sided test.

c. False. The null hypothesis is either true or it isn't. The *P*-value is the probability of getting a sample statistic as extreme or even more extreme than the one we got, *assuming the null hypothesis is true.*

d. True

Exercises

E14. D

E15. This is a two-tailed test of significance.

Check conditions. The Gallup poll uses what you can consider a simple random sample of adults in the United States. Both $np_0 = 506\left(\frac{2}{3}\right) \approx 337$ and $n(1 - p_0) = 506\left(\frac{1}{3}\right) \approx 169$ are at least 10. There are more than $10(506) = 5060$ adults in the United States. Thus, you can use a test for the significance of a proportion.

State your hypotheses.

H_0: $p = \frac{2}{3}$, where p is the proportion of all adults in the United States who would have said they would be willing to pay $500 more per year in higher prices so that industry could reduce air pollution.

H_a: $p \neq \frac{2}{3}$

Compute the test statistic and draw a sketch. The test statistic is

$$z = \frac{\hat{p} - p_0}{\sqrt{\frac{p_0(1 - p_0)}{n}}} = \frac{.63 - 2/3}{\sqrt{\frac{2/3(1 - 2/3)}{506}}} \approx -1.75$$

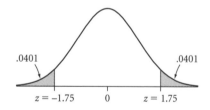

P-value. If the null hypothesis is true, the probability of getting a value of the test statistic that is smaller than -1.75 or larger than 1.75 is .0802.

Write a conclusion in context. You can not reject the null hypothesis at the 5% level. You have no evidence that if all U.S. adults had been asked, the proportion that would have said they were willing to pay $500 more per year would be different from $\frac{2}{3}$. The result from Gallup's sample is entirely consistent with a population with $\frac{2}{3}$ successes.

E16. This is a one-tailed test of significance.

Check conditions. The Gallup poll uses what you can consider a simple random

sample of adults in the United States. Both $np_0 = 1060(.5) = 530$ and $n(1 - p_0) = 1060(.5) = 530$ are at least 10. The population of all adults in the United States is much larger than $10(1060) = 10,600$. Thus, you can use a test for the significance of a proportion. This will be a one-tailed test.

State your hypotheses.

H_0: $p = .5$, where p is the proportion of all adults in the United States who would give a rating of excellent or good.

H_a: $p < .5$.

Compute the test statistic and draw a sketch. The test statistic is

$$z = \frac{\hat{p} - p_0}{\sqrt{\frac{p_0(1 - p_0)}{n}}} = \frac{.46 - .5}{\sqrt{\frac{.5(1 - .5)}{1060}}} \approx -2.605$$

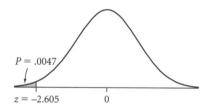

P-value. If the null hypothesis is true, the probability from Table A of getting a value of the test statistic that is smaller than -2.605 is only .0046 (halfway between .0047 and .0045). Using the test on the calculator with $x = 488$, you get $z = -2.58$ and a P-value of about .0049.

Write a conclusion in context. If you were to take a random sample from a population with 50% successes (or more), there is almost no chance of getting a result with as few or fewer successes as the one Gallup got in this sample. If the null hypothesis were true, Gallup would have a very unlikely result indeed. Thus you should reject the null hypothesis. The evidence supports the claim that fewer than half of adults would give a rating of excellent or good.

E17. This is a one-tailed test of significance.

Check conditions. The Gallup poll uses what you can consider a simple random sample of adults in the United States. Both $np_0 = 1003(.25) = 250.75$ and $n(1 - p_0) = 1003(.75) = 752.25$ are at least 10. The population of all adults in the United States is much larger than $10(1003) = 10,030$. Thus, you can use a test for the significance of a proportion. This will be a one-tailed test.

State your hypotheses.

H_0: $p = .25$, where p is the proportion of all adults in the United States who would pick cancer as the problem for science to solve in the next 25 years.

H_a: $p > .25$

Compute the test statistic and draw a sketch. The test statistic is

$$z = \frac{\hat{p} - p_0}{\sqrt{\dfrac{p_0(1 - p_0)}{n}}} = \frac{.30 - .25}{\sqrt{\dfrac{.25(1 - .25)}{1003}}} \approx 3.657$$

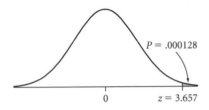

P-value. If the null hypothesis is true, the probability of getting a value of the test statistic that is larger than 3.657 is only .000128. Using the test on the calculator with $x = 301$, you get $z \approx 3.664$ and a P-value of about .000124.

Write a conclusion in context. If you were to take a random sample from a population with 25% successes (or fewer), there is almost no chance of getting a result with as many successes as the one Gallup got in this sample. If the null hypothesis were true, Gallup would have a very unlikely result indeed. Thus, it is not plausible that 25% (or fewer) of all adults would pick a cure for cancer.

E18. $.05(100) = 5$ people

E19. No matter what your null hypothesis, it probably isn't exactly true. For example, there is no pair of dice that has a probability of doubles of exactly $\frac{1}{6} = .1\overline{6}$. You might find a pair with probability of doubles equal to .166667, but exactly .16666666 . . . just won't happen. To reject the null hypothesis that $p = \frac{1}{6}$ ($\alpha = .05$) for the pair of dice with $p = .166667$, you would need a sample size of about

$$n = 1.96^2\left(\frac{\frac{1}{6}\left(1 - \frac{1}{6}\right)}{.00000033\ldots^2}\right)$$

$$\approx 5 \times 10^{12}$$

Admittedly, this is rather large.

E20. With a sample of size 20, a hypothesis test of $p = .5$ will not have much power to detect that this null hypothesis is false. To reject the null hypothesis that $p = .5$, you would have to have 5 heads or fewer or 15 heads or more. Using the exact binomial distribution with $p = .4$, the probability that this will happen is only about $.126 + .002 = .128$. A good suggestion would be to increase the sample size considerably.

E21. **a.** The test statistic for this test is

$$z = \frac{\frac{42}{80} - .55}{\sqrt{\dfrac{.55(1 - .55)}{80}}} \approx -0.449$$

This gives a P-value for this test of about .65. We can not reject the hypothesis that 55% of students prefer hamburgers.

b. The test statistic is $z = -1.35$. The P-value for this test is about .18. We can not reject the hypothesis that 55% of students prefer hot dogs.

c. The results of parts a and b may seem paradoxical to students. It looks like we are accepting the hypothesis that a majority prefer hamburgers and the hypothesis that a majority prefer hot dogs. This is precisely why we don't "accept" the null hypothesis. In this case, we don't have enough evidence to reject it, but we know that we have made a Type II error in at least one of these tests.

d. The test statistic is $z = -1.42$. Then the P-value for this test is about .155. We can not reject the hypothesis that 55% of the students prefer hamburgers.

e. The test statistic is $z = -4.264$. Then, the P-value for this test is .00002. We can reject the hypothesis that 55% of the students prefer hot dogs.

f. The results of parts d and e will look a lot better to students. The larger sample size makes it clear that more than half the students prefer hamburgers. Note that having students compare the four confidence intervals that can be constructed from this exercise would be a good exploration. Thanks to Dan Johnson, of Silver Creek High School in San Jose, California, for this idea.

E22. As with all investigative tasks, encourage students to do some exploratory analysis first. Students might make back-to-back stem-and-leaf plots of the heights of the winners and the heights of the losers. However, because the data come paired (by election), a complete exploratory analysis should take that into account. For example, students might examine a plot of the differences of winner's height minus loser's height. They also might make a scatterplot of (winner's height, loser's height) or make a plot of the differences over time.

When conducting a test of significance, the null hypothesis is that height doesn't matter. Specifically, the probability that the taller person will be elected is .50. Students could test the proportion of pairs where the taller person was elected against this standard. (They first should decide how to deal with the case where the two heights are the same.)

A Note about E22 and Other Situations Where Your "Sample" Is the Entire Population: Purists would say that we should not use a test of significance to determine whether the taller person is more likely to be elected president. They have two reasons. The first is that the numbers given are not a random sample from any population. We have all of the information for presidential elections from 1900 through 2000. And in fact, the taller candidate *did* win more than half of the elections.

The second reason is that this is a classic example of "data snooping." We probably could think of a hundred characteristics of the two candidates that we could have considered: older, heavier, more experienced, sharper dresser, and so on. The winner and the loser will not match exactly on all of these. By definition, if we check 100 characteristics, we expect that 5 will result in a rare event. Height simply may be one of those 5 characteristics and that's why people have noticed it.

However, you might use this example with your students as an example of how a test of significance can be used profitably even though we have the entire population. The question becomes, Can the fact that the taller man has won more often reasonably be attributed to chance? If the answer is yes, we have no reason to continue this investigation. If the answer is no, then we have to look for some other explanation. That explanation might in fact be that we did some data snooping and ended up with a Type I error. On the other hand, that explanation might be that being taller helps and future voters will also tend to favor the taller candidate.

So in situations like these, the mechanics of a significance test simply let us know whether or not there is something that needs to be investigated. The data first must pass the test that the results can't reasonably be attributed to chance before we take any further steps. Note that these comments apply to the Westvaco case as well, where we had information about the entire population of employees.

8.3 A Confidence Interval for the Difference of Two Proportions

Objectives

- to use simulation to construct an approximate sampling distribution for the difference of two proportions.
- to find the mean and standard error of the sampling distribution for the difference of two proportions.
- to construct and interpret a confidence interval for the difference of two proportions.
- to understand how randomization differs in surveys and experiments when comparing two proportions.

Important Terms and Concepts

- sampling distribution for the difference of two proportions
- confidence interval for the difference of two proportions

Lesson Planning

Class Time

Two to three days

Materials

For Activity 8.5, a large bag of plain M&M's and a large bag of peanut M&M's. Colored beads may be substituted.

Suggested Assignments

Classwork		
Essential	**Recommended**	**Optional**
Activity 8.5	D42–D44	
D39–D41	P35, P36	
P33, P34		

Homework		
Essential	**Recommended**	**Optional**
E23, E27	E24–E26, E28–E30	

Lesson Notes: Simulating the Sampling Distribution for the Difference of Two Proportions

Activity 8.5: Brown Plain and Peanut M&M's

In Activity 8.5, students construct an approximate sampling distribution for the difference of two proportions, $\hat{p}_1 - \hat{p}_2$. The first proportion comes from a random sample of size 20 taken from a population with 30% successes. The second proportion comes from a random sample of size 20 taken from a population with 20% successes.

You may wish to speed this along by counting out samples of size 20 ahead of time and placing them in small bags. Or, instead of a large bag of plain M&M's and a large bag of peanut M&M's, you could buy half of the class a small bag of plain M&M's and half the class a small bag of peanut M&M's. Pair the students up, have them take the first 20 M&M's out of their bags and get the difference of the proportion of plain that are brown and the proportion of peanut that are brown. This will give you only about 10 to 15 trials, depending on the size of your class. Do the remaining trials using the calculator.

Instead of using M&M's in Activity 8.5, you could have students do the entire simulation using their calculators. See step 4 below for instructions about how to use the calculator.

Alternatively, you could use two boxes of beads, one with 30% of a certain color and the other with 20% of a certain color. If there are several hundred beads in each box and each sample is replaced after it is drawn, then drawing samples of size 20 is roughly equivalent to random sampling from a binomial population.

Up-to-the-minute information about M&M's may be found at www.baking.m-ms.com.

1. Proportions will vary according to the sample. If, for example, the student gets 5 brown M&M's, the proportion would be $\frac{5}{20} = .25$.

2. Proportions will vary according to the sample. If, for example, the student gets 7 brown M&M's, the proportion would be $\frac{7}{20} = .35$.

3. Differences will vary. For the examples given in steps 1 and 2, the difference is $.25 - .35 = -.10$.

4. Differences will vary. A set of typical results appears in step 5.

If you prefer, students can do steps 1–4 on their calculators. On the TI-83, enter randBin(20,.3,100)→L1 to replicate step 1 one hundred times and store the results in list L1.

Divide list L1 by 20, L1/20→L1, to change to proportions. You can do this by using the command L1 $\div$ 20 STO →L1.

Then enter randBin(20,.2,100)→L2 to replicate step 2 one hundred times and place the results in list L2.

Divide L2 by 20, L2/20→L2, to change to proportions.

Finally, enter L1−L2→L3 to define list L3 as the 100 differences.

5. A typical dot plot for 100 sample differences appears below, along with the Minitab commands used to create it. The mean of this distribution is .0895, and the standard error is .1371. The theoretical mean is $.30 - .20 = .10$, and the theoretical standard error is approximately .136, as computed in D40 using the formula on the bottom of page 460 of the student text. The shape is approximately normal. A theorem of mathematical statistics says that if you take a value at random from one normal distribution and a second value independently and at random from a second normal distribution and add (or subtract) them, then the distribution of all possible sums (or differences) is also normal. (See E29.)

Minitab Simulation of M&M Differences

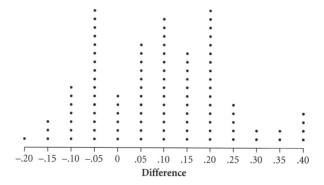

```
MTB > random 100 C1;
SUBC > binomial 20 .3.
MTB > random 100 C2;
SUBC > binomial 20 .2.
MTB > let C3 = (C1 − C2)/20
MTB > dotplot C3
```

The following is a dot plot of 2500 trials. It is very close to the theoretical distribution of $\hat{p}_1 - \hat{p}_2$. Each dot represents about 26 points.

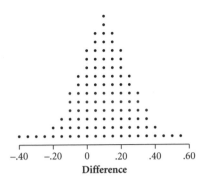

Difference

6. Students should identify the values that make up the middle 95% of the points on their dot plots. Their answers will vary depending on their simulation. On the theoretical distribution, the middle 95% falls between about $-.17$ and $.37$.

Discussion

D39. **a.** The mean is very close to zero, the standard error is about .1, and the shape is approximately normal.

b. The middle 95% of all differences are between about $-.2$ and $.2$.

c. The shapes of the two distributions are the same, approximately normal. The means of both distributions occur at about $p_1 - p_2$. And, as you would expect, the standard error for the samples of size 40 is smaller than that of the samples of size 20. It is about $\frac{3}{4}$ as large.

Practice

P33. The following is a sample dot plot.

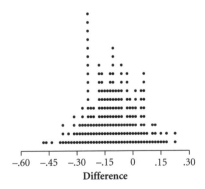

Difference

Results will vary according to the simulation, but the shape is approximately normal. The theoretical mean is $-.10$, and the theoretical standard error is .134. Thus the reasonably

likely values of $\hat{p}_1 - \hat{p}_2$ fall between about $-.36$ and $.16$ (for the middle 95%).

Lesson Notes: The Formula for the Confidence Interval

Using the TI-83

The 2-PropZInt function of the TI-83 calculator gives the same confidence interval as the formula in the section, subject to rounding error. You find this function by pressing STAT, arrowing to the TESTS menu, and selecting B:2-PropZInt. Note that although the formula in the student text requires $\hat{p}_1$ and $\hat{p}_2$, the calculator asks you to enter x_1 and x_2. These are the number of successes in the first sample and the number of successes in the second sample, respectively. This requirement can be a little bit of a problem if proportions are given, as in the dog ownership example on page 457 of the student text. Here, for example, we are given $\hat{p}_1 = .45$ and $\hat{p}_2 = .43$ and $n_1 = n_2 = 1016$. So the number of successes would be $n_1 \hat{p}_1 = 457.2$ and $n_2 \hat{p}_2 = 436.88$. Putting these values exactly into x_1 and x_2 will give an error, so the student will have to round and put in 457 and 437 respectively. This gives a 95% confidence interval $(-.0235, .06284)$.

Getting the Interpretation Right

Consider these two interpretations of the confidence interval in P34 of 5.4% ± 3.7% for the difference in the proportions of Americans who used the Internet in 2001 and 2000:

• You are 99% confident that the difference between the percentage of all Americans who used the Internet in 2001 and the percentage of all Americans who used the Internet in 2000 is in the interval 5.4% ± 3.7%.

• You are 99% confident that the percentage of all Americans who used the Internet increased between 1.6% and 9.1% from 2000 to 2001.

The first interpretation is correct and unambiguous. It reflects the meaning in this section of the confidence interval for the difference of two proportions. The meaning, for example, of the 5.4% is

$.054 = $ *proportion in 2001 $-$ proportion in 2000*

A student who writes the second interpretation may have the correct idea, but the words are ambiguous. Usually when we say that something increased by 5.4%, we are computing the increase as a proportion of the original base:

$$.054 = \frac{proportion \ in \ 2001 - proportion \ in \ 2000}{proportion \ in \ 2000}$$

However, this is not the case here. Encourage students to use wording like that of the first interpretation.

Discussion

D40. **a.** $\sqrt{.3(1-.3)/20 + .2(1-.2)/20} \approx .136$

b. Answers will vary. Because the simulation consisted of only 100 trials, the standard errors may not be very close.

D41. **a.** It is plausible that the two samples came from populations with the same proportion of successes because the observed value of $\hat{p}_1 - \hat{p}_2$ is a reasonably likely result if $p_1 - p_2 = 0$.

b. It suggests that the two samples didn't come from populations with the same proportion of successes unless a rare event occurred.

D42. **I.** A 95% confidence interval for the difference of two proportions $p_1 - p_2$ consists of those differences for which the observed difference of the two sample proportions $\hat{p}_1 - \hat{p}_2$ is a reasonably likely outcome. (That is, the confidence interval contains any differences in population proportions that could have produced the observed difference in sample proportions within the middle 95% of all possible outcomes.)

II. If you construct one hundred 95% confidence intervals, you expect that the difference of the population proportions $p_1 - p_2$ will be in 95 of them.

Practice

P34. We will let the "first" population be 2001, to have a positive difference.

Check conditions. The problem says that we may consider the two samples random and independent. Each of

$$n_1\hat{p}_1 = 2006(.723) \approx 1450$$
$$n_1(1 - \hat{p}_1) = 2006(1 - .723) \approx 556$$
$$n_2\hat{p}_2 = 2006(.669) \approx 1342$$
$$n_2(1 - \hat{p}_2) = 2006(1 - .669) \approx 664$$

is at least 5.

The number of Americans in each year was more than ten times the sample size given.

Do computations. The 99% confidence interval for 2001 minus 2000 is shown at the bottom of the page.

Write a conclusion in context. You are 99% confident that the difference between the percentage of all Americans who used the Internet in 2001 and the percentage of all Americans who used the Internet in 2000 is in the interval 1.7% to 9.1%. Because this confidence interval does not include zero, you are confident that the percentage increased.

P35. In general, as sample sizes get larger, the length of the confidence interval gets smaller. (If the sample size for only one sample gets larger, that part of the formula for the standard error goes to zero. This alone won't make the standard error itself go to zero unless the other sample size also gets larger.)

Lesson Notes: A Medical Experiment to Compare Two Treatments

Variations on Taking Two Independent Random Samples from Two Different Populations

If your students bring in examples of surveys from the media, quite often you will find that the design of the survey doesn't quite satisfy the conditions of this section. That is, the two samples were not taken independently from two different populations. Can the methods of this section (and of Section 8.4) still be used? The answer depends on the design used in the study. Four common designs are discussed next.

Two independent samples from the same population. Suppose you want to compare the proportion of households that own dogs this year and the proportion that owned dogs last year. It turns out that the households for the two years are exactly the same. Can you consider these "different" populations?

Yes. It is okay to use the methods of this section in cases like this as long as the households were

---

$$(.723 - .669) \pm 2.576 \sqrt{\frac{.723(1 - .723)}{2006} + \frac{.669(1 - .669)}{2006}} = .054 \pm .037, \text{ or about } .017 \text{ to } .091.$$

sampled independently in the two years. The populations meant in cases like this aren't really the households themselves, but rather the dog-ownership characteristic of the households, which may have changed over the year.

The same sample at two different times (repeated measures). A common survey design is, for example, to get a random sample of U.S. households and determine the percentage that own dogs. Then five years later, return to the same households and ask the same question.

This is a repeated measures design, and the methods of this section do not apply.

One sample from a mixed population divided into two samples (post-stratification). To compare, for example, the proportion of Republican voters who favor some issue and the proportion of Democratic voters who favor that issue, a survey organization might take one large random sample of voters and divide it into Republicans and Democrats. These groups are then treated as two independent random samples from the population of Republican voters and the population of Democratic voters.

Although the samples are now dependent, the formula for a confidence interval that is given in this section is approximately correct as long as both sample sizes are relatively large. Even if they are large, very unequal sample sizes would increase the margin of error.

Two questions asked of the same sample. The 2001 survey of 1016 U.S. households that found that 45% of the households owned a dog also found that 34% of these same households owned a cat. Can you use the formula for a confidence interval to estimate the difference in the proportion of U.S. households that own a cat and the proportion that own a dog?

It is not correct to use the methods of this section in a case like this. The households certainly can not be considered independent on the questions of dog and cat ownership. As students will see in E30, if a household owns one kind of pet, it is more likely to own the other kind of pet also.

Multiple-choice questions pose a similar problem of dependence. For example, suppose a survey asks each voter whether he or she is a Republican, Democrat, or Independent. If you want to compare the proportion of Republicans to the proportion of Democrats, the methods of this section will not work.

A Note on Effect Size

Although effect size is not usually covered in the introductory statistics course, it is a topic you may want to discuss with your students.

For example, from the table on page 458, there is only a 3% difference between the two treatments in the percentages who developed AIDS. This doesn't sound like much of a difference. However, the percentages who developed AIDS are relatively small to begin with, roughly 18% and 15%. Consequently, giving AZT+ACV rather than AZT alone reduced the chance of developing AIDS from 18% to 15% or by 3/18 = 17%. The effect size is said to be 17%. We estimate that using AZT+ACV prevents 17% of those who would develop AIDS if only AZT was used from developing AIDS.

$$effect\ size = \frac{\%\ difference\ between\ treatments}{percentage\ from\ original\ treatment}$$

But now suppose that 70% of patients given an old treatment are cured whereas 73% of patients given a new treatment are cured. It is still the case that there is a 3% difference between the two treatments, but here the effect size is only $\frac{3}{70} = 4\%$. Because the percentages were high to begin with, only 4% of those who wouldn't have been cured under the old treatment will be cured under the new treatment. See E28 for a situation where effect size is crucial.

Experiments to Compare Two Treatments

The difference between randomly selecting two independent samples from larger populations and randomly assigning the subjects you have to two different treatments is a fundamentally important concept in statistics. It's pretty amazing that the same confidence interval works (meaning it has a capture rate equal to that advertised) in both cases. To demonstrate to your students that random assignment of treatments leads to approximately the same standard error as for independent samples, you can use the simulation given on page 105 in Section 8.4. However, we suggest you wait until you get to Section 8.4 so students are more familiar with two-sample problems.

Discussion

D43. "Double-blind" means that neither the physician (who will decide whether the patient has developed AIDS) nor the patient know whether the patient is receiving AZT or AZT+ACV. "Randomized" means that the patients are assigned randomly to the two treatments. "Clinical trial" means a comparative experiment to evaluate a medical treatment that is based on actual patients in realistic situations.

D44. No, the proportions could be 0.07 and 0.02. No, the proportions could be 0.99 and 0.94, making Treatment B good in almost all situations.

Practice

P36. *Check conditions.* First, the conditions for an experiment are met, which allows the computing of a confidence interval for the difference of two proportions: Subjects were randomly assigned to treatments. Each of
$$n_1\hat{p}_1 = 169$$
$$n_1(1 - \hat{p}_1) = 10{,}868$$
$$n_2\hat{p}_2 = 138$$
$$n_2(1 - \hat{p}_2) = 10{,}896$$
is at least 5.

Do computations. The 95% confidence interval is as shown at the bottom of the page.

Write a conclusion in context. Suppose all of the subjects could have been given the aspirin treatment and all of the subjects could have been given the placebo treatment. Then you are 95% confident that the difference in the proportion who would get ulcers is in the interval .0028 ± .0031. Because 0 is in this interval, it is plausible that there is no difference in the proportions who would get ulcers. The term "95% confident" means that this method of constructing confidence intervals results in $p_1 - p_2$ falling in an

average of 95 out of every 100 confidence intervals you construct.

Exercises

E23. *Check conditions.* The conditions are met for constructing a confidence interval for the difference of two proportions:

• You were told that you may assume that the samples are equivalent to simple random samples.

• There are more than 81,310 male students and more than 81,310 female students in the United States.

• Each of
$$n_1\hat{p}_1 \approx 4513$$
$$n_1(1 - \hat{p}_1) \approx 3618$$
$$n_2\hat{p}_2 \approx 3439$$
$$n_2(1 - \hat{p}_2) \approx 4692$$
is at least 5.

Do computations. The 95% confidence interval for the difference in the proportions of male and female students who have played on sports teams run by their school during the 12 months preceding the survey is shown at the bottom of the page.

Write a conclusion in context. Because 0 isn't included in this confidence interval, it is acceptable to use the term "significantly more likely."

E24. Let x be the number of females in the survey. Then $16{,}262 - x$ is the number of males in the survey and
$$.495 = \frac{.555(16{,}262 - x) + .423x}{16{,}262}$$

Lesson 8.3, P36

$$(\hat{p}_1 - \hat{p}_2) \pm z^\star \cdot \sqrt{\frac{\hat{p}_1(1 - \hat{p}_1)}{n_1} + \frac{\hat{p}_2(1 - \hat{p}_2)}{n_2}} = (.0153 - .0125) \pm 1.96 \sqrt{\frac{(.0153)(.9847)}{11{,}037} + \frac{(.0125)(.9875)}{11{,}034}}$$
$$= .0028 \pm .0031 \text{ or } -.0003 \text{ to } .0059$$

Lesson 8.3, E23

$$(\hat{p}_1 - \hat{p}_2) \pm z^\star \cdot \sqrt{\frac{\hat{p}_1(1 - \hat{p}_1)}{n_1} + \frac{\hat{p}_2(1 - \hat{p}_2)}{n_2}} = (.555 - .423) \pm 1.96 \sqrt{\frac{(.555)(.445)}{8131} + \frac{(.423)(.577)}{8131}}$$
$$= .132 \pm .015 \text{ or } (.117, .147)$$

Solving, $x \approx 7392$. The number of females was about 7392, and the number of males was about 8870. There were more males in the sample than females, which must be the case because .495 is closer to .555 than it is to .423.

This does not change the conclusion to E23. Using these sample sizes, the confidence interval is .117 to .147.

E25. **Check conditions.** The conditions are met for constructing a confidence interval for the difference of two proportions:

- You were told that you may assume that the samples are equivalent to simple random samples.

- The number of men and number of women in the United States are more than 4250.

- Each of
$$n_1 \hat{p}_1 = 425(.23) \approx 98$$
$$n_1(1 - \hat{p}_1) = 425(1 - .23) \approx 327$$
$$n_2 \hat{p}_2 = 425(.34) \approx 145$$
$$n_2(1 - \hat{p}_2) = 425(1 - .34) \approx 281$$
is at least 5.

Do computations. The 99% confidence interval for the difference in the proportions of men and women who prefer their last name is shown at the bottom of the page.

Write a conclusion in context. You are 99% confident that the difference in the percentage of all men and the percentage of all women who prefer to be addressed by their last name is in the interval $-.189$ to $-.031$. (Alternatively, you are 99% confident that the difference in the percentage of all women and the percentage of all men who prefer to be addressed by their last name is in the interval .031 to .189.)

E26. The method is not correct because the respondents weren't selected independently from two different populations. These people were all from the same population and are differentiated only by their answer to the question. The appropriate method to use is a confidence interval for a proportion from a single population, as shown at the bottom of the page.

You are 95% confident that the proportion of online respondents who would support the proposed bill to eliminate the penny is in the interval .14 to .304. Because this interval doesn't contain 50%, it appears that less than half of the population of online respondents would support this bill.

E27. a. **Check conditions.** The conditions are met for constructing a confidence interval for the difference of two proportions:

Subjects were randomly assigned to treatments (the proportion who received the placebo was put first to keep things positive): Each of
$$n_1 \hat{p}_1 = 31$$
$$n_1(1 - \hat{p}_1) = 109$$
$$n_2 \hat{p}_2 = 17$$
$$n_2(1 - \hat{p}_2) = 122$$
is at least 5.

Lesson 8.3, E25

$$(\hat{p}_1 - \hat{p}_2) \pm z^* \cdot \sqrt{\frac{\hat{p}_1(1 - \hat{p}_1)}{n_1} + \frac{\hat{p}_2(1 - \hat{p}_2)}{n_2}} = (.23 - .34) \pm 2.576 \sqrt{\frac{(.23)(1 - .23)}{425} + \frac{(.34)(1 - .34)}{425}}$$
$$= -.11 \pm .079$$

Lesson 8.3, E26

$$\hat{p} \pm 1.96 \sqrt{\frac{\hat{p}(1 - \hat{p})}{n}} = .222 \pm 1.96 \sqrt{\frac{.222(1 - .222)}{99}}$$
$$\approx .222 \pm .082$$

Do computations. The 95% confidence interval is shown at the bottom of the page.

Write a conclusion in context. You are 95% confident that if all of the skiers in the experiment had been given the placebo and all of the skiers in the experiment had been given vitamin C, then the difference in the proportions who get colds would have been in the interval .0114 and .1868. Because 0 isn't in this confidence interval, you believe that vitamin C reduces the proportion of people who get colds.

b. Using $z^* = 2.576$, the 99% confidence interval is $-.0162$ to $.2144$. Because 0 is in this confidence interval, it is plausible that the same proportion of skiers would get a cold whether or not they took vitamin C.

E28. The conditions are met for constructing a confidence interval for the difference of two proportions:

Subjects were randomly assigned to treatments. Each of

$$n_1 \hat{p}_1 = 82$$
$$n_1(1 - \hat{p}_1) = 200{,}663$$
$$n_2 \hat{p}_2 = 162$$
$$n_2(1 - \hat{p}_2) = 201{,}067$$

is at least 5.

The 95% confidence interval for the difference in the proportions of children who developed polio is $-.0005$ to $-.0002$. That is, you are 95% confident that if all of the children in this experiment had been given the placebo and if all had been given the vaccine, the difference in the proportions who would have developed polio would have been between $-.0005$ and $-.0002$. This is a statistically significant difference because 0 isn't in the confidence interval. You believe that the vaccine reduced the proportion of children who developed polio. Although this looks like a very small difference, that's because the proportions who developed polio in the first place were very small.

Notice, however, that the effect size (see the earlier lesson notes on effect size) is quite large. The effect size is shown at the bottom of the page.

That is, with the vaccine, there are half the number of cases of polio.

E29. You can use z in this way only because the sampling distribution of the estimate $\hat{p}_1 - \hat{p}_2$ is approximately normal. How do you know that the distribution of $\hat{p}_1 - \hat{p}_2$ is approximately normal? A theorem in mathematical statistics given in the box on page 315 of the student text says that the sampling distribution of the difference of two normally distributed random variables is normal. So the sampling distribution of $\hat{p}_1 - \hat{p}_2$ will be approximately normal if the separate sampling distributions of $\hat{p}_1$ and $\hat{p}_2$ are normal. They are approximately normal if each of $n_1 \hat{p}_1$, $n_1(1 - \hat{p}_1)$, $n_2 \hat{p}_2$, and $n_2(1 - \hat{p}_2)$ is at least 10. However, this condition is stronger than necessary in the case of a difference—the sampling distribution of the difference will be approximately normal as long as each one of these is at least 5.

Lesson 8.3, E27

$$(\hat{p}_1 - \hat{p}_2) \pm z^* \sqrt{\frac{\hat{p}_1(1 - \hat{p}_1)}{n_1} + \frac{\hat{p}_2(1 - \hat{p}_2)}{n_2}}$$

$$= (.2214 - .1223) \pm 1.96 \sqrt{\frac{(.2214)(1 - .2214)}{140} + \frac{(.1223)(1 - .1223)}{139}}$$

$$= .0991 \pm .0877$$

Lesson 8.3, E28

$$\frac{proportion\ without\ vaccine - proportion\ with\ vaccine}{proportion\ without\ vaccine} = \frac{.0008 - .0004}{.0008}$$

$$= .5$$

E30. **a.** 41%

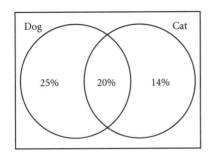

b. No, $P(own\ a\ dog) = .45$, but

$$P(own\ a\ dog \mid own\ a\ cat) = \frac{P(own\ a\ dog\ \text{and}\ own\ a\ cat)}{P(own\ a\ cat)}$$

$$= \frac{.2}{.34} \approx .588$$

So, in fact, households that have a cat are more likely to have a dog than households are overall.

Alternatively, students may use the fact that $P(own\ a\ dog$ and $own\ a\ cat) = .20$, but $P(own\ a\ dog) \cdot P(own\ a\ cat) = (.45)(.34) = .153$. Because the multiplication rule for independent events doesn't hold, the two events aren't independent.

c. No. The two percentages, 45% and 34%, did not come from independent samples.

8.4 A Significance Test for the Difference of Two Proportions

Objectives

- to review the sampling distribution for the difference of two proportions when $p_1 = p_2$
- to learn to use a test of significance to decide whether you should reject the claim that two samples were drawn from two binomial populations that have the same proportion of successes

Just as with a single proportion, a confidence interval for the difference of two proportions is introduced (in Section 8.3) before the associated significance test is introduced (in this section). This section is relatively short but is extremely important. Testing to see whether the difference of two sample proportions is statistically significant is a common situation.

Important Terms and Concepts

- significance test for the difference of two proportions
- pooled estimate for $\hat{p}$

Lesson Planning

Class Time

Three to four days

Materials

For Activity 8.6, one sheet of graph paper for each student and possibly a large bag of plain M&M's and a large bag of peanut M&M's

Suggested Assignments

Classwork		
Essential	**Recommended**	**Optional**
Activity 8.6	D47, D49	
D45, D46, D48	P39	
P37, P38		

Homework		
Essential	**Recommended**	**Optional**
E31, E33	E32, E34, E35, E37, E38	E36, E39–E41

Lesson Notes: A Difference When There Really Is No Difference

Activity 8.6: Differences When There Is No Difference

Again, you may wish to bring in large bags of plain and peanut M&M's or bags of beads to illustrate the sampling process visually before students move to simulation on the calculator. Each bag of beads should contain 20% of one particular color.

1. Results will vary. At this step, you may wish to use the real bag of plain M&M's. The TI-83 command that simulates this process is randBin(10,.2). Note that students must convert the number returned to a proportion. For example, if the result is 3, the answer would be $\frac{3}{10} = .3$.

2. Results will vary. At this step, you may wish to use the real bag of peanut M&M's. The TI-83 command that simulates this process is again randBin(10,.2).

    Again, students must convert the number returned to a proportion.

3. Results will vary.

4. To compute 999 differences at once on the TI-83, first store 999 values of $\hat{p}_1$ in list L1 by entering randBin(10,.2,999)/10→L1 and 999 values of $\hat{p}_2$ in list L2 by entering randBin(10,.2,999)/10→L2. Then store the differences, $\hat{p}_1 - \hat{p}_2$, in list L3 by entering L1–L2→L3.

5. Here's a typical dot plot and boxplot from this simulation of samples of size 10. Each dot represents 16 points.

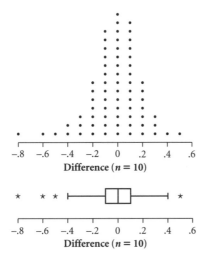

The distribution from this simulation has a mean of .0019 and standard error .174. Using the formulas at the bottom of page 460 in the student text, students may predict a mean of 0 and a standard error of about .179 (See D45).

The dot plot is mound-shaped, but this distribution has several outliers. Students may notice that $n_1 p_1 = n_2 p_2 = 10(.2) = 2$ is less than 5 and so too small to expect normality, as will be pointed out in D49. However, in most cases, the simulated distribution won't be too far from normal except in the tails.

6. Here's a typical dot plot and boxplot from this simulation using samples of size 40. The mean of this distribution is again near 0, actually $-.00540$, with a standard error of .090. The shape is approximately normal. Each dot represents 9 points.

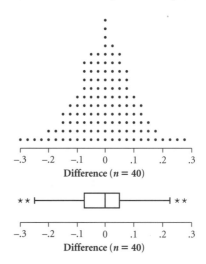

7. The distributions of both dot plots are centered around zero. The distribution for samples of size 40 is closer to being normally distributed than the one for samples of size 10. The distribution for samples of size 40 has a standard error about half that of the distribution for samples of size 10.

Discussion

D45. **a.** Because we know $p_1 = p_2 = .2$, we can compute the theoretical standard error:

$$\sigma_{\hat{p}_1 - \hat{p}_2} = \sqrt{\frac{p_1(1 - p_1)}{n_1} + \frac{p_2(1 - p_2)}{n_2}}$$

$$= \sqrt{\frac{.2(1 - .2)}{10} + \frac{.2(1 - .2)}{10}} \approx .179$$

This is very close to the estimate from the simulation, .174.

b. Again, the theoretical standard error can be computed:

$$\sigma_{\hat{p}_1 - \hat{p}_2} = \sqrt{\frac{p_1(1-p_1)}{n_1} + \frac{p_2(1-p_2)}{n_2}}$$

$$= \sqrt{\frac{.2(1-.2)}{40} + \frac{.2(1-.2)}{40}} \approx .089$$

Again, this is very close to the estimate from the simulation, .090.

D46. a. False. The values of $\hat{p}_1$ and $\hat{p}_2$ vary from sample to sample.

b. True. We are told that the proportion of successes in the two populations are equal.

c. True. (Refer to Activity 8.6 for an example.)

d. True. We have $\mu_{\hat{p}_1 - \hat{p}_2} = .2 - .2 = 0$.

e. True. As you can see from the dot plots in Display 8.16 in the student text, the sample differences $\hat{p}_1 - \hat{p}_2$ have less variability in the samples of size 40 than in the samples of size 10. They cluster more closely to 0, so we can see there is more of a chance of having the sample difference $\hat{p}_1 - \hat{p}_2$ nearer 0 with a larger sample size.

Practice

P37. a. A sample dot plot is shown here. Students may do the simulation on their calculators.

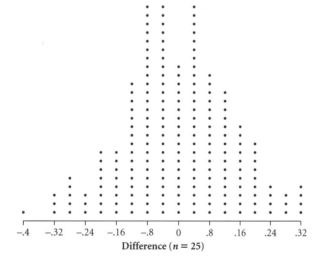

b. The mean of the distribution in the dot plot in part a is $-.00240$. Students' answers also should be close to zero. The standard error of the distribution in the dot plot is .13941. Students' answers should be close to .135.

c. The theoretical value of the mean is $\mu_{\hat{p}_1 - \hat{p}_2} = p_1 - p_2 = .35 - .35 = 0$, which is close to $-.00240$, the estimate in part b. The theoretical value of the standard error is

$$\sigma_{\hat{p}_1 - \hat{p}_2} = \sqrt{\frac{p_1(1-p_1)}{n_1} + \frac{p_2(1-p_2)}{n_2}}$$

$$= \sqrt{\frac{.35(1-.35)}{25} + \frac{.35(1-.35)}{25}} \approx .135$$

This is quite close to .139, the estimate in the simulation.

Lesson Notes: Significance Test for the Difference of Two Proportions

Situations Where You Use a Test of Significance for the Difference of Two Proportions

There are three different situations where you could use the significance test given in this section:

A sample survey from two different populations. You take a random sample independently from each of two populations and test to see whether the difference in the two sample proportions is statistically significant or could reasonably be attributed to chance variation. Examples of this situation occur in the student text in the survey about young adults living at home, on pages 469–471 and in P38, E31, and E32.

An experiment with two treatment groups. Deciding whether one treatment gives results that are different from another is the most important use of a test of significance for the difference of two proportions. Experimenters generally do not have independent random samples from larger populations. Instead they randomly assign the treatments to the subjects available. Examples in the student text include the AZT versus AZT + ACV experiment on pages 465–467 and in E33, E34, and the Chapter Review, E46.

Two entire populations. For example, in E35 students have Reggie Jackson's entire batting record. Of 9864 times at bat in regular season play, he had 2854 hits for a lifetime regular season batting average of .262. Of 98 times at bat in World Series play, he had 35 hits for a lifetime World Series batting average of .357. So, he had a larger percentage of hits during World Series play than during regular season play. There is a difference in the population proportions. However, this is unsatisfying, and we should be able to say more. Is the difference of .095 (or 9.5%) so small that we could reasonably expect something like this from chance variation alone? After all, it would be astounding to get *exactly* the same proportions even if everything else was equal. Or is the difference of 9.5% so large that we should look for some other explanation? Other examples in the student text include E36 and E45 of the Chapter Review. This use of a significance test is nonstandard, and the conclusion must be stated carefully.

Simulation of an Experiment

To demonstrate to your students that random assignment in an experiment leads to approximately the same standard error as for independent samples, you could have them do the following simulation.

Make up a bag of 40 beads (or M&M's) of two different colors, say 60% brown and 40% red. Draw out 20 at random without replacement. Calculate the difference between the proportion that are brown in your sample and the proportion that are brown in the sample remaining in the bag. Do his several hundred times to generate a simulated sampling distribution of the difference. Find the standard deviation of this distribution. It should be approximately the same as that given by the formula for the standard error of the difference from two independent samples:

$$\sigma_{\hat{p}_1 - \hat{p}_2} = \sqrt{\frac{p_1(1 - p_1)}{n_1} + \frac{p_2(1 - p_2)}{n_2}}$$

$$= \sqrt{\frac{.6(1 - .6)}{20} + \frac{.6(1 - .6)}{20}} \approx .155$$

Here are a histogram and boxplot of such a simulation where 500 samples were chosen and the differences were calculated as just described. That is, 20 beads (or M&M's) were chosen at random from a bag containing 24 brown and 16 red. The difference in the proportion of brown in the sample and the proportion of brown left in the bag was recorded. This was repeated 500 times. Here the

mean of the simulated sampling distribution of the difference is .0118 and the standard error is .154, just about the same as that from the preceding formula.

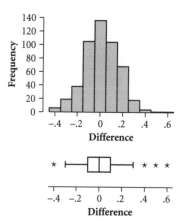

Note how this simulation is similar to a randomization procedure in a medical experiment. The null hypothesis is that it doesn't matter which treatment people get, the proportion who get well will be the same. The brown beads in the bag represent the people who get well, no matter which treatment they get. The red beads represent the people who don't get well. The sample you draw out of the bag represents the people who get Treatment A. The ones left in the bag represent the people who get Treatment B.

In H_0, $p_1 - p_2$ Is Not Necessarily Always 0

In a typical test of significance for the difference of two proportions, the null hypothesis states that the two population proportions are the same, or $p_1 - p_2 = 0$. In this case the test statistic simplifies to

$$z = \frac{(\hat{p}_1 - \hat{p}_2) - (p_1 - p_2)}{\sqrt{\hat{p}(1 - \hat{p})\left(\frac{1}{n_1} + \frac{1}{n_2}\right)}}$$

$$= \frac{(\hat{p}_1 - \hat{p}_2) - 0}{\sqrt{\hat{p}(1 - \hat{p})\left(\frac{1}{n_1} + \frac{1}{n_2}\right)}}$$

$$= \frac{(\hat{p}_1 - \hat{p}_2)}{\sqrt{\hat{p}(1 - \hat{p})\left(\frac{1}{n_1} + \frac{1}{n_2}\right)}}$$

It does not have to be the case that $p_1 = p_2$. In E41, for example, the hypothesized difference is $p_1 - p_2 = .02$, so the test statistic would be

$$z = \frac{(\hat{p}_1 - \hat{p}_2) - (p_1 - p_2)}{\sqrt{\dfrac{\hat{p}_1(1 - \hat{p}_1)}{n_1} + \dfrac{\hat{p}_2(1 - \hat{p}_2)}{n_2}}}$$

$$= \frac{\left(\dfrac{5}{64} - \dfrac{5}{100}\right) - .02}{\sqrt{\dfrac{\dfrac{5}{64}\left(1 - \dfrac{5}{64}\right)}{64} + \dfrac{\dfrac{5}{100}\left(1 - \dfrac{5}{100}\right)}{100}}}$$

Note About the Pooled Estimate of p

In a significance test for the equality of two proportions, the null hypothesis is that the proportion of successes in the first population is equal to the proportion of successes in the second population. Call that common proportion p. Because we conduct a hypothesis test as though the null hypothesis were true, that means that for each of the two populations we are sampling from, the sampling distribution of the sample proportion for samples of size n has mean p and standard error $\sqrt{p(1 - p)/n}$.

Thus, the sampling distribution of their difference has standard error

$$\sqrt{\frac{p(1 - p)}{n_1} + \frac{p(1 - p)}{n_2}} = \sqrt{p(1 - p)\left(\frac{1}{n_1} + \frac{1}{n_2}\right)}$$

Now we don't know p, but if the null hypothesis is true, the best estimate of p is the proportion $\hat{p}$ of successes in both samples put together:

$$\hat{p} = \frac{x_1 + x_2}{n_1 + n_2}$$

Why don't we do the same thing in the confidence interval for the difference of two proportions? We don't because the confidence interval doesn't involve any hypothesis that the proportions from the two populations are equal, so we can't assume a common p.

How About Doing a Test of the Significance of a Difference by Making a Confidence Interval for Each Proportion and Seeing Whether They Overlap?

As a substitute for the hypothesis test for the difference of two proportions, students sometimes suggest constructing two separate confidence intervals, one for p_1 and one for p_2, and then seeing whether they overlap. This suggestion shows that students have the basic idea of doing a significance test by using a confidence interval. And this method is almost okay, but it is too conservative. If the two don't overlap, then it is certain that the null hypothesis should be rejected. However, even if they do overlap, it is possible that the null hypothesis would be rejected at the level of α specified.

For example, suppose we were using a two-tailed test in the AZT/AZT+ACV example in Display 8.17 on page 466 of the student text. The null hypothesis would be rejected at a 5% level of confidence because the P-value is $2(.0078) = .0156$. However, the 95% confidence interval for the proportion who died when treated with AZT alone is .29 to .52. The 95% confidence interval for the proportion who died when treated with AZT+ACV is .11 to .31. The two intervals overlap.

An additional complication is that, although significance tests are sometimes one-sided, our confidence intervals are inherently two-sided. There is such a thing as a one-sided confidence interval, but students won't learn how to construct it in this textbook.

Note About the Sample Size in the *Young Men and Women Living at Home* Example

USA Today did not give the sample size for this survey. National polls of this type typically have a sample size of no more than about 1200. Let's assume that was the case here. However, there were four different age groups: 18–19, 20–24, 25–29, and 30–34. Thus, we estimate that there were about 300 in each age group, or 150 men and 150 women aged 20–24.

Discussion

D47. a. We rejected the null hypothesis that there is no difference between the results of the two treatments. If this hypothesis is in fact true, we made a Type I error.

b. These are the four numbers in the body of the table of Display 8.17 (not the totals), and they are all at least 5:

$$n_1\hat{p}_1 = 41$$
$$n_1(1 - \hat{p}_1) = 28$$
$$n_2\hat{p}_2 = 49$$
$$n_2(1 - \hat{p}_2) = 13$$

D48. a. The difference in the proportions in the two samples is small enough that it could reasonably have come from two populations with equal proportions of successes. This possibility suggests that either the two population proportions are equal or the sample sizes aren't large enough to distinguish between the two populations.

b. The difference in the proportions in the two samples is large enough that it isn't reasonable to assume that the samples came from two populations with equal proportions of successes.

D49. For the sample of size 10, $n_1\hat{p}_1$ and $n_2\hat{p}_2$ are equal to 2. And, in fact, the distribution wasn't as normal as we would have liked. Normality is necessary before we can use the table of the standard normal distribution to estimate probabilities.

On the other hand, for the samples of size 40, each of $n_1\hat{p}_1$, $n_1(1 - \hat{p}_1)$, $n_2\hat{p}_2$, and $n_2(1 - \hat{p}_2)$ is at least 5. The distribution of $\hat{p}_1 - \hat{p}_2$ is more symmetric, has no extreme outliers, and generally looks approximately normal. You can use the table of the standard normal distribution to estimate probabilities.

Practice

P38. This situation calls for a one-tailed significance test for the difference of two proportions because we are asked whether the data support the conclusion that there was a decrease in voter support for the candidate.

Check conditions. You are told that you have two random samples from a large population (potential voters in some city). It's reasonable to assume that the samples are independent. For the first survey $n_1 = 600$ and $\hat{p}_1 = \frac{321}{600} = .535$. For the second survey, $n_2 = 750$ and $\hat{p}_2 = \frac{382}{7500} \approx .5093$. Each of

$$n_1\hat{p}_1 = 321$$
$$n_1(1 - \hat{p}_1) = 279$$
$$n_2\hat{p}_2 = 382$$
$$n_2(1 - \hat{p}_2) = 368$$

is at least 5.

State your hypotheses.

H_0: The proportion, p_1, of potential voters who favored the candidate in the first survey is equal to the proportion, p_2, of potential voters who favored the candidate one week before the election, or $p_1 = p_2$.

H_a: The proportion, p_1, of potential voters who favored the candidate in the first survey is greater than the proportion, p_2, of potential voters who favored the candidate one week before the election, or $p_1 > p_2$.

Compute the test statistic and draw a sketch. The test statistic is

$$z = \frac{(\hat{p}_1 - \hat{p}_2) - (p_1 - p_2)}{\sqrt{\hat{p}(1 - \hat{p})\left(\frac{1}{n_1} + \frac{1}{n_2}\right)}}$$

$$\approx \frac{(.535 - .5093) - 0}{\sqrt{.521(1 - .521)\left(\frac{1}{600} + \frac{1}{750}\right)}} \approx 0.939$$

where

$$\hat{p} = \frac{total\ number\ of\ successes\ in\ both\ samples}{n_1 + n_2}$$

$$= \frac{321 + 382}{600 + 750} \approx .521$$

Using the table, the *P*-value for this one-tailed test is .1736. From the TI-83, the test statistic is $z = 0.938$ and the *P*-value is .1741. In this case, the 2-PropZTest gives us the most accurate answer because there is less rounding.

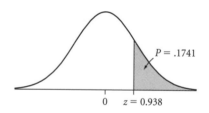

Write a conclusion in context. If there is no difference between the proportion of potential voters who favored the candidate at three weeks and the proportion of potential voters who favored the candidate at one week, then there is a .1741 chance of getting a difference of .0257 or larger with samples of these sizes. This difference is not statistically significant—it can reasonably be attributed to chance variation. We do not reject the null hypothesis and can not conclude that there has been a drop in support for the new candidate.

P39. We rejected the null hypothesis that there is no difference between the two proportions.

If this hypothesis is in fact true, and the two proportions are equal, we made a Type I error.

Exercises

E31. **a.** ***Check conditions.*** Although the situation probably is actually more complicated, you can assume that you have two independent random samples. All of

$$n_1\hat{p}_1 = 257(.76) \approx 195$$
$$n_1(1 - \hat{p}_1) = 257(1 - .76) \approx 62$$
$$n_2\hat{p}_2 = 256(.63) \approx 161$$
$$n_2(1 - \hat{p}_2) = 256(1 - .63) \approx 95$$

are at least 5. The number of boys and girls aged 12 to 17 in the United States is much larger than 10 times the sample size.

State your hypotheses.

H_0: The proportion, p_1, of all girls who would have said yes is equal to the proportion, p_2, of all the boys who would have said yes.

H_a: $p_1 > p_2$. (Note that you can use these symbols because you defined exactly what they stand for in the null hypothesis.)

Compute the test statistic and draw a sketch. The test statistic is

$$z = \frac{(\hat{p}_1 - \hat{p}_2) - (p_1 - p_2)}{\sqrt{\hat{p}(1 - \hat{p})\left(\frac{1}{n_1} + \frac{1}{n_2}\right)}}$$

$$= \frac{(.76 - .63) - 0}{\sqrt{.694(1 - .694)\left(\frac{1}{257} + \frac{1}{256}\right)}}$$

$$\approx 3.147$$

Here the pooled estimate, $\hat{p}$, is

$$\hat{p} = \frac{total\ number\ of\ successes\ in\ both\ samples}{n_1 + n_2}$$

$$\approx \frac{195 + 161}{257 + 256} \approx .694$$

The P-value from the calculator and the table for a one-tailed test is .0007, as shown in the following display. If you use the 2-PropZTest command on the TI-83, you get $z \approx 3.191$ and a P-value of about .00071.

NOTE: When using the TI-83, you must enter the number of successes as a whole number. If you multiply .76 by 257, for example, you

get 195.32. We use the rule of rounding to the nearest whole number, or 195. So we estimate that 195 girls said yes. But note that it also could have been 196 girls as $\frac{196}{257} \approx .7626$, which would also have been rounded to 76%. ■

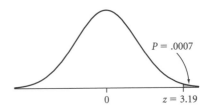

Write a conclusion in context. No significance level was given, so you should assume $\alpha = .05$. This difference is statistically significant, and so you reject the null hypothesis. If the proportions of all girls and all boys aged 12 to 17 who would have said yes were equal, the probability of getting a difference in proportions of 13% or larger from samples of these sizes is only .0007. Because this P-value is less than $\alpha = .05$, you can not reasonably attribute the difference of 13% to chance variation. You believe that if you could have asked all girls and all boys aged 12 to 17, the proportion of girls who would have said yes is higher than the proportion of boys who would have said yes.

b. Although random digit dialing ensures that unlisted numbers were included, this is not quite a simple random sample because not every teen has a phone, some share a phone with other teens, and some teens have more than one phone. Also, random digit dialing does not give a simple random sample as we have defined it because it randomly dials until a certain number of people answer rather than selecting a random sample of fixed size and then calling them until all have answered. However, the bias in this method is generally not too serious, so the formulas for random sampling usually work quite well.

Also, these samples were probably derived from a single sample that was divided by gender after the data were obtained. Again, this problem is not serious, especially for large samples.

Although the formula in this section for the standard error is based on simple random sampling, it is a close approximation in this case of random digit dialing.

Note: According to the U.S. Department of Housing and Urban Development (HUD), "Seven percent of households in the United States lack phones; in the rural South, the proportion is as high as 40 percent among renter households."

(Source: U.S. Department of Housing and Urban Development, Office of Policy Development and Research, Economic and Market Analysis Division. "Random Digit Dialing Surveys: A Guide to Assist Larger Housing Agencies in Preparing Fair Market Rent Comments," April 2000, http://www.huduser.org/publications/pubasst/rdd.html.)

Random digit dialing (RDD) usually does not mean simply dialing numbers at random. Dialing at random is not efficient because most of these numbers will not be in operation or will be the telephones of businesses. According to HUD, modern RDD methods "take advantage of the fact that residential telephone numbers are likely to be clustered among a small number of 100-blocks in which a large percentage of the possible numbers—more than 40 percent but often much higher—are in use." A 100-block is a set of 100 phone numbers that all have the same first eight digits. After one of these "residential" blocks is randomly selected, the last two digits are randomly selected from the numbers 00 to 99. For example, the telephone number 202-708-6677 is in the 100-block of 202-708-6600 through 202-708-6699.

c. The conditions were checked in part a. However, you need the additional assumption that there are about the same number of boys and girls in the United States. That is, the ratio in the sample of 257 girls to 256 boys is about right. The sample proportion is 69.4% because

$$\hat{p} = \frac{\text{total number of successes in both samples}}{n_1 + n_2}$$

$$= \frac{195 + 161}{257 + 256} \approx .694$$

The 95% confidence interval is

$$p \pm 1.96\sqrt{\frac{p(1-p)}{n}} = .694 \pm 1.96\sqrt{\frac{.694(1 - .694)}{513}}$$

$$\approx .694 \pm .040$$

You are 95% confident that if you asked all teens whether they feel like they are personally making a positive difference in their community, between 65.4% and 73.4% would say "yes."

E32. *Check conditions.* Although the situation probably is actually more complicated, you can assume that you have two independent random samples. All of

$$n_1\hat{p}_1 = 158(.35) \approx 55$$
$$n_1(1 - \hat{p}_1) = 158(1 - .35) \approx 103$$
$$n_2\hat{p}_2 = 435(.36) \approx 157$$
$$n_2(1 - \hat{p}_2) = 435(1 - .36) \approx 278$$

are at least 5. The number of people in each age group is much larger than 10 times the sample size.

State your hypotheses.

H_0: The proportion, p_1, of all people aged 18 to 29 who sleep eight hours or more on a workday is equal to the proportion, p_2, of all people aged 30 to 64 who sleep eight hours or more on a workday.

H_a: $p_1 \neq p_2$

Compute the test statistic and draw a sketch. The test statistic is

$$z = \frac{(\hat{p}_1 - \hat{p}_2) - (p_1 - p_2)}{\sqrt{\hat{p}(1 - \hat{p})\left(\frac{1}{n_1} + \frac{1}{n_2}\right)}}$$

$$= \frac{(.35 - .36) - 0}{\sqrt{.3575(1 - .3575)\left(\frac{1}{158} + \frac{1}{435}\right)}}$$

$$\approx -0.225$$

Here the pooled estimate, $\hat{p}$, is

$$\hat{p} = \frac{\text{total number of successes in both samples}}{n_1 + n_2}$$

$$= \frac{55 + 157}{158 + 435} \approx .3575$$

The *P*-value from the calculator for a two-tailed test is $2 \cdot \mathbf{normalcdf}(\text{-999,-0.225}) = .8220$, as can be seen in the display that follows.

Using the table with $z = -0.22$ gives a *P*-value of $2(.4129) = .8258$. Using the **2-PropZTest** command on your calculator with $x_1 \approx 55$ and $x_2 \approx 157$ gives a test statistic $z \approx -0.2879$ and a *P*-value of .7734.

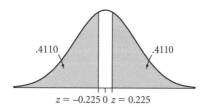

.4110   .4110

$z = -0.225 \quad 0 \quad z = 0.225$

Write a conclusion in context. No significance level was given, so you should assume $\alpha = .05$. This difference is not statistically significant, and so you do not reject the null hypothesis. If the proportion of all Americans aged 18 to 29 who sleep eight hours or more on a workday is equal to the proportion of all Americans aged 30 to 64 who do so, the probability of getting a difference in sample proportions of 1% or larger from samples these sizes is .8220. Because this *P*-value is larger than $\alpha = .05$, you can reasonably attribute the difference to chance variation. You have no evidence that the proportions would be different if you were to ask everyone in each of these two age groups whether they sleep more than eight hours on a workday.

E33. Because it was hypothesized before the experiment began that aspirin was beneficial, we will conduct a one-tailed significance test for the difference of two proportions. If students do a two-tailed test, the computations and conclusion will be the same.

Check conditions. The subjects weren't selected randomly from a larger population, but the treatments were randomly assigned to the subjects, so you can use this significance test for the difference of two proportions. For the group taking aspirin, $n_1 = 11,037$ and $\hat{p}_1 = \frac{139}{11,037} \approx .0126$. For the group taking a placebo, $n_2 = 11,034$ and $\hat{p}_2 = \frac{239}{11,034} \approx .0217$. Therefore, all of

$$n_1\hat{p}_1 = 139$$
$$n_1(1 - \hat{p}_1) = 10,898$$
$$n_2\hat{p}_2 = 239$$
$$n_2(1 - \hat{p}_2) = 10,795$$

are at least 5.

State your hypotheses.

H_0: If all of the men could have been given aspirin, the proportion, p_1, who had a heart attack would have been equal to the proportion, p_2, of the men who had a heart attack if all could have been given the placebo.

H_a: $p_1 < p_2$

Compute the test statistic. The test statistic is

$$z = \frac{(\hat{p}_1 - \hat{p}_2) - (p_1 - p_2)}{\sqrt{\hat{p}(1 - \hat{p})\left(\frac{1}{n_1} + \frac{1}{n_2}\right)}}$$

$$= \frac{(.0126 - .0217) - 0}{\sqrt{.0171(1 - .0171)\left(\frac{1}{11,037} + \frac{1}{11,034}\right)}}$$

$$\approx -5.214$$

or -5.191 without rounding.

Here,

$$\hat{p} = \frac{\textit{total number of successes in both samples}}{n_1 + n_2}$$

$$= \frac{139 + 239}{11,037 + 11,034} \approx .0171$$

The *P*-value is almost 0.

Write a conclusion in context. If there is no difference in the proportion of men who would have had a heart attack if they had all taken aspirin and the proportion who would have had a heart attack if they had all taken the placebo, then there is almost no chance of getting a difference of $-.0091$ or smaller in the two proportions from a random assignment of these treatments to the subjects. This difference can not reasonably be attributed to chance variation. You reject the null hypothesis.

Note that although the difference in proportions is very small, only .0091, this difference is statistically significant because of the large sample sizes. Further, men who take low-dose aspirin cut their chance of a heart attack almost in half.

E34. Because it was hypothesized before the experiment began that aspirin was beneficial, we will conduct a one-tailed test of the significance of the difference of two proportions.

Check conditions. The subjects weren't selected randomly from a larger population, but the treatments were randomly assigned to the subjects, so we can use this significance test for the difference of two proportions. (But note that the randomization wasn't done within the group of men who had heart attacks—that would have been impossible.) For the group taking aspirin, $n_1 = 139$ and $\hat{p}_1 = \frac{10}{139} \approx .072$. For the group taking a placebo, $n_2 = 239$ and $\hat{p}_2 = \frac{26}{239} \approx .109$. Therefore, all of

$$n_1\hat{p}_1 = 10$$
$$n_1(1 - \hat{p}_1) = 129$$
$$n_2\hat{p}_2 = 26$$
$$n_2(1 - \hat{p}_2) = 213$$

are at least 5.

State your hypotheses.

H_0: If all of the men who had a heart attack could have been given the same treatment, the proportion, p_1, who would have died of the heart attack after taking aspirin would be equal to the proportion, p_2, who would have died after taking the placebo.

H_a: $p_1 < p_2$

Compute the test statistic and draw a sketch. The test statistic is

$$z = \frac{(\hat{p}_1 - \hat{p}_2) - (p_1 - p_2)}{\sqrt{\hat{p}(1 - \hat{p})\left(\frac{1}{n_1} + \frac{1}{n_2}\right)}}$$

$$= \frac{(.072 - .1088) - 0}{\sqrt{.095(1 - .095)\left(\frac{1}{139} + \frac{1}{239}\right)}}$$

$$\approx -1.177$$

Here,

$$\hat{p} = \frac{\text{total number of successes in both samples}}{n_1 + n_2}$$

$$= \frac{10 + 26}{139 + 239} \approx .095$$

Using the table, the *P*-value for this one-tailed test is .1190. Using the TI-83, the *P*-value is .1197. The latter value is better because it was computed using less rounding.

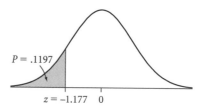

$$P = .1197$$
$$z = -1.177 \quad 0$$

Write a conclusion in context. If there would have been no difference in the proportion of men who would have died from their heart attack if they had all taken aspirin and the proportion who would have died if they had all taken the placebo, then there is a .1197 chance of getting a difference of $-.037$ or smaller in the proportions from random assignment of these treatments to the subjects. This difference can reasonably be attributed to chance variation. You do not reject the null hypothesis.

E35. *Is a significance test legal in this case?* Purists would say that we should not use a test of significance in this situation. They have two reasons. The first is that the numbers given are not a random sample from any population—in fact, they are the population of Reggie Jackson's "at bats." (He is retired, so there will be no further at bats.) We know all of his at bats, and we can see that, in fact, he did have a higher batting average in the World Series than in regular season play.

The second reason is that this is a classic example of "data snooping." There are hundreds of baseball players. Even if some underlying batting average is the same in regular season play as in the World Series for all players, by definition some players are certain to be rare events and do better in the World Series than in regular season play. Reggie is simply the player that stands out as the rarest of the predictable rare events.

However, you might use this example with your students as an example of how a test of significance can be used in a more limited sense. The question asks whether Reggie's better average in the World Series can reasonably be attributed to chance. This is the first question we should ask before assigning him the nickname "Mr. October." If it turns out that we can't reasonably attribute this to chance, then we have to look for some other explanation. That explanation might in fact be that we did some data snooping and ended up with a Type I error. On the other hand, the explanation might be that he came through in the World Series. At any rate, the data must pass the test that the results can't reasonably be attributed to chance before we take any further steps in comparing the performance of Reggie Jackson in the World Series to regular season play.

Check conditions. The two samples aren't random; they are the entire populations. Thus, a significance test will tell us only whether such a difference can reasonably be attributed to chance.

State your hypotheses.

H_0: The difference between the proportion of hits in regular season play and the proportion of hits in the World Series can reasonably be attributed to chance variation.

H_a: The difference between the proportion of hits in regular season play and the proportion of hits in the World Series is too large to be attributed to chance variation.

Compute the test statistic and draw a sketch. The test statistic is

$$z = \frac{(\hat{p}_1 - \hat{p}_2) - (p_1 - p_2)}{\sqrt{\hat{p}(1 - \hat{p})\left(\frac{1}{n_1} + \frac{1}{n_2}\right)}}$$

$$= \frac{(.262 - .357) - 0}{\sqrt{.263(1 - .263)\left(\frac{1}{9864} + \frac{1}{98}\right)}}$$

$$\approx -2.126$$

or, using the TI-83's 2-PropZTest, $z \approx 2.1299$. Here,

$$\hat{p} = \frac{total\ number\ of\ successes\ in\ both\ samples}{n_1 + n_2}$$

$$= \frac{2584 + 35}{9864 + 98} \approx .263$$

The one-sided P-value is about .017.

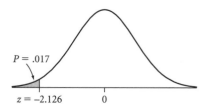

$P = .017$
$z = -2.126$ 0

Write a conclusion in context. A difference as large as Reggie's between regular season and World Series play would happen by chance to fewer than 17 players in 1000. Therefore, Reggie's record is indeed unusual. (It is interesting that Reggie hit only .227 in 163 bats in crucial League Championship Series play.)

E36. **I.** ***Check conditions.*** The two samples aren't random; they are the entire populations. Thus, a significance test will tell us only whether the difference in the percentages of casualties (43.9% vs. 27.4%) can reasonably be attributed to chance.

State your hypotheses.

H_0: The difference in the proportions of British and American troops wounded can reasonably be attributed to chance variation.

H_a: The difference is too large to be attributed to chance alone.

Compute the test statistic. The test statistic is

$$z = \frac{(\hat{p}_1 - \hat{p}_2) - (p_1 - p_2)}{\sqrt{\hat{p}(1 - \hat{p})\left(\frac{1}{n_1} + \frac{1}{n_2}\right)}}$$

$$= \frac{(.439 - .274) - 0}{\sqrt{.376(1 - .376)\left(\frac{1}{2400} + \frac{1}{1500}\right)}}$$

$$\approx 10.35$$

or 10.36 without rounding.
  Here,

$$\hat{p} = \frac{total\ number\ of\ wounded\ on\ both\ sides}{n_1 + n_2}$$

$$= \frac{1054 + 411}{2400 + 1500} \approx .376$$

The P-value is close to 0.

The test statistic is quite large and would be difficult to see in a sketch.

Write a conclusion in context. The difference in the proportion of casualties can not reasonably be attributed to chance alone. There is almost no chance of getting a difference this large unless British soldiers were more likely to be wounded.

II. *Check conditions.* The two samples aren't random; they are the entire populations. Thus, a significance test will tell us only whether the difference in the percentages of deaths (9.417% vs. 9.333%) can reasonably be attributed to chance.

State your hypotheses.

H_0: The difference in the proportion of British and American troops killed can reasonably be attributed to chance variation.

H_a: The difference is too large to be attributed to chance alone.

Compute the test statistic and draw a sketch.
The test statistic is

$$z = \frac{(\hat{p}_1 - \hat{p}_2) - (p_1 - p_2)}{\sqrt{\hat{p}(1 - \hat{p})\left(\frac{1}{n_1} + \frac{1}{n_2}\right)}}$$

$$= \frac{(.09417 - .09333) - 0}{\sqrt{.0938(1 - .0938)\left(\frac{1}{2400} + \frac{1}{1500}\right)}}$$

$$\approx 0.0875$$

Here,

$$\hat{p} = \frac{total\ number\ of\ successes\ in\ both\ samples}{n_1 + n_2}$$

$$= \frac{226 + 140}{2400 + 1500} \approx .0938$$

The TI-83 gives a test statistic $z = 0.087$ and a two-sided P-value of .9308.

Note: Here if $\hat{p}_1 = .094$ and $\hat{p}_2 = .093$ are used in the formula, the test statistic would be $z = 0.1042$ and the P-value would be .9170.

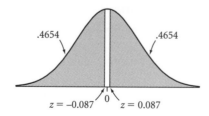

.4654   .4654

$z = -0.087$ 0 $z = 0.087$

Write a conclusion in context. The difference of only .001 in the proportions of deaths can reasonably be attributed to chance alone. There is no reason to conclude that British troops were more or less likely to be killed than American troops. This condition is true even though they were wounded at a much greater rate. Either the British wounds were less severe or they had better medical care available.

E37. a. An independent random sample is selected from each of two different populations.

b. The subjects, who usually do not constitute a random sample from any population, are assigned randomly to one of two different treatment groups.

E38. The test statistic would have to be at least

$$z = \frac{(\hat{p}_1 - \hat{p}_2) - (p_1 - p_2)}{\sqrt{\frac{p_1(1 - p_1)}{n_1} + \frac{p_2(1 - p_2)}{n_2}}}$$

$$= \frac{(\pm.10) - 0}{\sqrt{\frac{.35(1 - .35)}{40} + \frac{.35(1 - .35)}{50}}}$$

$$\approx \pm0.9883$$

A value of the test statistic this size or more extreme happens with probability $2(.1615) = .3230$.

E39. The test statistic would have to be at least

$$z = \frac{(\hat{p}_1 - \hat{p}_2) - (p_1 - p_2)}{\sqrt{\frac{p_1(1 - p_1)}{n_1} + \frac{p_2(1 - p_2)}{n_2}}}$$

$$= \frac{(-.20) - (.45 - .65)}{\sqrt{\frac{.45(1 - .45)}{30} + \frac{.65(1 - .65)}{25}}}$$

$$\approx 0$$

A value of the test statistic this size or smaller happens with probability .5.

E40. We made use of three facts that we learned in Chapters 5 and 7:

I. The mean of the distribution of the difference of two random variables is the difference of their individual means. We used this fact in stating that the mean of the sampling distribution of the difference $\hat{p}_1 - \hat{p}_2$ is equal to the difference of the means of the sampling distributions of $\hat{p}_1$ and $\hat{p}_2$, or

$$\mu_{\hat{p}_1 - \hat{p}_2} = \mu_{\hat{p}_1} - \mu_{\hat{p}_2} = p_1 - p_2$$

II. The variance of the distribution of the difference of two independent random variables is the sum of their individual variances. We used this fact in stating that the value of the variance of the sampling distribution of the difference $\hat{p}_1 - \hat{p}_2$ when $p_1 = p_2 = p$ is

$$\frac{p_1(1 - p_1)}{n_1} + \frac{p_2(1 - p_2)}{n_2} = p(1 - p)\left(\frac{1}{n_1} + \frac{1}{n_2}\right)$$

III. Under some not-very-restrictive assumptions, the distribution of the difference of two independent random variables is approximately normally distributed. Specifically, all of the values $n_1\hat{p}_1$, $n_1(1 - \hat{p}_1)$, $n_2\hat{p}_2$, and $n_2(1 - \hat{p}_2)$ must be at least 5.

E41. *Check conditions.* The conditions are met for doing a test of significance of the difference of two proportions. You have a random sample from each of two large populations. Each of $n_1\hat{p}_1 = 5$, $n_1(1 - \hat{p}_1) = 95$, $n_2\hat{p}_2 = 5$, and $n_2(1 - \hat{p}_2) = 59$ is at least 5.

State your hypotheses.

H_0: $p_1 - p_2 = .02$, where p_1 is the proportion of all mornings where Bus B is late and p_2 is the proportion of all mornings Bus A is late.

H_a: $p_1 - p_2 > .02$

Compute the test statistic and draw a sketch. The test statistic is

$$z = \frac{(\hat{p}_1 - \hat{p}_2) - (p_1 - p_2)}{\sqrt{\dfrac{\hat{p}_1(1 - \hat{p}_1)}{n_1} + \dfrac{\hat{p}_2(1 - \hat{p}_2)}{n_2}}}$$

$$= \frac{\left(\dfrac{5}{64} - \dfrac{5}{100}\right) - .02}{\sqrt{\dfrac{\dfrac{5}{64}\left(1 - \dfrac{5}{64}\right)}{64} + \dfrac{\dfrac{5}{100}\left(1 - \dfrac{5}{100}\right)}{100}}}$$

$$= 0.2031$$

The one-sided *P*-value is .4195.

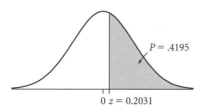

Write a conclusion in context. Suppose the proportion of all mornings that Bus B is late is equal to 2% more than the proportion of

all mornings that Bus A is late. Under this assumption, the chance of seeing a difference in sample proportions greater than the observed 2.8% is .4195. Because this probability is so large, the observed difference can be attributed to chance alone. You take Bus B.

Review

Homework	
Essential	E42–E47, E50
Recommended	E48, E51 (reading practice) or E52 (writing practice)
Optional	E49

Review Exercises

E42. **a.** *Blinded* means that a TT practitioner could not tell whether the investigator's hand was placed above their left hand or above their right hand. The way it was done was to have the TT practitioner rest their hands, palms up, on a flat surface. A tall screen with cutouts on its base was placed over the TT practitioner's arms so that they couldn't see the investigator's hand on the other side of the screen. Double-blinding would mean that the person who placed his or her hand above the TT practitioner's hands would not hear what the person's response was. Although this might have made the experiment a bit better, there was no judgment on the part of the investigator in evaluating the response from the TT practitioner. (The response was either right or wrong.)

b. First, note that the sample size in this experiment is not really 280 because there were only 21 practitioners (with 14 tested 10 times each and 7 tested 20 times each). The proper unit of analysis would be by practitioner. Because we don't have those data, let's carry through as a one-tailed test of a single proportion with $n = 280$.

Check conditions. As just discussed, the trials are not independent, and it's not quite correct to consider the number of successful trials as a binomial random variable. Both $np_0 = 280(.5) = 140$ and $n(1 - p_0) = 280(.5) = 140$ are at least 10. The population of all possible identifications is infinitely large, so it is at least 10 times their sample size of 280.

State your hypotheses.

H_0: The TT practitioners did no better than chance in identifying the correct hand. That is, $p = .5$, where p is the proportion of times the TT practitioners identified the correct hand.

H_a: The proportion of hands correctly identified was greater than .5.

Compute the test statistic and draw a sketch.

The test statistic is

$$z = \frac{123/280 - .5}{\sqrt{\dfrac{.5(1 - .5)}{280}}} \approx -2.032$$

The *P*-value is .9789.

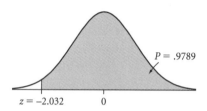

$P = .9789$

$z = -2.032 \qquad 0$

Write a conclusion in context. This looks like a statistically significant result, but note that the result from the sample, $\frac{123}{280} \approx .439$, is less than .5. It is in the wrong direction from the alternate hypothesis.

We can't reject the null hypothesis that the TT practitioners did no better than chance in identifying the correct hand. Even if a person is just guessing, there is a 97.9% chance of doing better than the TT practitioners did. So in fact, these TT practitioners were very, very unlucky.

c. This means that the sample size was large enough so that if TT practitioners could identify the correct hand with any consistency, the null hypothesis would have been rejected. Specifically, to reject the null hypothesis that the probability that they select the correct hand is .5, the value of z for a one-sided test would have to be 1.645. With

a sample size of 280, the practitioners would only have to get 54.9% correct:

$$z = \frac{.549 - .5}{\sqrt{\dfrac{.5(1 - .5)}{280}}} \approx 1.645$$

E43. a. Conditions were checked in P13. The 92% confidence interval is

$$\hat{p} \pm z^* \cdot \sqrt{\frac{\hat{p}(1 - \hat{p})}{n}} = .94 \pm 1.75 \sqrt{\frac{.94(1 - .94)}{754}}$$

$$= .94 \pm .015$$

or (.925, .955).

b. You are 92% confident that if you were able to ask *all* students aged 12 to 17 with Internet access, between 92.5% and 95.5% would say the Internet helped them with their homework.

c. Suppose you could repeat this survey with 100 different random samples each of size 754. Then you would expect the (unknown) proportion of all students aged 12 to 17 with Internet access who say the Internet helps them with their homework to be in 92 of the resulting confidence intervals. (But each of the 100 surveys probably would have a different interval.)

E44. **Check conditions.** The two samples may be considered random samples. They were taken independently from the population of U.S. adults in 2001 and in 2000. The number of adults in each year is larger than ten times 1108. Finally, each of

$$n_1\hat{p}_1 = 1108(.51) \approx 565$$
$$n_1(1 - \hat{p}_1) = 1108(1 - .51) \approx 543$$
$$n_2\hat{p}_2 = 1108(.47) \approx 521$$
$$n_2(1 - \hat{p}_2) = 1108(1 - .47) \approx 587$$

is at least 5.

Do computations. The 90% confidence interval for the difference of the two population proportions p_1 and p_2 is shown at the bottom of the page.

Review 8.4, E44

$$(\hat{p}_1 - \hat{p}_2) \pm z^* \cdot \sqrt{\frac{\hat{p}_1(1 - \hat{p}_1)}{n_1} + \frac{\hat{p}_2(1 - \hat{p}_2)}{n_2}} = (.51 - .47) \pm 1.645 \sqrt{\frac{(.51)(1 - .51)}{1108} + \frac{(.47)(1 - .47)}{1108}}$$

$$= .04 \pm .035$$

Alternatively, you can write this confidence interval as (.005, .075).

Write a conclusion in context. You are 90% confident that the difference between the proportion of all adults who would assign a grade of A or B in 2001 and in 2000 is between .005 and .075. Because 0 isn't in this confidence interval, there appears to be a small but "real" increase in the proportion of adults who would give their local public schools an A or a B.

E45. **a.** ***Check conditions.*** The two samples aren't random, they are the entire populations. Thus, a significance test will tell us only whether the difference in the proportions of snowboard injuries and ski injuries that were fractures (27.9% vs. 15.3%) can reasonably be attributed to chance.

State your hypotheses.

H_0: The difference in the proportion of snowboard injuries and ski injuries that were fractures can reasonably be attributed to chance variation.

H_a: The difference is too large to be attributed to chance alone.

Compute the test statistic and draw a sketch. The test statistic is

$$z = \frac{(\hat{p}_1 - \hat{p}_2) - (p_1 - p_2)}{\sqrt{\hat{p}(1-\hat{p})\left(\frac{1}{n_1} + \frac{1}{n_2}\right)}}$$

$$= \frac{(.279 - .152) - 0}{\sqrt{.198(1-.198)\left(\frac{1}{531} + \frac{1}{952}\right)}}$$

$$\approx 5.838$$

or 5.805 without rounding.

Here,

$$\hat{p} = \frac{\text{total number of successes in both samples}}{n_1 + n_2}$$

$$= \frac{148 + 146}{531 + 952} \approx .198$$

The *P*-value is close to 0.

z = −5.81   0   z = 5.81

Write a conclusion in context. The difference in the proportion of injuries that were fractures can not reasonably be attributed to chance variation. (One possible explanation is that snowboarders take more risks and so any injury is more likely to be serious. Another explanation may be that because skiers tend to be older, the same fall that would injure them slightly might not injure a younger person at all. Thus, the skiers have more injuries, but they tend to be less serious.)

b. In part a, you may have noticed that the number of fractures was about the same for skiers as for snowboarders. But now you are told that there are about twice as many skiers. Thus, snowboarders were twice as likely to have a fracture as a skier. However, you can't carry out a test to determine whether this is statistically significant without knowing about how many snowboarders and how many skiers there were.

E46. ***Check conditions.*** The treatments were assigned randomly to the subjects, so you can use this significance test for the difference of two proportions. For the group taking the medication, $n_1 = 25$ and $\hat{p}_1 = 13/25 = .52$. For the group taking a placebo, $n_2 = 26$ and $\hat{p}_2 = 10/26 \approx .385$. All of

$$n_1\hat{p}_1 = 13$$
$$n_1(1 - \hat{p}_1) = 12$$
$$n_2\hat{p}_2 = 10$$
$$n_2(1 - \hat{p}_2) = 16$$

are at least 5.

State your hypotheses.

H_0: The proportion, p_1, of people who would have responded if everyone had been given medication is equal to the proportion, p_2, of people who would have responded if everyone had been given the placebo.

H_a: $p_1 \neq p_2$

Compute the test statistic and draw a sketch.
The test statistic is

$$z = \frac{(\hat{p}_1 - \hat{p}_2) - (p_1 - p_2)}{\sqrt{\hat{p}(1 - \hat{p})\left(\frac{1}{n_1} + \frac{1}{n_2}\right)}}$$

$$= \frac{(.52 - .385) - 0}{\sqrt{.451(1 - .451)\left(\frac{1}{25} + \frac{1}{26}\right)}}$$

$$\approx 0.9686$$

or, using 2-PropZTest, $z = 0.9713$.

Here,

$$\hat{p} = \frac{total\ number\ who\ responded}{n_1 + n_2}$$

$$= \frac{13 + 10}{25 + 26} \approx .451$$

The two-sided *P*-value is .3314.

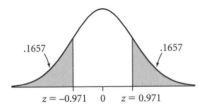

Write a conclusion in context. If there had been no difference between the proportion of people who would have responded if they had all taken the medication and the proportion who would have responded if they had all taken the placebo, then there is a .331 chance of getting a difference of .135 or larger in the two proportions from a random assignment of subjects to treatment groups. This difference can reasonably be attributed to chance variation. You do not reject the null hypothesis.

Note: Although the difference in the proportion who responded isn't statistically significant, the main point of the study was that "Brain physiology in placebo responders was altered in a different manner than in the medication responders."

E47. a. $.05(100) = 5$
b. $.95^{100} = .00592$

E48. Yes. Suppose that, in fact, the proportions of males and females who pass the bar exam are exactly equal in each state. Because we are doing 50 hypothesis tests at $\alpha = .05$, we

expect $.05(50) = 2.5$ Type I errors. We will conclude that there is some inequity in an average of 2.5 states even if there is no inequity in any state. In addition, students may say that the pass rates may be unequal for perfectly equitable reasons, such as females study harder.

So what do statisticians do in such a situation? There are three options:
1. If you have *n* hypotheses to check, reduce α to $\frac{\alpha}{n}$. Because *n* is 50 in this case, you would use $\alpha = \frac{.05}{50} = .001$. This makes the overall significance level less than or equal to .05. (This is called the Bonferroni method.)
2. In those states with statistically significant results, go out and get another sample to verify the results from the first one.
3. If it is impossible to get new data, randomly divide the sample from each state into two parts. Use the first sample in the first round of tests. For those states with a statistically significant result, verify this result in the second half of the sample.

E49. The method used for constructing 90% confidence intervals captures the true population percentage 90% of the time. Once again, the reasoning is rather subtle. See the explanation on page 424 in the dialogue in Section 8.1 of the student text and in the teacher's notes on pages 71–72. See also the explanation in E11 in Section 8.1.

E50. C

E51. There is one glaring error in the interpretation of a confidence interval: "To be more specific, the laws of probability say that if we were to conduct the same survey 100 times, asking people in each survey to rate the job Bill Clinton is doing as president, in 95 out of those 100 polls, we would find his rating to be between 47% and 53%."

This should say: "To be more specific, the laws of probability say that if we were to conduct the same survey 100 times, asking people in each survey to rate the job Bill Clinton is doing as president, *we expect that the proportion of the entire population that approves* would fall within 95 of the 100 confidence intervals."

There are many other sentences that students may be able to write more clearly or that students may not agree with. For example, "If Gallup were to—quite expensively—use a sample of 4,000 randomly selected adults each time it did its poll, the increase in accuracy over and beyond a well-done sample of 1,000 would be minimal and, generally speaking, would not justify the increase in cost."

Students may feel that cutting the margin of error in half from about 3% to about 1.5% might justify the increase in cost in a close election.

E52. Students should include some explanation of a margin of error and how it is relatively small (around 3%) even with a sample size as small as 1000. The part that people tend to have the hardest time understanding is that, for a fixed $\hat{p}$, the margin of error depends almost entirely on the sample size n and not on how large the population is. That is, a random sample of size 1000 from the residents of Seattle has about the same margin of error as a random sample of size 1000 from the residents of the United States. If the sample size n is large relative to the size N of the population (more than about 10% of the population size), then you should use a correction factor for the formula for the margin of error that makes it smaller. Specifically, an approximate confidence interval is

$$\hat{p} + z^* \cdot \sqrt{\frac{\hat{p}(1-\hat{p})}{n-1}} \sqrt{\frac{N-n}{N}}$$

where N is the size of the population.

See also the explanation from the Gallup Organization in E51.

9
INFERENCE FOR MEANS

Overview

In this chapter, students continue their formal study of statistical inference, but the parameters that are the objectives of the inference now switch from proportions to means.

As in Chapter 8, both confidence intervals and tests of significance are developed first graphically and then algebraically. The concepts are first developed for overly simplified situations in which the populations are normally distributed and the standard deviations are known. If students can grasp the basic concepts in these situations, they are better prepared to handle the more realistic situations that begin in Section 9.3.

To repeat the warning of Chapter 8, the logic of confidence intervals and tests of significance is difficult and the language used is somewhat technical, but using that logic and language correctly is one of the main goals of the introductory statistics course.

Goals

The six sections of this chapter will teach students

- to understand the concept of a confidence interval for estimating a population mean, compute a confidence interval, and interpret the results
- to perform a test of significance for deciding whether it is reasonable to reject a claim that a sample was drawn from a population with a specified mean
- to produce and interpret a confidence interval for the difference between the mean of one population and the mean of another population
- to perform a test of significance for deciding whether it is reasonable to reject a claim that two samples were drawn from two populations that have the same mean

Content Overview

In this chapter, students will use their understanding of sampling distributions, which was developed in Chapters 5 and 7 using simulation. The basic result is used again and again: If the sampling distribution can be considered approximately normal, 95% of all sample means will fall within two standard errors of the population mean. If students seem to be losing this concept of a sampling distribution as you teach this chapter, you may want to construct a few simulated sampling distributions once again, assigning, for example, D2 and P2 in Section 8.1.

Sections 1 and 2 are extremely important because they lay out the basics of inferential statistics for means: confidence intervals and significance tests.

Time Required

Traditional Schedule			Block	4 x 4 Block
Section 9.1				
3 days	Day 1	Overview, Activity 9.1, reasonably likely outcomes, confidence intervals	1 long, 2 short	2 days
	Day 2	Capture rate, sample size		
	Day 3	Summary, exercises		
Section 9.2				
4 days	Day 1	Overview, fixed-level testing, formal structure of tests of significance	3 long, 1 short	2 days
	Day 2	The meaning of reject, P-values		
	Day 3	One-sided alternatives, one-tailed tests		
	Day 4	Summary, exercises		
Section 9.3				
4 days	Day 1	Overview, Activity 9.2	3 long, 1 short	2 days
	Day 2	How to adjust for estimating σ, checking conditions		
	Day 3	Hypothesis tests for a mean when σ is unknown, P-values instead of fixed-level tests		
	Day 4	Summary, exercises		
Section 9.4				
3 days	Day 1	Overview, Activity 9.3	2 long, 1 short	2 days
	Day 2	Non-normal population, 15/40 rule		
	Day 3	Summary, exercises		

(continued)

Traditional Schedule			Block	4 x 4 Block
Section 9.5				
5 days	Day 1	Overview, Activity 9.4	3 long, 2 short	3 days
	Day 2	Confidence intervals for difference of means when shapes are normal and σ_1 and σ_2 are known		
	Day 3	Confidence intervals for difference of means when σ_1 and σ_2 are unknown		
	Day 4	Significance tests for difference when σ_1 and σ_2 are unknown, special case of pooling		
	Day 5	Summary, exercises		
Section 9.6				
5 days	Day 1	One sample or two?, Activity 9.5	3 long, 2 short	3 days
	Day 2	Completely randomized design, matched pairs design, repeated measures design		
	Day 3	Confidence interval for difference from paired comparisons (σ_1 and σ_2 unknown)		
	Day 4	Non-normal populations, comparing means, inference and chance		
	Day 5	Summary, exercises		
Review				
3 days			2 long	2 days

Materials

Section 9.1: None

Section 9.2: None

Section 9.3: None

Section 9.4: None

Section 9.5: None

Section 9.6: For Activity 9.5, rulers marked in millimeters

Suggested Assignments

Classwork

Section	Essential	Recommended	Optional
9.1	Activity 9.1 D1, D3, D4, D6, D9, D10 P1–P4	D5, D7, D8, D11 P5	D2
9.2	D12–D15, D17–D20 P6, P7, P10–P12	D16, D21, D22 P8, P9	D23 P13
9.3	Activity 9.2 D24–D26 P14, P15, P17–P20	D27 P16, P21	
9.4	Activity 9.3 D29, D30 P22	D28	
9.5	Activity 9.4 D34, D36 P23, P24, P26, P27	D32	D31, D33, D35, D37 P25
9.6	D38, D39, D41–D44, D47 P28, P29, P31	Activity 9.5 D40, D45, D46, D48 P30, P32, P33	

Homework

Section	Essential	Recommended	Optional
9.1	E1, E3–E5, E7	E2	E6, E8
9.2	E9–E12	E13, E14	
9.3	E15–E17, E20	E18, E19	
9.4	E21, E22, E25	E24	E23
9.5	E26, E27, E30	E29	E28, E31, E32
9.6	E33–E35	E36, E37	
Review	E38–E40, E42–E44, E47	E41, E45, E46, E48–E50	

9.1 Toward a Confidence Interval for a Mean

Objectives

- to find a confidence interval graphically from a sample taken from one of a fixed set of known populations
- to understand a confidence interval as consisting of those population means for which the result from the sample is reasonably likely
- to compute a confidence interval for a mean using the formula
- to interpret a confidence interval for a mean and understand the meaning of "confidence"
- to understand the relationship between capture rate and confidence level
- to compute the required sample size for a given margin of error

Important Terms and Concepts

- reasonably likely sample means and rare sample means
- confidence interval for a mean
- confidence level
- capture rate
- margin of error

Class Time

Three days

Materials

None

Suggested Assignments

Classwork		
Essential	**Recommended**	**Optional**
Activity 9.1	D5, D7, D8, D11	D2
D1, D3, D4, D6, D9, D10	P5	
P1–P4		

Homework		
Essential	**Recommended**	**Optional**
E1, E3–E5, E7	E2	E6, E8

Lesson Notes: Reasonably Likely Outcomes

You should emphasize the same general principles for inference about a population mean that you used for inference about proportions. In summary, that approach to inference is outlined as follows.

Goal: You want to draw a conclusion about an unknown parameter. For example, you want to estimate the mean μ of a population.

Model: Design a chance process that generates data. To estimate a population mean, draw a random sample from that population and compute the sample statistic $\bar{x}$.

Sampling distribution: Study the sampling distribution of $\bar{x}$ for various values of the parameter μ. Which values of $\bar{x}$ are reasonably likely for each value of μ?

Inference: Turn the logic around: Given the observed data, summarized by the sample statistic $\bar{x}$, which are the parameter values μ that would make the observed $\bar{x}$ a reasonably likely outcome?

Students should keep this summary in mind throughout the remainder of the chapter.

Activity 9.1: What Makes Strong Evidence?

The boxplots are summaries of the distributions of differences between standing and sitting pulse rates.

1. Still being guided by shape, center, and spread, the strongest evidence for a "significant" difference would be a plot that shows a nearly symmetric distribution with a positive center (greater than zero) and small variation. Experiment B fits the bill.

2. B gives the strongest evidence, followed by D, C, then A. Experiment D gives slightly stronger evidence than does C because boxplot D shows a slightly higher center and a little less spread. Experiment A shows no conclusive evidence of an increase because its center is near zero and it has tremendous spread, compared with the others.

3. It would be essential to know the sample size and the design of the experiment before proceeding with further analyses. (Experiments A and C were matched pairs designs with 28 observations each, whereas Experiments B and D were repeated measures designs with 28 observations each.)

Discussion

D1. **a.** Drawing a vertical line upward from an SAT combined score of 1390 on Display 9.2, you get the plot shown here. From this plot, you see that a score of 1390 is a reasonably likely outcome for North Carolina State, Wake Forest, and Notre Dame, but not for the other two universities.

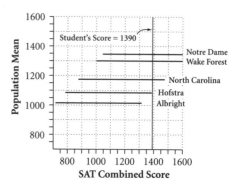

For your information, the following table shows the interval that is two standard deviations on each side of the mean for the five universities.

University	Interval of Reasonably Likely Outcomes
Notre Dame	1045 to 1645
Wake Forest	1000 to 1600
North Carolina State	875 to 1475
Hofstra	785 to 1385
Albright	715 to 1315

Note that Display 9.2 shows the upper end of Notre Dame's interval cut off at 1600 because the maximum SAT score reported for any student is 1600. A blackline master similar to Display 9.2 is provided at the end of this section.

b. To be reasonably likely, the score, x, must be within $2(150) = 300$ points of μ. That implies that μ must be within 300 points of x. So, any value of μ between $x - 300$ and $x + 300$ would be plausible. That is, any value of μ in that interval could have produced score x as a reasonably likely outcome.

D2. **a.** The horizontal line segments in Display 9.2 have endpoints $\mu - 2\sigma$ and $\mu + 2\sigma$, where μ is the population mean on the vertical scale. Except for the fact that Notre Dame's line was cut off at 1600, all of the horizontal segments are of equal length and are centered at $x = \mu$, where x is measured along the horizontal axis. Therefore the slopes of the parallel lines joining the endpoints must be 1. The line joining the left endpoints is $x = \mu - 2\sigma$, or $\mu = x + 2\sigma$. The line joining the right endpoints is $x = \mu + 2\sigma$, or $\mu = x - 2\sigma$.

b. A vertical line at a fixed x will intersect these lines at $\mu = x - 2\sigma$ and $\mu = x + 2\sigma$.

c. For any value of μ between $x - 2\sigma$ and $x + 2\sigma$, the observed value of x will cross the line of reasonably likely outcomes. Therefore, those are the values of μ that are plausible for that particular x.

D3. **a.** In this case, the σ of 150 is simply replaced by 100 and the set of plausible values for μ is the interval $x - 2(100)$ to $x + 2(100)$, or $x - 200$ to $x + 200$.

b. Similarly, if σ is 210, the set of plausible values for μ is the interval $x - 2(210)$ to $x + 2(210)$, or $x - 420$ to $x + 420$.

Lesson Notes: Confidence Intervals

Students are now looking for plausible values for a population mean, rather than for a population proportion, but the methodology is the same as that used in Chapter 8. Students will use a sample mean with a normal sampling distribution to estimate a population mean. Emphasize that random sampling or assignment is still the key ingredient that makes the theory work.

To construct confidence intervals with the TI-83 calculator where σ is known, use ZInterval in the TESTS menu.

Discussion

D4. **a.** 90% interval: $1000 \pm (1.645)(150)$, or from 753 to 1247

95% interval: $1000 \pm (1.960)(150)$, or from 706 to 1294

99% interval: $1000 \pm (2.576)(150)$, or from 614 to 1386

b. The mean for Notre Dame (1345) belongs to the 99% interval, but not to the two narrower intervals.

D5. If $n = 16$, $\sigma = 150$, then $\sigma_{\bar{x}} = 150/\sqrt{16} = 37.5$.

a. 90% interval: $1000 \pm (1.645)(37.5)$, or from 938 to 1062

95% interval: $1000 \pm (1.96)(37.5)$, or from 926 to 1074

99% interval: $1000 \pm (2.576)(37.5)$, or from 903 to 1097

The first confidence interval, for example, is interpreted this way: We are 90% confident that the students in the sample come from a university that has a mean combined SAT score for all students of between 938 and 1062. Alternatively, if a university has a mean combined SAT score for all students of between 938 and 1062, it is reasonably likely to have a random sample of 16 students with a mean SAT combined score of 1000.

b. The mean of 1345 for Notre Dame does not fall into any of the three intervals.

D6. It is never possible to be 100% confident with less than 100% of the data in hand. If you knew all the values in a population perfectly, then that level of accuracy could be achieved. For samples, high levels of confidence produce long intervals, so a level of 99.5% may produce an interval that is so long that it is of little practical value. For example, what good does it do to estimate the mean annual income of families in your community as being somewhere between ten dollars and a billion dollars? In statistics, there is always tension between level of confidence and usefulness of the answer.

D7. From a geometric point of view, if the standard deviations differed, the horizontal lines in Display 9.2 would be different lengths. There would then be no easy way to relate lengths of vertical segments to lengths of horizontal segments.

If you tried to use the formula, you wouldn't have a fixed value to substitute in for σ.

D8. In this method of constructing confidence intervals, the values used as multipliers of the standard errors (1.645, 1.960, 2.576) are taken from the normal distribution. They are the multipliers that cut off, respectively, the middle 90%, 95%, and 99% of a normal distribution, but typically not of other distributions. If the population is normal, then the sampling distribution of the sample mean will be normal as well, and so these multipliers are the correct ones to use. (Now, the sampling distribution of the sample mean may be approximately normal in other situations—large samples, for example, from slightly skewed populations—but normality of the population is the only way to guarantee the normality of sample means for all sample sizes.) See also the solution to D11.

D9. a. The margin of error increases.
b. The margin of error decreases.
c. The margin of error increases.

Practice

P1. If $n = 9$, $\sigma = 150$, then $\sigma_{\bar{x}} = 150/\sqrt{9} = 50$.

a. 90% interval: $1110 \pm (1.645)(50)$, or from 1028 to 1192
95% interval: $1110 \pm (1.960)(50)$, or from 1012 to 1208
99% interval: $1110 \pm (2.576)(50)$, or from 981 to 1239

The resulting intervals are the values of the population means that could have produced an observed sample mean of 1110 as a reasonably likely outcome. Here, "reasonably likely" is interpreted, respectively, as the middle 90%, 95%, or 99% of the possible values of the sample mean. In other words, for the 90% confidence interval, we are 90% confident that the mean SAT score of all students at this university falls between 1028 and 1192.

b. The mean of 1015 for Albright belongs to the 99% and 95% intervals, but not to the 90% interval.

P2. A confidence interval may be shortened by either increasing the sample size or decreasing the confidence level, assuming the standard deviation remains constant. For vital decisions it is not a good idea to reduce the confidence in the answer; the better alternative is to increase the sample size.

P3. Because the only thing that might change in the construction of the confidence interval is the sample mean, the intervals would have the same width but are likely to have differing locations. Thus, B is the best answer.

Lesson Notes: Capture Rate

The population mean is constant but unknown; it is the sample mean that moves around from sample to sample! Therefore, the intervals constructed in repeated samples of the same size will have differing locations, and some intervals will miss the population mean altogether. This is sometimes a difficult idea for students to grasp, so careful and thorough discussion is needed. You may want to use an example like the one provided in the answer to D11 to show how the capture rate is sensitive to the conditions underlying the confidence interval.

Discussion

D10. The capture rate depends entirely on z^*. Therefore,

a. it is not affected by changes to the sample size,

b. it is not affected by changes to the population standard deviation,

but

c. it is affected by changes to the confidence level because the capture rate is equivalent to the confidence level.

This may confuse students because they typically want a larger n to result in a higher capture rate. An increase in sample size, for example, for a 95% confidence interval decreases the margin of error and the length of the interval, but the shorter interval still has a 95% chance of capturing the population mean in repeated sampling.

D11. "The capture rate equals the confidence level." The answer to both parts a and b hinges on the normality of the sampling distribution of the sample mean, which is the basis of the method used here for constructing confidence intervals. This normality is guaranteed only for random samples from normal populations.

Think of an extremely skewed population consisting of a thousand 3's and one 3,000. The population mean is about 6, and the population standard deviation is about 94. Suppose you take random samples of size 4 from this population. Almost always a sample will consist of all 3's and the sample mean will be 3. The standard error of the sample mean is about $94/\sqrt{4} = 47$. Thus, virtually all of the nominal 95% confidence intervals, calculated by the rules of this chapter, will capture the population mean. The same is true for 90% confidence intervals, and even for 50% confidence intervals. An example of this type will help convince students that the capture rate (for these intervals) can change dramatically once you move away from normality.

Even if the population of interest is normally distributed, nonrandom samples in general will produce confidence intervals with capture rates far different from what was anticipated. For example, suppose you want to estimate the mean diameter of a pile of rocks, but the rocks are sampled with a sieve so that only the largest ones remain in the sample. Confidence intervals based on such data will most often miss the true population mean size.

Lesson Notes: What Sample Size Should You Use?

This would be a good place to remind students of the principles of good design of studies, as discussed in Chapter 4. Randomization is key, but samples must be selected from well-defined populations and treatments must be randomized to a specified collection of experimental units. But how large should the sample or collection of units be? The answer is to be found in the margin of error. A good investigator will look ahead to the planned analysis before collecting any data and think about how he or she would like that analysis to look. If you are estimating mean household income of your community, will a margin of error of $20,000 be meaningful from a practical point of view? How about $10,000? Does it make sense to think in terms of a margin of error of $500? What will be a useful answer after the project is finished should be

considered before the data collection begins. Otherwise, you may be wasting time and money.

Practice

P4. For 95% confidence, z^* is 1.96 or approximately 2.0. The width of the confidence interval is twice the margin of error, so the margin of error must be set at 0.5. Using the formula for sample size,

$$n = \left(\frac{z^* \cdot \sigma}{E}\right)^2 = \left(\frac{2 \cdot 10}{0.5}\right)^2 = 1600$$

If you use $z^* = 1.96$, then $n = 1537$.

P5. When the confidence level is not given, it is common practice to assume it is 95%. The standard deviation here is in hours but the margin of error is in minutes, so these must be changed to common units. Using hours for both, the sample size is

$$n = \left(\frac{z^* \cdot \sigma}{E}\right)^2 = \left(\frac{2 \cdot 2}{1/6}\right)^2 = 576$$

If you use $z^* = 1.96$, then $n = 554$.

Exercises

E1. **a.** The information given suggests that the distribution of acceptance rates might be approximately normal, with a range of 19 to 90. A normal curve actually has infinitely long tails, so these boundaries can not be the extremes of any normal distribution. However, you also know that about 95% of the area under a normal curve lies within two standard deviations of the mean, so it is reasonable to think that the interval from 19 to 90 for a sample of only 50 colleges might cover about four standard deviations. That makes the standard deviation approximately 18. Using the standard construction, the 95% confidence interval then is

$$\bar{x} \pm z^* \cdot \frac{\sigma}{\sqrt{n}} \text{ or } 52 \pm 1.96 \frac{18}{\sqrt{4}}$$

which yields an interval of 52 ± 17.6, or approximately (34, 70). This is a long interval because the sample size is small and the population has lots of variability.
b. The variable is the acceptance rate per college, and the cases are the colleges (not the individual students within those colleges).

c. The population of interest consists of the acceptance rates of the 50 top liberal arts colleges in the United States. You are 95% confident that the mean acceptance rate of these 50 colleges falls between 34% and 70%. This is not the same as saying that you are 95% confident that between 34% and 70% of all students who apply to these colleges are accepted. It is impossible to make any statement like that because the same number of students do not apply to each college.

E2. In order to achieve this mean and standard deviation, most of the Dartmouth scores must be up close to the upper boundary of 1600, with a pronounced skewness toward the lower values. In other words, the distribution of scores for Dartmouth can not be normal. (Notre Dame's scores have something of the same nature, but not as pronounced.)

E3. B. The 99% confidence interval will have a better chance of capturing the true mean. It will be longer than the 90% interval. The capture rate does not depend on the sample size; it depends only on the confidence level.

E4. **a.** False. A confidence interval is a statement about plausible values for a population mean, not about the individual values within a population.

b. False. A confidence interval is a statement about plausible values for a population mean, not about the values in the sample.

c. False. The method has a 95% chance of success, but after this particular interval is calculated, it either is successful or it isn't.

d. False. The sample mean is the center of the confidence interval.

e. True. The capture rate equals the confidence level provided the population is nearly normal and the sample is random.

E5. For a sample size approximation, it is satisfactory to use $z^* = 2$.

a. $n = \left(\dfrac{z^* \cdot \sigma}{E}\right)^2 = \left(\dfrac{2 \cdot 2}{2}\right)^2 = 4$

b. $n = \left(\dfrac{z^* \cdot \sigma}{E}\right)^2 = \left(\dfrac{2 \cdot 2}{1}\right)^2 = 16$

c. $n = \left(\dfrac{z^* \cdot \sigma}{E}\right)^2 = \left(\dfrac{2 \cdot 2}{0.5}\right)^2 = 64$

Notice that the sample sizes increase by a factor of 4 each time the margin of error is cut in half.

E6. Here are the key steps:

$$z^* \cdot \frac{\sigma}{\sqrt{n}} = E$$

$$\frac{(z^* \cdot \sigma)^2}{n} = E^2$$

$$n = \left(\frac{z^* \cdot \sigma}{E}\right)^2$$

E7. The sample mean is $\bar{x} \approx 15.97$. You could use a confidence interval to estimate the true mean of the weight of the water, which results in

$$\bar{x} \pm z^* \cdot \frac{\sigma}{\sqrt{n}} = 15.97 \pm 1.96 \cdot \frac{0.06}{\sqrt{10}}$$

or an interval of (15.93, 16.01). Because 16 is one of the plausible values for the population mean, there is no need to adjust the machine. (This is an example of an important principle in quality improvement; don't make adjustments until you are pretty sure things need adjusting.)

E8. For the 95% intervals, the margin of error is $1.96 \cdot 5.11/\sqrt{n} \approx 10/\sqrt{n}$.

For the 90% intervals, the margin of error is $1.645 \cdot 6.09/\sqrt{n} \approx 10/\sqrt{n}$.

So, the margins of error are equal but the capture rates are not. The former captures the population mean about 95% of the time, and the latter only about 90% of the time. Therefore, the 90% intervals must have more variable locations than the 95% intervals. They "bounce around" more because the sampling distribution of the sample mean has greater variability.

The plots that follow each show 25 confidence intervals based on random samples of size 9 selected from populations with mean 10. The 95% confidence intervals come from a population with standard deviation 5.11, and the 90% confidence intervals come from a population with standard deviation 6.09. All confidence intervals are the same length, but it is obvious that the 90% confidence intervals, from the more variable population, have greater variation in their locations. The boxplots display the lower and upper confidence bounds for these intervals and, again, show that the 90% intervals have greater variation in their endpoints. (Each boxplot contains results from 25 confidence intervals.)

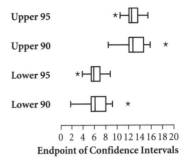

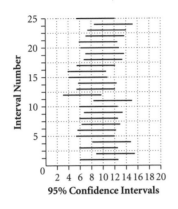

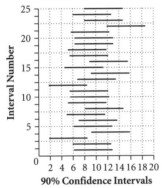

Reasonably Likely Outcomes for Combined SAT Scores
for $\sigma = 150$

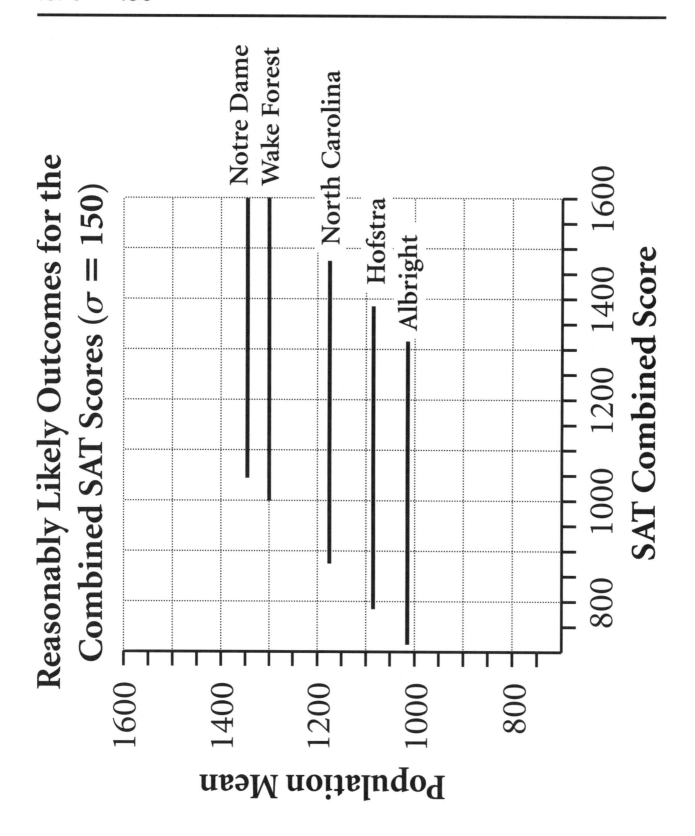

9.2 Toward a Significance Test for a Mean

Objectives

- to understand the logic of a significance test for a mean
- to perform the four steps in a significance test for a mean
- to understand the meaning of the following terms in the context of inference for means: statistical significance, null hypothesis and alternate hypothesis, test statistic, level of significance, and one-tailed test and two-tailed test
- to compute and interpret a *P*-value in testing a mean

Important Terms and Concepts

- significance test for a mean
- statistical significance
- fixed-level testing
- conditions (assumptions) for a test
- null hypothesis and alternate hypothesis
- test statistic

- level of significance
- *P*-value
- observed significance level
- one-tailed test and two-tailed test
- conclusion in context

Class Time
Four days

Materials
None

Suggested Assignments

Classwork		
Essential	**Recommended**	**Optional**
D12–D15, D17–D20	D16, D21, D22	D23
P6, P7, P10–P12	P8, P9	P13

Homework		
Essential	**Recommended**	**Optional**
E9–E12	E13, E14	

Lesson Notes: Plausible Values for Means

How to reason from a sample back to the population from which the sample came is the key issue of statistical inference. In this chapter, we are looking for values of the population mean that are consistent with the sample data; we call these plausible values. A population having a mean equal to any one of the plausible values could have produced the observed sample mean as a reasonably likely outcome. A blackline master of Display 9.4 is provided at the end of this section.

Discussion

D12. a. In Display 9.4 and in the following plot, the sample mean of 1300 cuts the middle of the Wake Forest line segment but is far to the right of the Hofstra line segment. So it is plausible that the sample came from Wake Forest, but not from Hofstra.

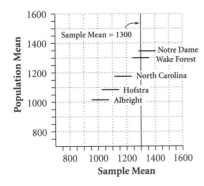

b. The mean for Hofstra scores is 1085, and the z-statistic corresponding to a sample mean of 1300 is

$$z = \frac{\bar{x} - \mu}{\sigma/\sqrt{n}} = \frac{1300 - 1085}{150/\sqrt{25}} \approx 7.2$$

An outcome 7 standard deviations away from the mean almost never occurs from random sampling, so it is implausible that the sample mean came from Hofstra.

The z-statistic for Wake Forest is 0; the mean for Wake Forest is exactly 1300. So, it is plausible that the sample came from Wake Forest.

Lesson Notes: Fixed-Level Testing

Classical statistics has approached tests of significance in two different ways. One is to calculate a probability—the *P*-value—that shows how unusual your sample result is when the null hypothesis is true and then use that *P*-value to weigh the evidence in the data for or against the null hypothesis. The decision whether to reject the null hypothesis is left up to the experimenter, who makes a judgment in light of the context surrounding that decision. The other approach is to set a boundary—the significance level α—for this probability and then automatically reject the null hypothesis whenever the *P*-value falls below this boundary.

Fixed-level testing has an advantage in that it allows the experimenter to study the power of the test to reject the null hypothesis under various alternatives and to select a sample size accordingly. In fact, there is a one-to-one correspondence between a confidence interval estimate of a mean and a two-sided test of significance for that mean. The plausible values produced by the confidence interval are precisely those that would not be rejected in a test, so long as the significance level for the test is the complement of the confidence level for the interval. (For example, $\alpha = 5\%$ is the complement of a confidence level of 95%.) A disadvantage of fixed-level testing is that it sets decision making in stone before the data have been reviewed and may be too stringent to allow the experimenter to use good judgment.

Historically, the *P*-value approach was developed and promulgated by a very experienced data analyst and brilliant scientist, R. A. Fisher (whose name you have seen earlier in the text). The fixed-level approach was developed by outstanding mathematical statisticians, J. Neyman and E. Pearson. Not surprisingly, Neyman also developed the notion of confidence intervals. The argument between these approaches goes on even today, but most applied scientists appear to favor a combination of approaches, using the fixed-level ideas when designing studies and estimating with confidence intervals and the *P*-value approach when weighing the evidence from a test of significance.

Discussion

D13. For a two-tailed test, the critical value $z^\star$ for the 10% significance level must cut off a .05 area in each tail of the standard normal distribution. This value is 1.645. The critical value for the 5% significance level must cut off a .025 area in each tail of the standard normal distribution, and that value is 1.960. Similarly, the critical value for the 1% significance level must cut off a .005 area in each tail of the standard normal distribution, and that value is 2.576.

For a one-tailed test, the tail areas equal the significance levels, and therefore the critical values are 1.28, 1.645, and 2.33, respectively.

D14. **a.** The z-statistic for this situation is

$$z = \frac{\bar{x} - \mu}{\sigma/\sqrt{n}} = \frac{1170 - 1100}{210/\sqrt{25}} = 1.67$$

This is larger than the critical value for the 10% level, so UOP would be rejected as a plausible university for this sample. However, this z-statistic is smaller than the critical values for either the 5% or 1% levels, so UOP would not be rejected as plausible at these levels.

b. No. The significance test asks a question about a specific population, such as "Does the observed sample mean come from the set of reasonably likely outcomes for samples of size 25 from the University of the Pacific?" Thus, no larger group need be considered to answer this question.

Lesson Notes: The Formal Structure of Tests of Significance

Note that the text asks students to check "conditions," rather than having them make "assumptions." The techniques of inference will not work without randomness, and "assuming" you have a random sample when you need to analyze data is about as effective as imagining you have a can opener when you need to open a can. It is better for students to think of random sampling or random assignment of treatments as required conditions before they can use an inferential procedure rather than as assumptions they can make.

For the procedures of this chapter to work you also need the condition of an approximately normal

sampling distribution for the sample mean. As students saw in Chapter 5, this will be the case when you have a nearly normal population or when you have a sample that is large enough that the Central Limit Theorem takes over. In a later section you will see how badly things can fail if this condition is not met.

The last condition is that you must know the standard deviation σ of the population. In practice, you won't know σ. But that unrealistic assumption is made here to advance the theory. In Section 9.3, students learn how to handle the realistic case where σ is estimated by s, the sample standard deviation.

Discussion

D15. *Check conditions.* The sample was randomly selected from an approximately normal population of scores with known σ.

State your hypotheses.

H_0: The students' scores have been selected from Notre Dame, which has a mean score of 1345.

H_a: The students are not from Notre Dame.

Compute the test statistic and draw a sketch.
The z-statistic for a sample mean of 1173, with sample of size 4, and a hypothesized population mean of 1345 is

$$z = \frac{1173 - 1345}{150/\sqrt{4}} = -2.293$$

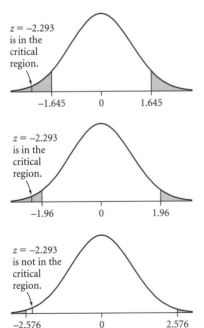

Write a conclusion in context. For $\alpha = .05$, $z^* = 1.96$, and for $\alpha = .10$, $z^* = 1.645$, so there is sufficient evidence at either of these two levels to reject the hypothesis that the students come from Notre Dame. For $\alpha = .01$, $z^* = 2.576$, so you do not reject the null hypothesis.

D16. For the 5% test it must be the case that $(x - 1175)/(150/\sqrt{1}) > 1.96$ or < -1.96, but for the 1% level test it must be the case that $(x - 1175)/(150/\sqrt{1}) < 2.576$ or > -2.576, where x represents the student's score. Therefore,

$$x > 1175 + 150(1.96) = 1469$$

and

$$x < 1175 + 150(2.576) = 1561$$

or

$$x < 1175 - 150(1.96) = 881$$

and

$$x > 1175 - 150(2.576) = 789$$

So her score is between 789 and 881, or between 1469 and 1561.

Practice

P6. *Check conditions.* From the description of the acceptance rates, the population is approximately normal, with σ equal to about one-fourth of the range, or approximately 18. (See the solution to E1 shown earlier in Section 9.1.) The sample was selected at random.

State your hypotheses. Letting μ denote the mean acceptance rate for the top 50 liberal arts colleges:

H_0: $\mu = 50$
H_a: $\mu \neq 50$

Compute the test statistic and draw a sketch: The test statistic is

$$z = \frac{\bar{x} - \mu_0}{\sigma/\sqrt{n}} = \frac{52 - 50}{18/\sqrt{4}} \approx 0.22$$

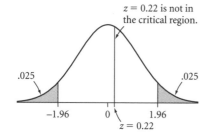

Using $z^* = 1.96$, this value of z isn't statistically significant.

Write a conclusion in context. A test statistic of $z \approx 0.22$ is too close to 0 to reject the null hypothesis at any of the prescribed levels. Based on a random sample of four colleges selected from the top 50 liberal arts colleges in the country, there is insufficient statistical evidence to conclude that the mean acceptance rate for all 50 of these colleges differs from 50%.

P7. Conditions have been checked previously in the text. For the null hypothesis that the population mean from which this sample came is 1300 (Wake Forest), the z-statistic is

$$z = \frac{\bar{x} - \mu_0}{\sigma/\sqrt{n}} = \frac{1350 - 1300}{150/\sqrt{9}} = 1.0$$

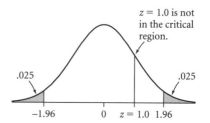

This value is smaller than the critical value of 1.96 for a 5% level test. Therefore, the null hypothesis that the sample came from Wake Forest can not be rejected.

P8. Conditions have been checked previously in the text. For the null hypothesis that the population mean from which this sample came is 1300 (Wake Forest), the z-statistic is

$$z = \frac{\bar{x} - \mu_0}{\sigma/\sqrt{n}} = \frac{1150 - 1300}{150/\sqrt{36}} = -6.0$$

The test statistic is quite large and would be difficult to see in a sketch. A sample mean that is 6 standard deviations from the population mean practically never occurs with random sampling, so the null hypothesis can be rejected at the 10% level (where $z^* = 1.645$). It's not plausible that this sample came from Wake Forest.

P9. Conditions have been checked previously in the text. For the null hypothesis that the population mean from which this sample came is 1085, the z-statistic is

$$z = \frac{\bar{x} - \mu_0}{\sigma/\sqrt{n}} = \frac{1000 - 1085}{150/\sqrt{9}} = -1.70$$

$z = -1.70$ is in the critical region.

.05   .05

−1.645   0   1.645

This value (in absolute value) is larger than the critical value for a test at the 10% level but is smaller than the critical values for tests at the 5% and 1% levels. Thus, you can reject the hypothesis that the sample came from a university with mean 1085 at the 10% level, but not at the 5% or 1% levels.

Lesson Notes: The Meaning of Reject

When your data show that you should reject the null hypothesis, there are only three possibilities. The model may not fit the situation that produced the data, the null hypothesis is true but you were unlucky enough to see a rare sample, or rejecting the null hypothesis is the correct decision. Discuss these options with students and point out that the first option can be ruled out if good data collection practices are followed.

Remind students that not rejecting a null hypothesis is not the same as accepting it. You may fail to reject that the average annual household income in your town is $60,000, but that does not establish the fact that it is exactly $60,000. This figure is just one plausible value among many.

Discussion

D17. The components of a significance test (check conditions, state hypotheses, do computations, make a conclusion linked to computations and in context) are the same for proportions and means. As presented in this book, both tests rely on approximately normal sampling distributions for the sample statistic (either sample proportion or sample mean). In both cases, you need to know n and you need to have some sense of the shape of the population in order to verify approximate normality of the sampling distribution. The shape of the sampling distribution is easier to verify for proportions where there is a simple test using np and $n(1 - p)$. The main difference

between the two procedures is that when working with means you must account for a second parameter—the standard deviation.

D18. Only II can be answered. The probability of rejecting a true null hypothesis is .01; the probability of not rejecting it is .99.

Lesson Notes: *P*-Values: The Observed Significance Level

Refer to the notes for the section on fixed-level testing and remind students of the difference between these two approaches. The *P*-value gives you a measure of the strength of the evidence against the null hypothesis; a large *P*-value implies weak evidence whereas a small *P*-value implies strong evidence. In relating the two approaches, the significance level can be thought of as the maximum *P*-value for which you would reject a null hypothesis. There is no direct analogy between *P*-values and confidence intervals as there is with confidence intervals and fixed-level testing.

Discussion

D19. a. As the standard deviation increases, with everything else remaining the same, the value of the test statistic z decreases. Therefore, the *P*-value will increase. It is harder to reject a false null hypothesis in the face of more variation in the data.

b. As the sample size increases, with everything else remaining the same, the value of the test statistic increases. Therefore, the *P*-value will decrease. There is more evidence against a false null hypothesis as you gather more data.

Practice

P10. For P6 the value of the test statistic was 0.22, which was smaller than the critical values for testing at the 10%, 5%, and 1% levels. The *P*-value is approximately .8241 (calculator) or .8258 (Table A), which is so large as to indicate that the observed outcome, or a more extreme outcome, is not at all unusual under the null hypothesis. So you should not reject the null hypothesis.

For P7 the value of the test statistic was 1.0, smaller than the critical value for a test at the 5% level. The *P*-value is approximately .3173 (calculator) or .3174 (Table A), which allows the conclusion that the observed outcome, or a more extreme outcome, is not unusual under the null hypothesis. You should not reject the null hypothesis.

For P8 the value of the test statistic was -6.0, which is larger in absolute value than the critical value for a test at the 10% level. The P-value here is essentially 0, which implies that an outcome at least as extreme as the one observed is very unusual under the null hypothesis. You should reject the null hypothesis.

P11. With a sample size of 100, a hypothesized population mean of 1175, and a standard deviation of 150, we have

$$z = \frac{\bar{x} - 1175}{150/\sqrt{100}} \text{ or } \bar{x} = 1175 + z \cdot \frac{150}{\sqrt{100}}$$

a. Here $z = \pm 1.645$, so $\bar{x}$ is about 1150, or 1200.

b. Here $z = \pm 1.96$, so $\bar{x}$ is about 1146, or 1204.

c. Here $z = \pm 2.576$, so $\bar{x}$ is about 1136, or 1214.

Lesson Notes: One-Sided Alternatives, One-Tailed Tests

Discuss possible investigations that might lead to a research hypothesis that is one-sided, such as "Does exercise lower cholesterol?" or "Does an extra lab session improve exam scores?" Then, discuss how the set-up of the hypotheses and the calculation of the P-value changes. For the same value of the z-statistic, the P-value is now half what it was in the two-sided test.

We chose to present one-sided tests using the P-value approach, but you can construct these as fixed-level tests just as well. There is an analogy between fixed-level, one-sided tests and one-sided confidence intervals, but the latter are used so seldom that they are not presented here.

Discussion

D20. a. The two-sided P-value corresponds to the pair of shaded areas.

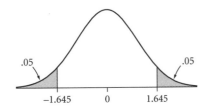

b. The right-hand area ($z \geq 1.645$) corresponds to evidence that $\mu > \mu_0$. For any given value of the test statistic, z, the one-tailed P-value will be exactly half as large as the two-tailed P-value.

c. If $z = 1.645$, the two-tailed P-value is .10. A value of $z = 1.28$ gives a one-tailed P-value of .10.

d. The P-value will be larger for a two-tailed test.

D21. a. This situation calls for a one-sided (right-tailed) alternate because the claim (research or alternate hypothesis) is that the mean price increased.

b. $\bar{x}$ = mean selling price for a sample of houses sold this month.

μ = true mean selling price of all houses sold in the city for this month.

c. The null hypothesis is that μ is the same as the mean for last month. The alternate is that it is greater.

D22. a. A one-sided (left-tailed) test is appropriate because the research hypothesis is that the freezing point will be lower for saltwater.

b. $\bar{x}$ = mean freezing point for a sample of bowls of saltwater.

μ = the true freezing point for saltwater with this degree of salinity.

c. The null hypothesis is that the true freezing point of saltwater μ is the same as for pure water. Or, using symbols:

$H_0: \mu = 32°F$ or $H_0: \mu = 0°C$

The alternate hypothesis is that the true freezing point of saltwater is lower than it is for pure water. Symbolically:

$H_a: \mu < 32°F$ or $H_a: \mu < 0°C$

D23. Answers will vary, of course, but for the one-sided scenarios, the context should provide a natural reason to use a one-sided alternate. The alternate in the opposite direction should be irrelevant, uninteresting, impossible, or meaningless.

Practice

P12. A one-sided (left-tailed) test is appropriate because the research hypothesis is that water boils at a lower temperature at high altitude.

$\bar{x}$ = mean boiling point for a sample of pots of water boiled at Denver airport.

μ = true boiling point of water in Denver.

The null hypothesis is that the true boiling point is the same as at sea level. Or, using symbols:

$H_0: \mu = 212°F$ or $H_0: \mu = 100°C$

The alternate is that the true boiling point is lower than at sea level. Symbolically:

$H_a: \mu < 212°F$ or $H_a: \mu < 100°C$

P13. A company that produces a gasoline additive would test that it gives greater gas mileage. A group concerned about energy usage and environmental impact of cars might claim a lower gas mileage if it was suspicious of the manufacturer's claim.

Exercises

To do a test of significance for a mean using the TI-83 calculator, use Z-Test in the TESTS menu.

E9. Choice D is the correct answer. Many students will want to say that the P-value measures the chance that the null hypothesis is true because we reject the null hypothesis when the P-value is small. We can never calculate this probability based on sample data alone; all we can do is calculate the conditional probability of getting particular results from a random sample under the condition that the null hypothesis is true.

E10. Choice A is the correct answer, for reasons that have been discussed thoroughly in the last two chapters. You might remind students, however, that the confidence level and the capture rate are equal only if the underlying conditions of the test (normality of the population and random sampling) are satisfied.

E11. All three conditions are met for the tests in parts a and b: random sample, nearly normal sampling distribution of the sample mean, and σ known.

a. If the students are assuming the true mean is at least $650, then the real question is "Could a population with a mean of 650 have produced the observed sample mean as a likely outcome?" If we reject this claim, we would certainly reject a claim of any value larger than 650. The logical alternate to this claim is the one-sided alternate hypothesis that the true mean is less than 650. Thus, using symbols, we have

$H_0: \mu = 650$

$H_a: \mu < 650$

where μ is the mean monthly rent advertised for all two-bedroom apartments in Gainesville.

The z-statistic is

$$z = \frac{\bar{x} - \mu_0}{\sigma/\sqrt{n}} = \frac{575 - 650}{165/\sqrt{25}} \approx -2.27$$

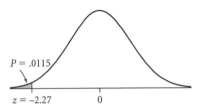

The P-value (one-sided) is about .0115 (calculator) or .0116 (Table A), and this gives sufficient evidence to reject the claim that the population mean is 650 in favor of the alternative that it is less than 650. Therefore, there is sufficient evidence against the student's claim that it is 650 or larger.

b. The newspaper is looking for a change in either direction so the hypotheses, using symbols, are

$H_0: \mu = 500$

$H_a: \mu \neq 500$

The z-statistic is

$$z = \frac{\bar{x} - \mu_0}{\sigma/\sqrt{n}} = \frac{575 - 500}{165/\sqrt{25}} \approx 2.27$$

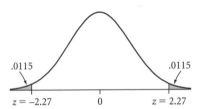

The P-value is, therefore, exactly twice the one for part a, or about .0230. This is sufficient evidence to reject the hypothesis that the population mean remains at $500.

c. Yes; the hypothesized value of 500 does not lie inside the 95% confidence interval for this year's mean rent, which is approximately (510, 640). Remind students that two-sided tests are equivalent to confidence intervals, but one-sided tests are not.

E12. The answer depends on the sample size, n. The key to making the inference procedures work is that the sampling distribution of the sample mean $\bar{x}$ must be approximately normal. If n is very large, that will be true even if the population is highly skewed. ("Large" here remains undefined because it depends on how skewed the population is, but n should be at least 40.) If n is small, the distribution of the sample mean will be skewed and the inferential technique will not work correctly. "Not working" means that the real P-value might be quite different from the calculated P-value.

E13. **Check conditions.** The data are stated to be a random sample from a normal population with $\sigma = 0.06$.

State your hypotheses.
H_0: $\mu = 16$
H_a: $\mu \neq 16$
where μ is the true mean number of ounces of water filled by the machine today.

Compute the test statistic and draw a sketch.
The z-statistic is

$$z = \frac{\bar{x} - \mu_0}{\sigma/\sqrt{n}} = \frac{15.974 - 16}{0.06/\sqrt{10}} = -1.37$$

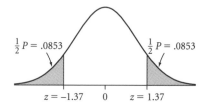

Write a conclusion in context. The (two-sided) P-value is .1706, which is fairly small but not small enough for a recommendation to adjust the machine. Remember, one of the problems of maintaining quality in manufacturing is that machines are adjusted too often, so you might want to be a little conservative in rejecting the null hypothesis. It looks like Jack and Jill should wait before adjusting this machine.

E14. **a.** The population of heights is known to be approximately normal, and the sample was randomly selected, but we must use 2 as an estimate of σ, the standard deviation of the heights of the population of female runners.
H_0: $\mu = 65$
H_a: $\mu \neq 65$
where μ is the mean height of all female runners. The test statistic is

$$z = \frac{\bar{x} - \mu_0}{\sigma/\sqrt{n}} = \frac{66 - 65}{2/\sqrt{36}} = 3$$

which is larger than the critical value for a 5% level test. We would reject the hypothesis that the mean height for all female runners is 65 inches.

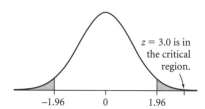

b. There are two different populations and so two "true" means. The first is the population of the heights of all women, and the second is the population of the heights of all female runners. When the problem says that the mean is 65, it is referring to the first population, that of the heights of all women. The mean of the heights of all female runners is unknown. Thus, when the null hypothesis is written as $\mu = 65$, it is saying that the mean height, μ, of all female runners is equal to the mean height, 65 inches, of all women. If this hypothesis is rejected, we are rejecting that the mean height of all female runners is 65 inches, not that the mean height of all women is 65 inches.

Reasonably Likely Outcomes for Sample Means
for $n = 25$

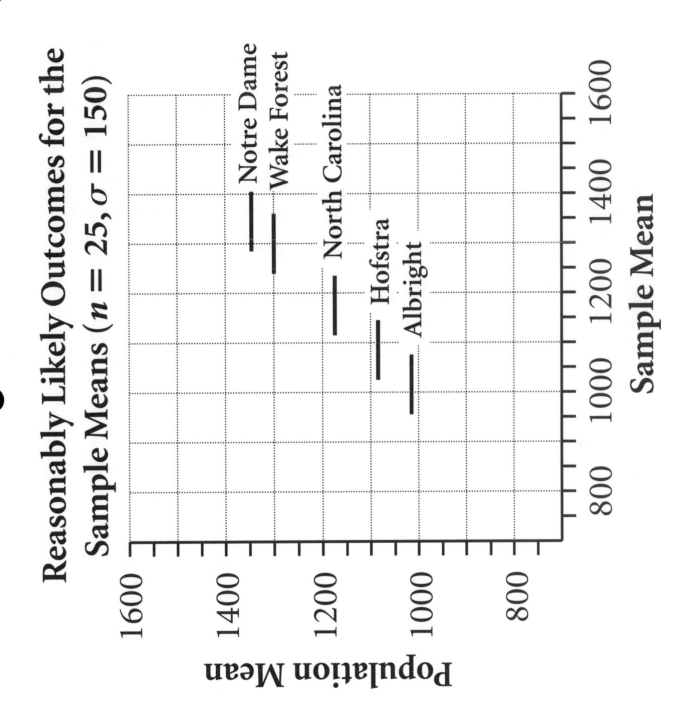

9.3 When You Estimate σ: The *t*-Distribution

Objectives

- to understand that the capture rate for a confidence interval is less than advertised when the population standard deviation is estimated by the sample standard deviation unless you adjust by using *t* instead of *z*
- to construct a confidence interval for a mean using the sample standard deviation and *t*-procedures
- to perform the four steps in a significance test for a mean using the sample standard deviation and *t*-procedures
- to deepen the understanding of these terms in the context of inference for means: confidence interval, capture rate, statistical significance, null hypothesis and alternate hypothesis, test statistic, level of significance, and one-tailed test and two-tailed test
- to compute and interpret a *P*-value in testing a mean

Important Terms and Concepts

- using *s* as an estimate of σ
- *t*-procedures
- *t*-table
- degrees of freedom
- *t*-distribution

Class Time

Four days

Materials

None

Suggested Assignments

Classwork		
Essential	**Recommended**	**Optional**
Activity 9.2	D27	
D24–D26	P16, P21	
P14, P15, P17–P20		

Homework		
Essential	**Recommended**	**Optional**
E15–E17, E20	E18, E19	

Lesson Notes: The Effect of Estimating σ

The first person to realize that the intervals based on z must be adjusted when the population standard deviation is estimated from the sample was W. S. Gossett, a scientist working for the Guinness brewery in Dublin in the early 1900s. By making an assumption about the true form of the sampling distribution of the sample variance and by assuming that the sample mean and the sample variance are independent, Gossett was able to work out the form of the t-distribution and come up with a table of t-values, much the same as we have today. He checked the agreement between his theory and practice by collecting many small samples of data from known populations—and doing the calculations by hand! In other words, Gossett did simulation without the aid of technology. Gossett was supposed to keep his work private because his employer had strict rules on sharing trade secrets, so he published his early papers under the pen name Student. To this day his distribution is often called Student's t.

R. A. Fisher, one of the greatest scientists of the 20th century, was intrigued by Gossett's work and proceeded to work out the mathematical theory based on sampling from a normal distribution. Among other things, Fisher proved that Gossett's assumptions were correct, but he could not make much improvement on Gossett's tables.

A blackline master of the t-table is provided at the end of this section.

Activity 9.2: The Effect of Estimating the Standard Deviation

1–2. Answers will depend on the student's random sample.

3. 95%; no

4–5. Answers will depend on the student's random samples.

6. Typically, out of 100 runs of this simulation, you will see about 9 or 10 intervals that do not overlap 511. These should be about evenly divided between those that miss on the low side and those that miss on the high side. Because the capture rate should be about 95%, these intervals are too short. The proper adjustment for using s instead of σ will make the intervals a little longer than these intervals based on $z = 1.96$.

7. See E18 on page 516 of the student text for a typical histogram of sample standard deviations. Here, the shape is slightly skewed right, the mean value of s is 105.80, and the standard deviation is 36.33. The mean value of s is smaller than σ. The sample standard deviation s is smaller than σ in about 240 of the 405 samples and larger in about 165.

Discussion

D24. **a.** Although the average value of s in repeated sampling is close to σ, the sampling distribution of s is skewed toward the larger values. Thus, the chance is greater than .5 that an observed sample standard deviation will be smaller than σ. This causes the confidence intervals to be too short more than half the time and the capture rate to be smaller than the advertised value.

b. The larger sample size will give capture rates closer to 95% because the skewness of the sampling distribution of s decreases as n increases. (See the paragraph above D24 on page 504 of the student text.)

D25. If an interval's true capture rate is lower than what you want it to be, you can get a higher capture rate by using a wider interval; if the true capture rate is higher than you want it to be, you can get a lower capture rate by using an interval that is narrower.

Note: For example, when $n = 1000$, the value needed to replace z^* to produce a 95% confidence interval is 1.962, just a bit larger than 1.96. But the value needed when $n = 2$ is 12.71!

Practice

P14. **a.** The interval is (4.32, 5.68).

b. When σ is estimated by s, the centers of the intervals are the same as if you were using σ. However, the width will vary directly with s rather than being constant. Because s is smaller than σ more often than it is larger, the confidence interval will be too short more often than it is too long. This makes the capture rate smaller than the advertised value.

Lesson Notes: Confidence Intervals Based on *t*

You should reinforce the fact that confidence intervals based on *t* will be a little wider than confidence intervals based on *z*, all else being equal. The adjustment gets smaller, though, as *n* gets larger. In fact, as *n* tends to infinity, the *t*-distribution tends toward the *z*-distribution (standard normal distribution).

Discussion

D26. a. By comparing directly with each of the other two, you can see that the widest interval is for $n = 4$, $s = 10$, confidence level 99%. It has a higher confidence level than the first interval and a higher confidence level, smaller sample size, and larger standard deviation than the second.

b. The confidence levels are all equal, so the comparison depends on *n* and *s*. The third interval ($n = 5$, $s = 10$) is narrower than both the other two, so it remains to compare $n = 3$, $s = 10$ (with $t^* = 4.303$, $t^* \cdot s/\sqrt{n} = 24.84$) and $n = 4$, $s = 12$ (with $t^* = 3.182$, $t^* \cdot s/\sqrt{n} = 19.09$). The widest interval is the first one, ($n = 3$, $s = 10$).

c. Here you can see that the first will be narrower than the second because the first has a smaller confidence level. Also, the second will be narrower than the third because the second has a smaller value of *s*.

90%, $n = 10$, $s = 5$: $t^* = 1.833$, $t^* \cdot s/\sqrt{n} = 2.90$
95%, $n = 10$, $s = 5$: $t^* = 2.262$, $t^* \cdot s/\sqrt{n} = 3.58$
95%, $n = 10$, $s = 10$: $t^* = 2.262$, $t^* \cdot s/\sqrt{n} = 7.15$

The third interval is the widest.

D27. a. With respective degrees of freedom of 5, 5, 5, and 4, the four 95% confidence intervals are

$$8.61 < \mu(special) < 11.64$$
$$9.39 < \mu(exercise) < 13.36$$
$$10.00 < \mu(weekly) < 13.25$$
$$11.16 < \mu(final) < 13.54$$

Note: See Lesson Notes at the beginning of Section 9.5 for an explanation of this notation.

b. It looks as though there is good evidence to say that $\mu(special)$ is smaller than $\mu(final)$, but there is so much overlap among the other intervals that it is impossible to order the means in any rigorous way from this information. This is a good opportunity to begin making a case for comparison of means, which will come in Section 9.5.

Practice

P15. a. 2.262 **b.** 2.447 **c.** 3.106
d. 2.920 **e.** 63.66 **f.** 5.841

P16. a. $n = 4$, $\bar{x} = 27$, $s = 12$: $t^* = 3.182$, $t^* \cdot s/\sqrt{n} = 19.092$
The interval is 27 ± 19.092, or 7.908 to 46.092. The calculator gives (7.905, 46.095). We are 95% confident that the unknown mean is in the interval 7.908 to 46.092.

b. $n = 9$, $\bar{x} = 6$, $s = 3$: $t^* = 2.306$, $t^* \cdot s/\sqrt{n} = 2.306$
The interval is 6 ± 2.306, or 3.694 to 8.306. The calculator gives the same values. We are 95% confident that the unknown mean is in the interval 3.694 to 8.306.

c. $n = 16$, $\bar{x} = 9$, $s = 48$: $t^* = 2.131$, $t^* \cdot s/\sqrt{n} = 25.572$
The interval is 9 ± 25.572, or -16.572 to 34.572. The calculator gives (-16.58, 34.577). We are 95% confident that the unknown mean is in the interval -16.572 to 34.572.

P17. The confidence interval is

$$\bar{x} \pm t^* \cdot \frac{s}{\sqrt{n}} \text{ or } 5.0 \pm 2.262 \cdot \frac{1.1}{\sqrt{10}}$$

which yields an interval of (4.21, 5.79). This is just a little longer than the *z*-interval constructed in P14, which was (4.32, 5.68). We are 95% confident that the mean level of aldrin in the Wolf River downstream from the toxic waste site is in the interval 4.21 to 5.79.

Lesson Notes: Fixed-Level Testing

Fixed-level testing here works just as it did in the previous section, except that critical values are found from the *t*-table rather than from the *z*-table and will be a little larger for the same level of significance.

Practice

P18. The hypotheses, in symbols, are

H_0: $\mu = 4$

H_a: $\mu \neq 4$

where μ is the mean Aldrin level downstream. With the sample mean and standard deviation as given in P17, the test statistic is

$$t = \frac{\bar{x} - \mu_0}{s/\sqrt{n}} = \frac{5.0 - 4.0}{1.1/\sqrt{10}} \approx 2.875$$

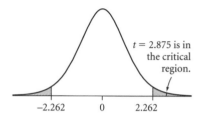

t = 2.875 is in the critical region.

−2.262   0   2.262

For $\alpha = .05$, the critical *t*-value for 9 degrees of freedom is $t^* = 2.262$. Because the observed *t*-value exceeds the critical value, we have sufficient evidence to reject the null hypothesis. The data suggest that the mean aldrin level differs from 4 nanograms.

Lesson Notes: P-Values

Again, a *P*-value here has the same definition as in the previous section, except that it is calculated from the *t*-distribution rather than the *z*-distribution. If you are using technology you can get the exact *P*-value for a test. If you are using a table, you can only approximate a *P*-value because of the limited entries in the table.

Practice

P19. The test statistic ($t = 2.875$) and the degrees of freedom ($df = 9$) are the same as in P18. The *P*-values shown in intervals are taken from a table; the single, more exact, values are taken from a graphing calculator.

  a. $.01 < P\text{-value} < .02$; *P*-value = .0183

  b. $.990 < P\text{-value} < .995$; *P*-value = .9908

  c. $.005 < P\text{-value} < .01$; *P*-value = .0092

P20. The two probabilities are the same: both are equal to .05.

P21. A: The test of H_0 vs. H_a: $\mu > 0$ has the greatest probability of rejecting H_0.

Exercises

E15. **a.** The confidence interval can be constructed automatically from a computer or graphing calculator, but to show the steps you will need a *t*-value with 45 degrees of freedom, which does not appear on the table. When this situation arises use the t^* for the next smallest tabled degrees of freedom, which would be 1.684 in this case. (For a 90% confidence interval and 45 degrees of freedom, $t^* = 1.680$, very close to 1.684.) The interval is

$$\bar{x} \pm t^* \cdot \frac{s}{\sqrt{n}} \text{ or } 10.93 \pm 1.684 \cdot \frac{6.22}{\sqrt{46}}$$

or (9.39, 12.47). Any population mean in this interval could have produced the observed sample mean as a reasonably likely outcome. Note that you are estimating the mean study hours for the population of females taking this course. This would not be a valid estimate of the mean for all females in the university.

    Also, there is one extremely large value in each of the subgroups, and this value may cause a problem with the techniques being used here. To see how much this outlier affects the confidence interval, you could re-analyze the data with this point taken out. The resulting interval is (9.11, 11.91), so the effect of the outlier is marginal. This is due to the large sample size.

  b. This calls for a one-sided test.

H_0: $\mu = 11$, where μ denotes the mean weekly study time for males

H_a: $\mu < 11$

The *t*-statistic is

$$t = \frac{\bar{x} - \mu_0}{s/\sqrt{n}} = \frac{8.20 - 11.0}{5.94/\sqrt{15}} \approx -1.826$$

and the one-sided *P*-value is .045. This is small, so there is sufficient evidence to say that, on the average, the males study less than the females.

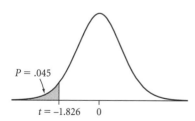

P = .045

t = −1.826   0

Here, removing the outlier among the males reduces the sample mean to 7, the t-statistic to -3.894, and the P-value to .001. Now the evidence is much stronger in favor of the males having a significantly lower mean for weekly study hours.

c. For the overall sample of 61 students,

$$\bar{x} = \frac{46(10.93) + 15(8.20)}{61} \approx 10.26$$

You could reconstruct a data file from the stemplots and calculate a sample standard deviation for the combined sample, giving (8.67, 11.86), but this is too much work. Note that both of the sample standard deviations for the subgroups are close to 6.0 and the females have the larger sample size. Thus, the standard deviation of the combined sample is going to be very close to the one for females. In fact, you can use 6.2 as a good approximation. The resulting 95% confidence interval is

$$\bar{x} \pm t^* \cdot \frac{s}{\sqrt{n}} \text{ or } 10.26 \pm 2.00 \cdot \frac{6.20}{\sqrt{61}}$$

or (8.67, 11.85). We are 95% confident that the mean number of hours studied per week for all students in this course is between 8.67 and 11.85.

E16. **a.** With 95% confidence, $17{,}219.66 < \mu < 22{,}238.34$ for all models of sedans.

b. With 90% confidence, $4024.7 < \mu < 4369.7$ for all models of SUVs.

c. With 98% confidence, $25.86 < \mu < 32.13$ for all models of sedans.

With 98% confidence, $18.68 < \mu < 20.52$ for all models of SUVs.

d. The question of "least informative" can have a variety of answers that depend on the subjective judgments of the students. One way of looking at this is to compare the length of the confidence interval to the center (which is the sample mean). For that measure of "information," the first confidence interval (price of sedans) is least informative. The interval length is about 25% of the value of the mean, which implies that you are not estimating mean price very precisely. Students may come up with other intriguing definitions of "information."

The basic way to increase information is to increase the sample size. Students may

also mention stratifying by size or by manufacturer.

E17. **a.** Yes.
H_0: $\mu = 3.04$
H_a: $\mu \neq 3.04$
where μ is the mean hot dog price at all 31 stadiums. With $n = 3$, $\bar{x} = 3.25$, and $s \approx 0.433$, the t-statistic is $t = 0.84$ and the P-value is .4893 for a two-sided alternate ($\mu \neq 3.04$). The population mean of 3.04 is consistent with these data. That is, there is not sufficient evidence to reject \$3.04 as a plausible mean price of hot dogs. This all assumes that the sample comes from a population that is approximately normal.

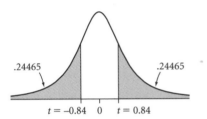

b. The sample data and t-statistic are the same as in part a, but now the alternate should be one-sided ($\mu > 3.04$). The P-value for this alternate is .2447, half the value given in part a. Your friend's claim is not supported by these data.

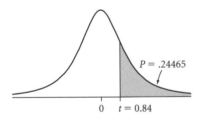

c. No. Ten teams sampled out of 31 violates the guideline that the sample size must be at most 10% of the population size. Such a large sampling fraction would cause the standard error of the sample mean to be much smaller than the standard error $s/\sqrt{n}$ used in the t-procedures of this chapter.

E18. **a.** At first glance, the shape looks to be approximately normal, but closer inspection will reveal slight skewness toward the large values. Both the mean and the median of the distribution are slightly below the population standard deviation of 112, so s tends to underestimate σ.

b. Because the median is smaller than 112, you know that more than half of the values of the sample standard deviation must be below 112. A rough count on the histogram shows that at least 240 of the 405 sample standard deviations fall below the population standard deviation of 112. Therefore, s is more often smaller than σ.

c. Because s tends to underestimate σ, the advertised 95% confidence intervals will be too short when s is used as an estimate of σ. This means the actual capture rate will be less than 95%.

E19. **a.** There are n deviations, and their sum is 0.

b. No. It gives you some indication of the center of the population, but no information at all about how spread out the values are.

c. The deviations sum to zero, $3 + (x_2 - \bar{x}) = 0$, so the second deviation is $(x_2 - \bar{x}) = -3$.

d. The deviations sum to zero, $3 + (-1) + (x_3 - \bar{x}) = 0$, so the third deviation is $(x_3 - \bar{x}) = -2$.

e. If you have the first $n - 1$ deviations, $(x_1 - \bar{x}), (x_2 - \bar{x}), \ldots, (x_{n-1} - \bar{x})$, you can solve for the last $(x_n - \bar{x})$ using the equation shown at the bottom of the page.

Only the first $n - 1$ deviations are independent. The last is redundant because you can always find it from the others using this equation.

f. The number of degrees of freedom is the number of independent deviations from your sample available for estimating the standard deviation of the population, σ. For the t-statistic, df is $n - 1$, because you only have $n - 1$ independent deviations to use to estimate σ.

E20. **a.** They are both mound-shaped and centered at about zero. The spread of A is less than that of B.

b. B is the simulated t-distribution. The respective formulas are

$$z = \frac{\bar{x} - 100}{20/\sqrt{4}} \text{ and } t = \frac{\bar{x} - 100}{s/\sqrt{4}}$$

Because s tends to be smaller than σ more often than it is larger, t will tend to be larger in absolute value than z.

Lesson 9.3, E19e

$$(x_1 - \bar{x}) + (x_2 - \bar{x}) + \cdots + (x_{n-1} - \bar{x}) + (x_n - \bar{x}) = 0$$

TABLE B   *t*-Distribution Critical Values

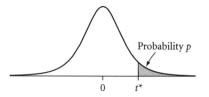

Table entry for *p* and *C* is the point *t** with probability *p* lying above it and confidence level *C* given by the probability of lying between –*t** and *t**.

Probability *p*

Tail Probability *p*

df	.25	.20	.15	.10	.05	.025	.02	.01	.005	.0025	.001	.0005
1	1.000	1.376	1.963	3.078	6.314	12.71	15.89	31.82	63.66	127.3	318.3	636.6
2	.816	1.061	1.386	1.886	2.920	4.303	4.849	6.965	9.925	14.09	22.33	31.60
3	.765	.978	1.250	1.638	2.353	3.182	3.482	4.541	5.841	7.453	10.21	12.92
4	.741	.941	1.190	1.533	2.132	2.776	2.999	3.747	4.604	5.598	7.173	8.610
5	.727	.920	1.156	1.476	2.015	2.571	2.757	3.365	4.032	4.773	5.893	6.869
6	.718	.906	1.134	1.440	1.943	2.447	2.612	3.143	3.707	4.317	5.208	5.959
7	.711	.896	1.119	1.415	1.895	2.365	2.517	2.998	3.499	4.029	4.785	5.408
8	.706	.889	1.108	1.397	1.860	2.306	2.449	2.896	3.355	3.833	4.501	5.041
9	.703	.883	1.100	1.383	1.833	2.262	2.398	2.821	3.250	3.690	4.297	4.781
10	.700	.879	1.093	1.372	1.812	2.228	2.359	2.764	3.169	3.581	4.144	4.587
11	.697	.876	1.088	1.363	1.796	2.201	2.328	2.718	3.106	3.497	4.025	4.437
12	.695	.873	1.083	1.356	1.782	2.179	2.303	2.681	3.055	3.428	3.930	4.318
13	.694	.870	1.079	1.350	1.771	2.160	2.282	2.650	3.012	3.372	3.852	4.221
14	.692	.868	1.076	1.345	1.761	2.145	2.264	2.624	2.977	3.326	3.787	4.140
15	.691	.866	1.074	1.341	1.753	2.131	2.249	2.602	2.947	3.286	3.733	4.073
16	.690	.865	1.071	1.337	1.746	2.120	2.235	2.583	2.921	3.252	3.686	4.015
17	.689	.863	1.069	1.333	1.740	2.110	2.224	2.567	2.898	3.222	3.646	3.965
18	.688	.862	1.067	1.330	1.734	2.101	2.214	2.552	2.878	3.197	3.611	3.922
19	.688	.861	1.066	1.328	1.729	2.093	2.205	2.539	2.861	3.174	3.579	3.883
20	.687	.860	1.064	1.325	1.725	2.086	2.197	2.528	2.845	3.153	3.552	3.850
21	.686	.859	1.063	1.323	1.721	2.080	2.189	2.518	2.831	3.135	3.527	3.819
22	.686	.858	1.061	1.321	1.717	2.074	2.183	2.508	2.819	3.119	3.505	3.792
23	.685	.858	1.060	1.319	1.714	2.069	2.177	2.500	2.807	3.104	3.485	3.768
24	.685	.857	1.059	1.318	1.711	2.064	2.172	2.492	2.797	3.091	3.467	3.745
25	.684	.856	1.058	1.316	1.708	2.060	2.167	2.485	2.787	3.078	3.450	3.725
26	.684	.856	1.058	1.315	1.706	2.056	2.162	2.479	2.779	3.067	3.435	3.707
27	.684	.855	1.057	1.314	1.703	2.052	2.150	2.473	2.771	3.057	3.421	3.690
28	.683	.855	1.056	1.313	1.701	2.048	2.154	2.467	2.763	3.047	3.408	3.674
29	.683	.854	1.055	1.311	1.699	2.045	2.150	2.462	2.756	3.038	3.396	3.659
30	.683	.854	1.055	1.310	1.697	2.042	2.147	2.457	2.750	3.030	3.385	3.646
40	.681	.851	1.050	1.303	1.684	2.021	2.123	2.423	2.704	2.971	3.307	3.551
50	.679	.849	1.047	1.295	1.676	2.009	2.109	2.403	2.678	2.937	3.261	3.496
60	.679	.848	1.045	1.296	1.671	2.000	2.099	2.390	2.660	2.915	3.232	3.460
80	.678	.846	1.043	1.292	1.664	1.990	2.088	2.374	2.639	2.887	3.195	3.416
100	.677	.845	1.042	1.290	1.660	1.984	2.081	2.364	2.626	2.871	3.174	3.390
1000	.675	.842	1.037	1.282	1.646	1.962	2.056	2.330	2.581	2.813	3.098	3.300
∞	.674	.841	1.036	1.282	1.645	1.960	2.054	2.326	2.576	2.807	3.091	3.291
	50%	60%	70%	80%	90%	95%	96%	98%	99%	99.5%	99.8%	99.9%

Confidence Level *C*

9.4 The Effect of Long Tails and Outliers

Objectives

- to understand what happens to the capture rate for a confidence interval when the population is not normally distributed
- to consider transformations of the data before constructing a confidence interval or performing a test of significance for a mean
- to investigate a rule for when to use the t-procedures for means and when to be careful
- to deepen the understanding of these terms: confidence interval, capture rate, statistical significance, null hypothesis and alternate hypothesis, test statistic, level of significance, P-value, and one-tailed test and two-tailed test in the context of inference for means

Important Terms and Concepts

- transforming to normality using logs and reciprocals
- robustness of t-procedures
- 15/40 rule for using t-procedures

Class Time

Three days

Materials

None

Suggested Assignments

Classwork		
Essential	**Recommended**	**Optional**
Activity 9.3	D28	
D29–D30		
P22		

Homework		
Essential	**Recommended**	**Optional**
E21, E22, E25	E24	E23

Lesson Notes: Departures from Normality

The main idea of this section is that the *t*-procedures are fairly robust—that is, they work well for modest departures from normality. However, they do not work well when the population is highly skewed unless the sample sizes are large or the data are transformed.

There is a further problem with skewed data. If you take repeated random samples from a population that is skewed to the right, you will find that $\bar{x}$ and s are positively correlated. If the population is skewed left, $\bar{x}$ and s are negatively correlated. However, for a normal distribution, $\bar{x}$ and s are uncorrelated.

Discussion

D28. The capture rate will be substantially less than 95%. Students have seen that replacing σ with s lowers the capture rate, and they may speculate that the same thing happens for skewed distributions. That's true, and that is why there is a whole section on this! Here is an extreme example to show why the capture rate will be too small. Suppose you have a population with 9999 values all very close to 1 and one value of 1,000,000. Then $\mu \approx 101$. Random samples of size, say, 10 will almost always consist of 10 values close to 1 and so have a small s, yielding a confidence interval that is too short. In addition, the observed sample means almost always will be approximately equal to 1, much smaller than the population mean. Thus, the confidence intervals almost always will be centered too far to the left, in addition to being too short.

D29. Using a longer confidence is the more cautious procedure. Suppose, for example, that μ represents the mean daily yield of a production process and you know what the true value of this mean was for yesterday's production. A sample from today's production produces a 90% confidence interval that lies entirely below yesterday's mean value. That might set all sorts of checks into motion to find out why production is "down" when, in reality, it is just that the interval was too short. When big decisions are at stake, the analysis should tend toward the cautious side.

Activity 9.3: The Effect of Skewness on Confidence Intervals

1. Number the species from 01 to 68 and use a table of random digits to select five different pairs of digits from 01 to 68. These animals are your sample.

2. Students should use $t^* = 2.776$ in constructing the 95% confidence intervals based on samples of size 5.

3–4. Confidence intervals will vary depending on the samples selected.

5–6. The next plot shows the results of a simulation involving 50 random samples of size 5 each from the brain weight data. For each sample, an advertised 95% confidence interval was constructed, using the method of Section 9.3 based on the *t*-distribution. It turned out that 18 intervals did not capture the population mean of 394.49 grams, and all missed on the low side. Thus, the observed capture rate is only $\frac{32}{50}$ or 64% rather than 95%!

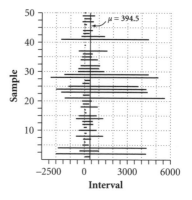

Note: If you repeat this procedure on the logarithms of the brain weights, the confidence intervals look like those in the next plot. Here the population mean of the natural logs of the brain weights is 2.977 grams, and the observed capture rate from the simulation is $\frac{46}{50}$ or 92%.

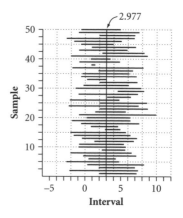

Lesson Notes: The 15/40 Rule

Although the 15/40 rule is a handy guideline, it is difficult to judge the shape of a population by looking at a small sample. Students should be advised to think carefully about the nature of the population that underlies each data set they encounter. Some populations (the maximum height of a river, for example) are naturally skewed. Others (the proportion of active ingredient in a medication) can not be terribly skewed because their possible values are constrained. The following Discussion and Practice questions attempt to get students thinking in this direction.

Discussion

D30. a. This is a small sample from a population that may be strongly skewed toward the larger values. The data must be studied carefully for skewness and outliers. You may want to remove the risk of outliers in the sample by confining the sampling (and the results) to certain sections of the city that do not have exorbitantly priced houses. A transformation may take care of the skewness.

b. This is now a large sample from a population that may be strongly skewed toward the larger values. Now you need not be so concerned about skewness, but you should still look for outliers that might affect the results.

c. The population of SAT scores is generally quite normal in shape, so there is little cause for concern here. Methods based on normality should work fine.

d. Waiting times are notoriously skewed. A typical distribution of data of this type would show many small to moderate times, but a few very long ones. With a medium-sized sample, a transformation would be necessary to bring the data into the normal fold.

Practice

P22. a. III. Here is a dot plot of 16 outcomes for the activity of flipping a penny until the first head occurs. Plots will vary, but they should all be skewed toward the larger values. These

data must be transformed before using any of the methods of this chapter.

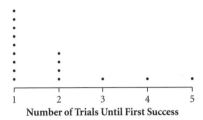

b. I. The data were collected separately for men and women and should be analyzed that way. The boxplots that follow show reasonable symmetry and no outliers, although not much can be inferred about the shape of the population from such small samples. On thinking about these populations, students may come to the conclusion that normal body temperatures can not vary a great deal, so there can not be strong skewness in the population distribution. Methods based on t are probably appropriate here.

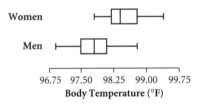

c. IV. These data were analyzed in E15. There is an outlier in each data set, but only moderate skewness. For these sample sizes you should analyze the data with and without the outliers, but a transformation is not needed.

d. III. There is some evidence of skewness in this very small sample, as seen in the next dot plot. However, if you think about SUV prices, you will realize that the population is skewed toward the larger values. If a price of an SUV is going to be far away from the center, then it almost has to be on the large side. You can not buy a cheap SUV, but you can buy a very expensive one!

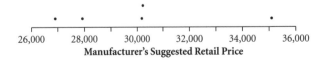

Exercises

E21. **a.** The sample is random; however, the mercury levels are skewed toward the higher values and need a transformation. The logarithm does a good job of bringing the distribution back to approximate normality.

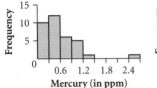 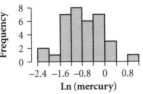

b. The boundary of 0.5 ppm is not stated to be a mean (it could be a median or even a 90th percentile), but it will be considered a mean for this analysis. On the natural log scale this boundary value becomes $\ln(0.5) \approx -0.69$.

For testing $H_0: \mu = -0.69$ versus $H_a: \mu > -0.69$ where μ is the mean mercury content of all Maine lakes.

The test statistic is about

$$t = \frac{\bar{x} - \mu_0}{s/\sqrt{n}} = \frac{-0.792 - (-.69)}{0.693/\sqrt{35}} \approx -.87$$

Depending on how much rounding is done, the *P*-value is about .80 or .81. There is certainly no evidence to suggest that the population mean mercury level, measured on the log scale, exceeds -0.69.

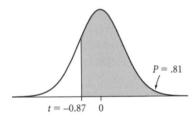

Note that you also could use a confidence interval approach. The 95% confidence interval for the population mean on the log scale (using the value for 30 degrees of freedom from Table B on page 701 in the student text) is given by

$$\bar{x} \pm t^* \cdot \frac{s}{\sqrt{n}} = -0.792 \pm (2.042) \cdot \frac{0.693}{\sqrt{35}}$$

$$= -0.792 \pm 0.239$$

or $(-1.03, -0.55)$. This interval includes $\ln(0.5) \approx -0.69$ well within its boundaries, so 0.5 is a plausible value for the population mean mercury level.

Does Maine deserve the headline? If health advisories are not issued until there is conclusive evidence that the average level of mercury exceeds 0.5, then perhaps an advisory is not justified, as there is no evidence to reject 0.5 (and even lower levels) as a plausible mean. On the other hand, because 0.5 ppm is a plausible value for the mean mercury level of Maine lakes and this level is considered contaminated, the conservative approach is to declare the lakes contaminated and the headline is justified.

E22. **a.** Yes. The data from the sample are slightly skewed toward the larger values, but the sample size is so large that the sampling distribution of the sample mean would not reflect this skewness; the sampling distribution would appear nearly normal.

b. The 90% confidence interval is

$$\bar{x} \pm t^* \cdot \frac{s}{\sqrt{n}} = 2.32 \pm 1.660 \cdot \frac{1.23}{\sqrt{393}}$$

$$= 2.32 \pm 0.103$$

yielding an interval of (2.22, 2.42) for the mean loss for Insurer A.

c. No for $n = 40$, but yes for $n = 4$. For this amount of skewness, sample sizes of 40 would probably produce nearly normal sampling distributions for the sample means. However, for samples of size 4, a transformation would be in order.

E23. **a.** Here are the averages:

		Report	
		Verbal	Visual
Task	Verbal	12.85	13.69
	Visual	9.01	18.17

One way to compare times is to hold the task fixed and look at the effect of the reporting method. For the verbal task (row 1), the verbal reporting method took less time, on average (12.85 seconds), than visual reporting (13.69 seconds). Taken at face value, this result seems at odds with the theory.

However, common sense suggests that visual reporting is inherently more time-consuming than verbal reporting, no doubt in part because it is much less familiar. The column averages (about 11 seconds for verbal reporting, 16 seconds for visual reporting) bear this out.

Holding the report method fixed in order to compare times for the two kinds of tasks makes the pattern a little easier to see:

Report	Task	
	Same Kind	Opposite
Verbal	12.85	9.01
Visual	18.17	13.69

For both kinds of reporting methods, average times were slower when the task was of the same kind, faster when opposite.

b. Boxplots of the response times show skewed distributions with a few outliers. However, these times are not so much exceptions as they are part of the overall pattern of strong skewness toward high values. (Such a pattern is quite common for waiting times, for example.)

Scatterplots also show the skewness. This is easiest to see in a plot of visual versus verbal tasks with verbal report. The points form a wedge, with crowding in the lower left (both times low) and scatter that increases as you move up or to the right.

These patterns strongly suggest transforming, and a common choice for times is the reciprocal transformation, from time (how long?) to $\frac{1}{\text{time}}$ (how frequently?).

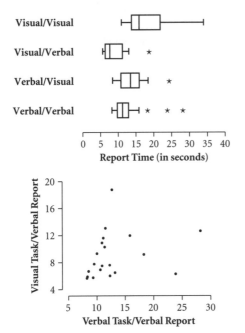

c. The 90% confidence intervals for the untransformed data are given in this Minitab printout:

```
Variable   N    Mean    StDev   SE Mean    90.0 % C.I.
Vis/Vis    20   18.17   6.12    1.37      (15.80, 20.54)
Vis/Ver    20   9.012   3.371   0.754     (7.708, 10.316)
Ver/Vis    20   13.688  3.979   0.890     (12.150, 15.227)
Ver/Ver    20   12.85   5.17    1.16      (10.85, 14.85)
```

For example, the first interval is interpreted as: We are 90% confident that if all subjects were given the visual task with a visual report, the mean reporting time would be in the interval 15.80 to 20.54 seconds.

The 90% confidence intervals for the data first transformed by taking reciprocals are

```
Variable    N    Mean     StDev   SE Mean     90.0 % C.I.
1/VisVis    20   0.06058  0.01831  0.00409   (0.05350, 0.06766)
1/VisVer    20   0.12365  0.03787  0.00847   (0.10900, 0.13830)
1/VerVis    20   0.07890  0.02238  0.00501   (0.07025, 0.08756)
1/VerVer    20   0.08630  0.02378  0.00532   (0.07710, 0.09549)
```

For example, the first interval is interpreted as: We are 90% confident that if all subjects were given the visual task with a visual report, the mean number of tasks completed in one second would be in the interval (0.05350, 0.06766).

From part b, we know that we should have more faith in the confidence intervals constructed using the reciprocals of the times.

In Fathom, you can calculate the means, standard deviations, and standard errors with a summary table. You can calculate the confidence intervals with an estimate (**Analyze | Estimate Parameters**). The summary table and an estimate for the 90% confidence interval of the untransformed visual task/visual report data are at the bottom of the next page. (This estimate is in unverbose mode—deselect **Verbose** in the Analyze menu.)

E24. a. The 68 original brain weights have mean 394.49 and standard deviation 1207, so a 95% confidence interval for the mean brain weight of all species from which we assume these are a random sample is (102.3, 686.7). However, as you observed in Activity 9.3 (and as can be verified by the histogram at the top of the next page), the brain weights are highly skewed. Thus, you shouldn't have 95% confidence in this "95% confidence" interval.

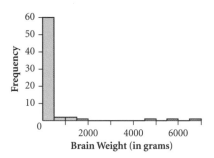

Brain Weight (in grams)

b. With the three extreme outliers removed, the resulting sample is still skewed and will not produce a reliable confidence interval. The confidence interval from the *t*-procedure is (69.3, 229.4).

c. The interval in part b is much shorter than the one in part a and is shifted a long way to the left. Still, both intervals are unreliable because of the skewness of the data.

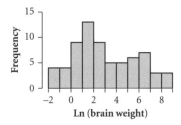

Ln (brain weight)

d. Using a natural log transformation on all 68 brain weights gives a distribution that is

much more normal looking, as seen in the histogram in part c. Now the interval produced by the *t*-procedure will be quite reliable. The mean is 2.977, and the standard deviation is 2.686, so the 95% confidence interval is (2.327, 3.627). We are 95% confident that the mean ln brain weight of all of the species from which this sample came is in this interval. If you transform the endpoints back to the original scale, you get the interval of 10.247 to 37.637 grams. Note how different this is from that in part a and part b.

Note: This interval estimates the mean of the natural log transformed data, so interpreting its meaning back on the original scale is a bit problematic. The problem arises from the fact that the mean of the logs of a set of values is not equal to the log of their mean, so exponentiating the mean of the log-transformed data does not give an estimate of the mean on the original scale. The log transformation does, however, preserve order, so the median of the log-transformed data is the log of the median of the nontransformed data. Once the data are transformed to a nearly symmetric distribution, the mean

---

Lesson 9.4, E23c

Mount Holyoke	Summary Table			
⬇ ➡	**VisVis**	**VisVer**	**VerVis**	**VerVer**
	18.173	9.012	13.6885	12.8495
	6.1247059	3.371393	3.979314	5.1658519
	1.3695259	0.75386638	0.88980166	1.1551196

S1 = mean ( )
S2 = sampleStdDev ( )
S3 = stdError ( )

Estimate of Mount Holyoke	Estimate Mean ▼
Attribute (continuous): VisVis	

Interval estimate for population mean of **VisVis**

Count:	20		
Mean:	18.173		
Std dev:	6.12471		
Std error:	1.36953		
Confidence level:	90 %		
Estimate:	18.173	+/-	2.36809
Range:	15.8049	to	20.5411

and median will be about equal, so a confidence interval estimate of the population mean is, in effect, estimating the population median as well. Thus, exponentiating the endpoints of the interval calculated above back to the original scale produces an interval estimate of the population median of (10.2, 37.6). (The sample median of the brain weights is 11.45.)

E25. **a.** The stemplots show marked skewness for the *P/H* data but near symmetry for the *H/P* data. These are small samples, however, so you should give some thought as to whether this would happen in general. Persons per housing unit could get very large for some types of housing units and in some locations, but it can not fall below one, and most units will have few people. So it seems that this variable will tend to have a skewed distribution. On the other hand, housing units per person will not go above one and can not fall below zero, so it is impossible for this variable to be highly skewed.

```
Stem-and-leaf of P/H
Leaf Unit = 0.10
  2   1  37
 (7)  2  0112234
  1   3
  1   4
  1   5
  1   6 8

Stem-and-leaf of H/P
Leaf Unit = 0.010
  1   1  4
  1   2
  1   3
 (7)  4  0235677
  2   5  7
  1   6
  1   7  1
```

b. The 95% confidence interval for the mean number of persons per housing unit by county, with 9 degrees of freedom, is

$$\bar{x} \pm t^* \cdot \frac{s}{\sqrt{n}} = 2.570 \pm (2.262) \cdot \frac{1.544}{\sqrt{10}}$$
$$= 2.570 \pm 1.104$$

or (1.465, 3.674). This interval contains the set of plausible values for the mean number of persons per housing unit in the population of Florida counties.

c. The 95% confidence interval for the mean number of housing units per person is

$$\bar{x} \pm t^* \cdot \frac{s}{\sqrt{n}} = 0.457 \pm (2.262) \cdot \frac{0.143}{\sqrt{10}}$$
$$= 0.457 \pm 0.102$$

or (0.355, 0.559). Thus, we are 95% confident that the true mean number of housing units per person by county is between 0.355 and 0.559.

d. The reciprocal of housing units per person is persons per housing unit, so another confidence interval for the mean of the latter is produced by taking the reciprocals of the endpoints of the interval in part c, which turns out to be (1.789, 2.817). This is quite different from the confidence interval in part b, showing once again that back-transforming the endpoints of the confidence interval for transformed data isn't the same as the confidence interval for the original values.

e. Because of the skewness in the data on persons per housing unit, the *t*-procedures will work better on the data for housing units per person. Thus, the answers to parts c and d are more reliable than that for part b.

9.5 Inference for the Difference Between Two Means

Objectives

- to understand the concepts of a confidence interval and a test of significance in the context of comparing two population means
- to construct a confidence interval for the difference between two means using the sample standard deviations and t-procedures
- to perform the four steps in a significance test for a difference between two means using the sample standard deviations and t-procedures
- to deepen the understanding of the following terms in the context of comparing means: confidence interval, capture rate, statistical significance, null hypothesis and alternate hypothesis, test statistic, level of significance, P-value, and one-tailed test and two-tailed test

Important Terms and Concepts

- random assignment of treatments to subjects
- independent random samples
- pooling sample variances versus unpooled t-procedures

Class Time

Five days

Materials

None

Suggested Assignments

Classwork		
Essential	**Recommended**	**Optional**
Activity 9.4	D32	D31, D33, D35, D37
D34, D36		P25
P23, P24, P26, P27		

Homework		
Essential	**Recommended**	**Optional**
E26, E27, E30	E29	E28, E31, E32

Lesson Notes: The Strength of Evidence

A note about notation: Statisticians use two slightly different notations for, say, the mean concentration of Aldrin at the bottom of the river. One notation uses parentheses (see the Data Desk printout at the top of page 540 in the student text), and the other uses subscript (see the null hypothesis at the top of page 539 in the student text):

$$\mu(bottom)$$

$$\mu_{bottom}$$

Because students may see either one of these, we have used both in the student text and here in the Instructor's Guide.

Activity 9.4 The Strength of Evidence

1. The hypothetical data sets differ from the real one in terms of the distance between centers, the spreads, and the sample sizes. Other things being equal, the evidence of a difference is stronger (1) if the distance between centers is greater, (2) if the spreads are smaller, and (3) if the sample sizes are larger.

Hypothetical data set 1: The evidence here of a difference in the mean aldrin concentration at the bottom and at mid-depth is stronger than in the actual data. For the hypothetical data, the distributions are shifted farther apart, but otherwise are identical.

Hypothetical data set 2: The evidence here is stronger than in the actual data, because the spreads are smaller, while the sample sizes are the same and distance between centers is about the same.

Hypothetical data set 3: The evidence here is weaker than in the actual data because the spreads are greater, while the sample sizes are the same and the distance between centers is about the same.

Hypothetical data set 4: The evidence is stronger in the hypothetical data because the sample sizes are larger than in the actual data. The hypothetical data set was created by repeating each value from the actual data a second time, so the means are un- changed and the standard deviations are virtually unchanged.

Hypothetical data set 5: The evidence here is weaker than in the actual data because the sample sizes are smaller and the spreads are somewhat greater.

Hypothetical data set 6: The evidence of a difference here is exactly the same as in the actual data: Both distributions have been shifted up by one unit, but the shapes, spreads, sample sizes, and difference between centers are all unchanged.

Hypothetical data set 7: Although the sample sizes and distribution shapes are the same as in the actual data, the means are closer together, so the evidence here is weaker.

2. The strength of evidence that two groups differ in their means depends on

- the distance between the group means (greater distances provide stronger evidence)
- the spreads of the distributions (smaller spreads provide stronger evidence)
- the sizes of the samples (larger samples provide stronger evidence)

Lesson Notes: Confidence Intervals When Shapes Are Normal and σ_1 and σ_2 Are Known

Discussion

D31. The standard deviations given are for the entire populations in a previous year. It's true that they are only approximations to the current population standard deviations, but they probably are quite close. Further, sample size calculations are rough approximations anyway, so we might as well use the simpler normal distribution in the approximation process.

D32. For the allocation of 150 data points to the region with the larger amount of variation, the margin of error becomes

$$z^* \cdot \sqrt{\frac{\sigma_1^2}{n_1} + \frac{\sigma_2^2}{n_2}} = 2\sqrt{\frac{271^2}{150} + \frac{79^2}{50}} = 49.6$$

which is smaller than the margin of error of 56 for the equal sample size allocation. As you can discern from the formula, it is better to allocate a larger sample size to the more variable population. See the note to the solution for D33.

D33. Let the common variance be σ^2. You want to find the value of n_1 that minimizes

$$z^* \cdot \sqrt{\frac{\sigma^2}{n_1} + \frac{\sigma^2}{n - n_1}}$$

Because z^* is a constant and the square of a function is increasing, this is equivalent to minimizing

$$\frac{\sigma^2}{n_1} + \frac{\sigma^2}{n - n_1} = \frac{\sigma^2 n}{n_1(n - n_1)}$$

Because σ^2 and n are constants, to minimize the fraction you need to maximize the denominator. Let

$$y = n_1(n - n_1) = n_1 n - n_1^2$$

This is a parabola that opens down, so its maximum occurs at the vertex

$$n_1 = \frac{-n}{2(-1)} = \frac{n}{2}$$

You should split the total sample equally between the two populations.

Alternatively, methods of calculus could be used to find the value of n_1 that minimizes the margin of error, but this is probably beyond the scope of most students.

A third alternative is to look for patterns in the margins of error for differing values of the sample sizes. For example, let $n = 200$. By letting n_1 vary you can produce the following table. The margin of error is minimized when the two sample sizes each equal 100.

n_1	n_2	Margin of Error
70	130	$z^*\sigma(.148)$
80	120	$z^*\sigma(.144)$
90	110	$z^*\sigma(.142)$
100	100	$z^*\sigma(.141)$
110	90	$z^*\sigma(.142)$
120	80	$z^*\sigma(.144)$
130	70	$z^*\sigma(.148)$

Note: When $\sigma_1 \neq \sigma_2$ the minimum margin of error is achieved by the following allocation:

$$n_1 = n \cdot \frac{\sigma_1}{\sigma_1 + \sigma_2} \quad \text{and} \quad n_2 = n \cdot \frac{\sigma_2}{\sigma_1 + \sigma_2}$$

The sample should be allocated to the populations in direct proportion to their standard deviations. This makes sense because the more variable population should have the larger sample size (see page 25).

Practice

P23. **a.** The z-interval for the difference in means is shown at the bottom of the page. Any difference in true means in this interval could have produced the sample result as a reasonably likely outcome. We are 95% confident that if we got the SAT score of all students in these two districts and computed the difference of the two mean scores, that difference would be in the interval -15.4 to 95.4.

This interval is appropriate as long as these are independently selected random samples (which the problem says that they are) and the populations of student scores are approximately normal in each school district. The former is a condition of the sampling process. The latter should be true if the school districts have reasonably large numbers of students. It is known that the distribution of all scores for any particular SAT math exam is approximately normal.

b. The confidence interval overlaps zero, which implies that the difference between the mean SAT scores of all students in these two districts could well be zero. That is, you could reasonably attribute the observed difference in the sample means (510 versus 470) to chance.

P24. The margin of error is to be

$$z^* \cdot \sqrt{\frac{\sigma_1^2}{n_1} + \frac{\sigma_2^2}{n_2}} = 2\sqrt{\frac{100^2}{n_1} + \frac{100^2}{n_1}} = 40$$

Solving for n_1,

$$2 \cdot \sqrt{\frac{2(100)^2}{n_1}} = 40$$

$$\sqrt{n_1} = \frac{2}{40}(100)\sqrt{2} \approx 7.07$$

$$n_1 = 50$$

(If students use $z^* = 1.96$, $n_1 = 49$.)

$$(\bar{x}_1 - \bar{x}_2) \pm z^* \cdot \sqrt{\frac{\sigma_1^2}{n_1} + \frac{\sigma_2^2}{n_2}} = (510 - 470) \pm 1.96 \cdot \sqrt{\frac{100^2}{25} + \frac{100^2}{25}} \text{ or } 40 \pm 55.4 \text{ or } (-15.4, 95.4)$$

You should take a random sample of 50 students from each district.

P25. If you allocate 100 counties to the South and 100 counties to the West, your estimated margin of error is

$$z^* \cdot \sqrt{\frac{\sigma_1^2}{n_1} + \frac{\sigma_2^2}{n_2}} = 1.96 \cdot \sqrt{\frac{244^2}{100} + \frac{837^2}{100}} \approx 170.88$$

If you allocate so that the sample sizes are proportional to the standard deviations, the sample sizes should be chosen so that

$$n_1 = n \cdot \frac{\sigma_1}{\sigma_1 + \sigma_2} = n \cdot \frac{244}{244 + 837} = n(.226)$$

$$n_2 = n \cdot \frac{\sigma_2}{\sigma_1 + \sigma_2} = n \cdot \frac{837}{244 + 837} = n(.774)$$

for a total sample size of 200, $n_1 = 45$ and $n_2 = 155$. The margin of error is then smaller:

$$z^* \cdot \sqrt{\frac{\sigma_1^2}{n_1} + \frac{\sigma_2^2}{n_2}} = 1.96 \cdot \sqrt{\frac{244^2}{45} + \frac{837^2}{155}}$$

$$\approx 149.8$$

This gives the optimum allocation of resources. (See the note for the solution to D33.)

Lesson Notes: Confidence Intervals for Differences When σ_1 and σ_2 Are Unknown

Determining the degrees of freedom associated with two-sample t-procedures is an issue that is troubling to many teachers and students (and many statisticians, too). In the one-sample case, the adjustment for not knowing the population variance was easy: Replace z by t and use $n - 1$ degrees of freedom in the analysis. However, when two population variances have to be estimated by two sample variances, the adjustment is not so simple. The reason it isn't simple is that the sampling distribution of the statistic

$$\frac{\bar{x}_1 - \bar{x}_2}{\sqrt{\frac{s_1^2}{n_1} + \frac{s_2^2}{n_2}}}$$

is not a z-distribution or a t-distribution. The exact distribution is unknown, and determining it is called the Behrens-Fisher problem. However, it is known that the distribution is reasonably close to a t-distribution if the right degrees of freedom are used.

Three approaches to finding the number of degrees of freedom are commonly mentioned in introductory textbooks: Use the smaller of the degrees of freedom in the two samples, pool the sample variances, and then add the degrees of freedom from the two samples, or use a rather complicated and mysterious formula to approximate the degrees of freedom.

The easy but conservative approach is to use the smaller of the two degrees of freedom from the individual samples, the minimum of $(n_1 - 1)$ and $(n_2 - 1)$. This procedure is too conservative and will fail to find real differences in means more often than it should, but it will not get you into trouble by finding too many significant differences where they do not exist. Overall, though, this is a poor procedure that should be used only as a rough approximation or a last resort when you do not have a calculator or computer available.

Pooling the sample variances by taking their weighted average is justified only in those cases for which it is known beyond a reasonable doubt that the population variances are equal. Generally, this can happen only in carefully designed experiments. When pooling is justified, the degrees of freedom are simply $(n_1 - 1) + (n_2 - 1) = n_1 + n_2 - 2$.

The "best" solution is to adjust the degrees of freedom according to the sample sizes and the sample variances using the formula given in D35 on page 536 of the student text. This is the approximation built into the TI-83 and many software packages. It may give fractional degrees of freedom, but that is not a problem for the computer.

Discussion

D34. *Note:* An efficient way to handle this discussion question is to split the work among eight groups of students.

a. Do computations. With 95% confidence, $-.31 < \mu(BA) - \mu(MA) < 2.29$, where $\mu(BA)$ stands for the true mean aldrin concentration on the bottom and $\mu(MA)$ stands for the true mean aldrin concentration at mid-depth in this part of the Wolf River.

Write a conclusion in context. The interval overlaps zero just slightly, so for the actual data there is insufficient evidence to say that the mean for the bottom measurements differs from the mean for the mid-depth measurements (but it is close).

b. Do computations. Here, $n_1 = 10$ and $n_2 = 10$. With 95% confidence, $.69 < \mu(B1) - \mu(M1) < 3.29$ where $\mu(B1)$ stands for the true mean aldrin concentration on the bottom and $\mu(M1)$ stands for the true mean aldrin concentration at mid-depth for the population from which the sample in hypothetical data set 1 was taken.

Write a conclusion in context. Because this interval does not contain zero, the evidence in favor of a difference between means is stronger than in the actual data.

c. *Do computations.* With 95% confidence, $-0.04 < \mu(B2) - \mu(M2) < 2.02$.

Write a conclusion in context. The confidence interval just barely contains 0, so the evidence here that the mean concentrations differ is stronger than in the actual data.

d. *Do computations.* With 95% confidence, $-1.45 < \mu(B3) - \mu(M3) < 2.03$.

Write a conclusion in context. The evidence here is weaker than in the actual data. It is quite plausible that the difference in the mean concentrations is zero.

e. *Do computations.* With 95% confidence, $.15 < \mu(B4) - \mu(M4) < 1.83$.

Write a conclusion in context. The evidence is stronger in the hypothetical data because zero isn't in the confidence interval and so we are confident that the means differ.

f. *Do computations.* With 95% confidence, $-0.82 < \mu(B5) - \mu(M5) < 2.66$.

Write a conclusion in context. The evidence here is weaker than in the actual data because zero is closer to the middle of the confidence interval.

g. *Do computations.* With 95% confidence, $-0.31 < \mu(B6) - \mu(M6) < 2.29$.

Write a conclusion in context. The evidence of a difference here is exactly the same as in the actual data: both distributions have been shifted up by one unit, but the shapes, spreads, sample sizes, and difference between centers are all unchanged.

h. *Do computations.* With 95% confidence, $-1.31 < \mu(B7) - \mu(M7) < 1.29$.

Write a conclusion in context. Zero is near the center of the confidence interval, so the evidence here is almost nonexistent for a difference in mean concentration at the bottom and at mid-depth.

D35. a. The calculations are as follows:

$$\frac{\left(\frac{s_1^2}{n_1} + \frac{s_2^2}{n_2}\right)^2}{df} = \frac{\left(\frac{s_1^2}{n_1}\right)^2}{n_1 - 1} + \frac{\left(\frac{s_2^2}{n_2}\right)^2}{n_2 - 1}$$

$$\frac{\left(\frac{1.447^2}{6} + \frac{1.896^2}{6}\right)^2}{df} = \frac{\left(\frac{1.447^2}{6}\right)^2}{5} + \frac{\left(\frac{1.896^2}{6}\right)^2}{5}$$

$$\frac{.8989}{df} = \frac{.4807}{5}$$

$$df = \frac{.8989}{.0961} \approx 9.35$$

b. If the sample sizes are equal, then the df calculation simplifies to

$$\frac{\left(\frac{s_1^2}{n_1} + \frac{s_2^2}{n_1}\right)^2}{df} = \frac{\left(\frac{s_1^2}{n_1}\right)^2}{n_1 - 1} + \frac{\left(\frac{s_2^2}{n_1}\right)^2}{n_1} - 1$$

$$\frac{(s_1^2 + s_2^2)^2}{df} = \frac{s_1^4 + s_2^4}{n_1 - 1}$$

$$df = (n_1 - 1)\left(\frac{(s_1^2 + s_2^2)^2}{s_1^4 + s_2^4}\right)$$

c. If, in addition, the sample standard deviations are equal, then the calculation simplifies even further to

$$df = (n_1 - 1)(2)$$

Practice

P26. With 90% confidence, $-0.32 < \mu(F) - \mu(M) < 5.78$. However, each sample contains one outlier on the high side. To see the effect of these outliers, a re-analysis should be conducted with these points removed. Such an analysis gives the 90% confidence interval as

$$1.26 < \mu(F) - \mu(M) < 5.73$$

which no longer overlaps 0. Because the lower bounds of these confidence intervals are so different, these results must be used with caution. Ideally, it would be good to get more data to resolve the issue of whether the population means for males and females actually differ.

Lesson Notes: Significance Tests for Differences When σ_1 and σ_2 Are Unknown

Discussion

D36. *Check conditions.* Conditions for the *t*-procedures were checked for the Special and Control groups in the example on page 533, where it was observed that each sample contains a value that is relatively large. A dot plot of all four data sets is shown below. The Weekly and Final data have more symmetric distributions; nevertheless, results here should be viewed with some caution.

The treatments were randomly assigned to the babies, so the condition of random assignment is met.

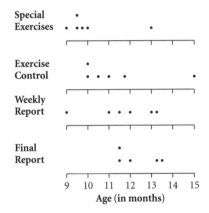

a. *State your hypotheses.*

H_0: $\mu(special) - \mu(weekly) = 0$

H_a: $\mu(special) - \mu(weekly) < 0$

where $\mu(special)$ is the mean age of walking if all of the babies could have been given the special exercises treatment and $\mu(weekly)$ is the mean age of walking if all of the babies could have been given the weekly report treatment.

Compute the test statistic and draw a sketch.

$$t = \frac{\bar{x}_1 - \bar{x}_2}{\sqrt{\dfrac{s_1^2}{n_1} + \dfrac{s_2^2}{n_2}}} = \frac{10.125 - 11.625}{\sqrt{\dfrac{1.447^2}{6} + \dfrac{1.547^2}{6}}} = -1.734$$

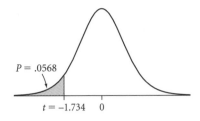

With 9.96 degrees of freedom, the *P*-value is .0568.

Write a conclusion in context. The *P*-value is just a bit larger than .05, so this is not quite sufficient evidence to reject the hypothesis of equal mean walking time, at the $\alpha = .05$ level of significance, for the special exercises and weekly report groups. An observed difference in means of this size could simply be the result of the randomization of the treatments to the babies.

b. *State your hypotheses.*

H_0: $\mu(exercise) - \mu(weekly) = 0$

H_a: $\mu(exercise) - \mu(weekly) < 0$

Compute the test statistic and draw a sketch.

$$t = \frac{\bar{x}_1 - \bar{x}_2}{\sqrt{\dfrac{s_1^2}{n_1} + \dfrac{s_2^2}{n_2}}} = \frac{11.375 - 11.625}{\sqrt{\dfrac{1.896^2}{6} + \dfrac{1.547^2}{6}}} = -0.250$$

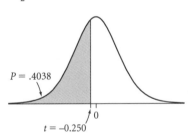

With 9.61 degrees of freedom, the *P*-value is .4038.

Write a conclusion in context. The *P*-value is large, which makes it clear that there is not sufficient evidence to reject the hypothesis of equal means for the control and weekly report groups. An observed difference in means of this size could quite reasonably be due to the randomization of the treatments to the babies.

c. From the example on page 541, a significance test of special exercises versus exercise control yields a *P*-value of .1150.

The special exercises group is very close to having a significantly lower mean than the weekly report group, with a *P*-value that is just slightly larger than 0.05. The next strongest comparison is between the special exercises and exercise control groups, with a *P*-value of .1150. The weakest evidence of a difference in means comes from the comparison of exercise control group versus the weekly report group. Good advice to the experimenter might be to suggest that larger sample sizes be obtained for the first two comparisons.

Practice

P27. *Check conditions.* These can be thought of as random samples of students taking an introductory statistics course (but not as random samples of all students at the university). As was noted in the solution to P26, each sample contains one unusually large value, which may have great influence on the results. The data will be analyzed both with and without these values.

State your hypotheses.
H_0: $\mu(F) - \mu(M) = 0$
H_a: $\mu(F) - \mu(M) \neq 0$
where $\mu(F)$ is the mean study time of all female students taking this course and $\mu(M)$ is the mean study time of all male students taking this course.

Compute the test statistic and draw a sketch.

$$t = \frac{\bar{x}_1 - \bar{x}_2}{\sqrt{\dfrac{s_1^2}{n_1} + \dfrac{s_2^2}{n_2}}} = \frac{10.93 - 8.20}{\sqrt{\dfrac{6.22^2}{46} + \dfrac{5.94^2}{15}}} = 1.53$$

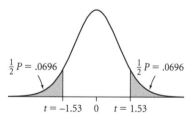

The calculator gives $df = 24.8$ and a *P*-value of .1392.

Write a conclusion in context. The *P*-value of .1392 shows that there is not sufficient evidence to reject the null hypotheses of equal mean weekly study hours for males and females.

This result is consistent with the interpretation of the confidence interval in the solution to P26. Because the 90% confidence interval found in P26 overlaps zero, there will be no statistically significant difference between the means at the 10% level. The 95% confidence interval would be even longer, so there is no statistically significant difference at the 5% level either.

However, to see the effect of these outliers, we will re-analyze with these points removed. Such an analysis gives the following results:
H_0: $\mu(F) - \mu(M) = 0$
H_a: $\mu(F) - \mu(M) \neq 0$
t-statistic = 2.653 with 31 *df*.

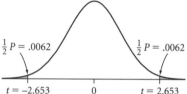

The *P*-value of .0124 now supports rejection of the hypothesis of equal population means. All things considered, it seems that the analysis without the outliers is the better one for these data. The two outliers inflate the standard deviations to the extent that the test statistic is unduly small.

Lesson Notes: The Pooled *t*-Procedure

D37. For III ($n_1 = 5$, $n_2 = 25$, $\sigma_1 = 10$, $\sigma_2 = 1$), the *SD*s are unequal and pooling is wrong. For II ($n_1 = 10$, $n_2 = 10$, $\sigma_1 = 10$, $\sigma_2 = 10$), pooling is reasonable, but with sample sizes equal and not tiny, pooling won't bring much of an advantage. For I ($n_1 = 5$, $n_2 = 25$, $\sigma_1 = 10$, $\sigma_2 = 10$), pooling is appropriate and useful: Pooling lets you use information from the larger sample to estimate the *SD* for the smaller sample.

The t^*-values for 95% confidence intervals are shown here.

Situation	Pooled t		Unpooled t	
	df	t^*	df	t^*
I: $n_1 = 5$, $n_2 = 25$, $\sigma_1 = 10$, $\sigma_2 = 10$	28	2.048	$5.7 \approx 6$	2.447
II: $n_1 = 10$, $n_2 = 10$, $\sigma_1 = 10$, $\sigma_2 = 10$	18	2.101	18	2.101
III: $n_1 = 5$, $n_2 = 25$, $\sigma_1 = 10$, $\sigma_2 = 1$	28	2.048	4.0	2.776

Notice that the pooled t gives narrower intervals in situations I and III. For I, pooling is appropriate, and the narrower interval is the correct one, in the sense that its capture rate will be equal to the advertised rate of 95%. For III, the narrower interval is wrong. Its capture rate will be substantially below the advertised rate of 95%. For II, it makes no difference which procedure you use.

On balance, these examples suggest that to be safe, you should use the pooled *SD* only when you have strong reason to believe that the population standard deviations are equal.

Exercises

E26. **a.** Before using an inference procedure, you should plot the data. The following boxplots indicate that there are no outliers and that the data distributions are reasonably symmetric. The two-sample *t*-interval should work fine.

Page 507 of the student text says these were random samples from a larger population.

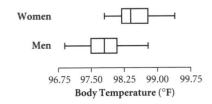

Summary of Men's Body Temperatures

Mean	97.88
Standard Deviation	0.555

Summary of Women's Body Temperatures

Mean	98.52
Standard Deviation	0.527

The 90% confidence interval for the difference between the population mean body temperature for men and for women is shown at the bottom of the page.

The plausible values for the true difference in mean body temperatures lie in the interval $(-1.06, -0.22)$, which is entirely on the negative side of zero.

b. This claim calls for a one-sided test of significance; the details are as follows.

Check conditions. These were checked above.

State your hypotheses.

H_0: $\mu(women) - \mu(men) = 0$

H_a: $\mu(women) - \mu(men) > 0$

where $\mu(men)$ is the mean body temperature for all men in this population and $\mu(women)$ is the mean body temperature for all women in this population.

Compute the test statistic and draw a sketch.

$$t = \frac{(\bar{x}_1 - \bar{x}_2) - (\mu_1 - \mu_2)_0}{\sqrt{\dfrac{s_1^2}{n_1} + \dfrac{s_2^2}{n_2}}}$$

$$= \frac{(98.52 - 97.88) - 0}{\sqrt{\dfrac{0.527^2}{10} + \dfrac{0.555^2}{10}}}$$

$$\approx 2.64$$

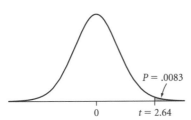

With 17.95 degrees of freedom, the *P*-value is .0083.

Lesson 9.5, E26a

$$(\bar{x}_1 - \bar{x}_2) \pm t^* \cdot \sqrt{\frac{s_1^2}{n_1} + \frac{s_2^2}{n_2}} = (97.88 - 98.52) \pm 1.740 \cdot \sqrt{\frac{0.555^2}{10} + \frac{0.527^2}{10}}$$

where the degrees of freedom as given by the calculator is 17.95.

Write a conclusion in context. The very small *P*-value indicates that these data provide rather strong evidence to say that women have a higher mean temperature than men.

E27. *Check conditions.* Boxplots of the data show that there is one unusually small heart rate for the males. This may cause problems with the analysis and will be checked out. Otherwise, the distributions look fairly symmetric. These are random samples.

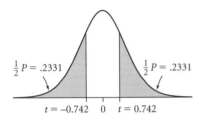

Summary of Men's Heart Rates

Mean	75.69
Standard Deviation	7.11

Summary of Women's Heart Rates

Mean	73.08
Standard Deviation	10.53

Do computations. With 95% confidence, $-4.71 < \mu(men) - \mu(women) < 9.94$ where $\mu(men)$ is the mean heart rate for all men in this population and $\mu(women)$ is the mean heart rate for all women in this population.

Write a conclusion in context. Because zero is in the confidence interval, there is insufficient evidence to say that the mean heart rate for men differs from the mean heart rate for women.

A test of significance can be used to answer the question as well.

State your hypotheses.
H_0: $\mu(men) - \mu(women) = 0$
H_a: $\mu(men) - \mu(women) \neq 0$

Compute the test statistic and draw a sketch. *t*-statistic = 0.742. With 21.06 degrees of freedom, the *P*-value is .4662.

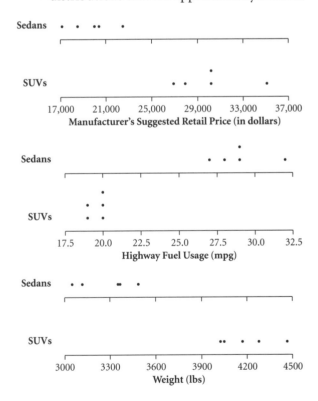

Write a conclusion in context. Again, there is no evidence to say that the mean heart rates differ for the two groups.

If the outlier among the men's heart rates is dropped, the 95% confidence interval for the difference in means becomes $-2.76 < \mu(men) - \mu(women) < 10.94$, and there is still no evidence of a difference between the two population means.

E28. *Check conditions.* These are random samples (vouched for by one of the authors). The following plots do not reveal any reason why these data could not have come from distributions that are approximately normal.

a. *Do computations.* With 95% confidence, $6347.71 < \mu(SUV{:}MSRP) - \mu(Sedan{:}MSRP) < 14{,}326.28$.

Write a conclusion in context. We are 95% confident that the mean price for models of SUVs exceeds the mean price for models of sedans by some amount between $6348 and $14,326.

b. *Do computations.* With 95% confidence, $655.35 < \mu(SUV{:}Weight) - \mu(Sedan{:}Weight) < 1186.65$.

Write a conclusion in context. We are 95% confident that the mean weight of models of SUVs exceeds the mean weight of models of sedans by an amount between 655 and 1187 pounds.

c. *Do computations.* With 95% confidence, $-11.69 < \mu(SUV{:}MPG) - \mu(Sedan{:}MPG) < -7.11$.

Write a conclusion in context. We are 95% confident that the mean gas mileage of models of sedans exceeds the mean gas mileage of models of SUVs by an amount between 7 and 12 mpg.

d. Each of the preceding intervals provides enough evidence to say that the two population means differ. Answers as to which interval is least informative may differ, but one way to look at "information" is to compare the length of the interval to the smaller mean making up the difference. For price (MSRP) the interval length is nearly half the smaller mean, whereas for both weight and MPG the length is only about one-eighth the smaller mean. In that sense, the interval on price is least informative.

e. All three intervals are advertised as 95% confidence intervals, so you should have equal confidence in each of them. The only reason this might not be the case is if the data do not meet the conditions (random samples from normal distributions). These are random samples (selected by one of the authors), but normality of the populations can not be guaranteed. In fact, it is virtually a certainty that these populations are not normal; all are probably skewed toward the larger values. Which one has the potential to be most skewed? Probably price again because there is almost no upper limit as to how much a person can spend for some

models in either of these classes. So, the interval on price loses on both "information" and "confidence."

E29. a. *Check conditions.* The source for these data quoted in E21 on page 525 of the student text states that the data are from random samples. Recall from E21 that a log transformation is used here because of the skewness of the distribution on the original scale of parts per million.

State your hypotheses.

H_0: $\mu(lnHG \text{ for lakes with dams}) - \mu(lnHG \text{ for lakes without dams}) = 0$

H_a: $\mu(lnHG \text{ for lakes with dams}) - \mu(lnHG \text{ for lakes without dams}) > 0$

Compute the test statistic and draw a sketch. t-statistic $= 0.396$. With 31.95 degrees of freedom, the P-value is .3474.

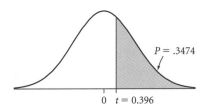

Write a conclusion in context. The large P-value indicates that there is no evidence that lakes with dams have higher mean mercury content than lakes without dams.

b. *Do computations.* With 95% confidence, $0.37 < \mu(lnHG \text{ for type 2 lakes}) - \mu(lnHG \text{ for type 1 lakes}) < 1.72$.

Write a conclusion in context. The mean mercury content, on a log scale, is between .37 and 1.72 points higher in lakes of type 2 (eutrophic) as compared to lakes of type 1 (oligotrophic). That is, any two population means differing by an amount in this interval could have produced the observed difference in means of two samples as a reasonably likely outcome.

c. The question asks about a difference in either direction, so the answer could be obtained through a confidence interval or a test of significance. Here is the result of the latter.

State your hypotheses.

H_0: $\mu(lnHG \text{ for type 2 lakes}) - \mu(lnHG \text{ for type 3 lakes}) = 0$

H_a: $\mu(lnHG$ *for type 2 lakes*$) -$
   $\mu(lnHG$ *for type 3 lakes*$) \neq 0$

Compute the test statistic and draw a sketch.
t-statistic $= 1.292$. With 27.93 degrees of freedom, the *P*-value is .2070.

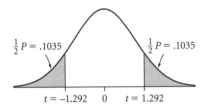

$\frac{1}{2}P = .1035$ $\frac{1}{2}P = .1035$

$t = -1.292$ 0 $t = 1.292$

Write a conclusion in context. The large *P*-value indicates that there is no evidence of a difference in mean mercury content between all lakes of types 2 and 3.

E30. **Check conditions.** These data sets are slightly skewed toward the larger values, but the sample sizes are so large that the sampling distributions of the sample means would not reflect this skewness; the sampling distributions would appear nearly normal. The source of the data indicates that these are random samples.

a. Do computations. With 95% confidence, $-0.79 < \mu($ *length of stay for Insurer A*$) - \mu($ *length of stay for Insurer B*$) < -0.39$.

Write a conclusion in context. Because zero isn't a plausible difference, there is evidence that the true mean lengths of stay differ for the two insurers.

b. Do computations. With 95% confidence, $-1.79 < \mu($ *staff per bed for Insurer A*$) - \mu($ *staff per bed for Insurer B*$) < -1.21$.

Write a conclusion in context. Because zero isn't a plausible difference, there is evidence that the mean number of staff per bed differs for the two insurers. (A significance test gives $t = -10.14$ and $P \approx 0$.) Insurer A serves hospitals that appear to have smaller staff-per-bed ratios. It might be, then, that these hospitals have patients who require less care because they are not as seriously ill as those in hospitals served by Insurer B. That could explain why the length of stay also appears to be smaller for hospitals served by Insurer A.

c. Do computations. We are now back in the realm of proportions, so this question must be answered by methodology from Chapter 8. Let p_1 be the proportion of

private hospitals used by all patients of Insurer A and p_2 be the proportion for Insurer B. The interval

$$(\hat{p}_1 - \hat{p}_2) \pm z^* \cdot \sqrt{\frac{\hat{p}_1(1 - \hat{p}_1)}{n_1} + \frac{\hat{p}_2(1 - \hat{p}_2)}{n_2}}$$

yields the 95% confidence interval (.16, .26).

Write a conclusion in context. The evidence shows that the proportions of all patients who are in private hospitals differ for the two companies. (A significance test gives $z = 7.77$ and $P \approx 0$.) Public hospitals are often general hospitals that have a wide range of facilities and accept almost all kinds of cases, whereas private hospitals are often more specialized and accept a narrower range of illnesses. Thus, more of the serious illnesses, often among patients with a history of illness, may show up at public hospitals. Again, this points to the possibility that Company A may be insuring a preponderance of less ill patients.

E31. **Check conditions.** Dot plots of the values of %LS for each elapsed time show that as the percentages get closer to 100, there is a tendency to show skewness toward the smaller values, but the skewness is not extreme for these data. Because the data come from a designed experiment, standard inference methods should work here.

a. Do computations. With 90% confidence, $1.22 < \mu($ *%LS after 40 minutes in NJ*$) - \mu($ *%LS after 40 minutes in PR*$) < 9.45$.

Write a conclusion in context. The mean %LS appears to differ for the two laboratories at the 40-minute time period.

b. Do computations. With 90% confidence, $-1.46 < \mu($ *%LS after 60 minutes in NJ*$) - \mu($ *%LS after 60 minutes in PR*$) < 4.79$.

Write a conclusion in context. Because 0 is contained in the confidence interval, there is no evidence of a difference in the mean %LS for the two laboratories at the 60-minute time period.

c. The %LS measurements for the 40-minute time period are below 90%, so the limit of 15 percentage points applies. The entire confidence interval is within $(-15, +15)$, so the 40-minute results would be considered to be equivalent. That is, there is no evidence that the true means differ by more than 15 percentage points in either direction.

Similarly, the limit of 7 percentage points applies to the 60-minute test results. The 90% confidence interval lies entirely within the interval $(-7, +7)$, so the 60-minute results would be declared equivalent as well.

E32. **a.** ***Check conditions.*** Letting μ_1 denote the mean score increase for coached students and μ_2 the mean increase for uncoached students, the test of significance must be designed to detect a change of more than 25 points in these means.

State your hypotheses.

H_0: $\mu_1 - \mu_2 = 25$

H_a: $\mu_1 - \mu_2 > 25$

Compute the test statistic and draw a sketch.

$$t = \frac{(\bar{x}_1 - \bar{x}_2) - (\mu_1 - \mu_2)_0}{\sqrt{\dfrac{s_1^2}{n_1} + \dfrac{s_2^2}{n_2}}}$$

$$= \frac{(60 - 13) - 25}{\sqrt{\dfrac{42^2}{9} + \dfrac{30^2}{50}}}$$

$$= 1.50$$

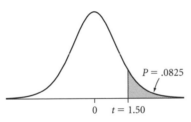

With $df \approx 9.52$, the P-value is about .0825.

Write a conclusion in context. This small value of the test statistic would not allow rejection of the null hypothesis that the coaching does not improve SAT math scores.

b. There is no evidence of a control group here, so we will compare the average gain of 73 with the expected mean gain of $25 + 13 = 38$.

State your hypotheses.

H_0: $\mu = 38$

H_a: $\mu > 38$

where μ is the mean increase from this coaching program.

Compute the test statistic and draw a sketch.

$$t = \frac{73 - 28}{42/\sqrt{12}} \approx 3.7115$$

With 11 degrees of freedom, the P-value is .0017.

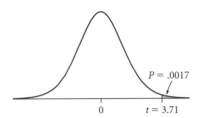

For these data, we do have sufficient evidence to reject the null hypothesis and conclude that the coaching seems to have improved the average gain by more than the expected 38 points.

c. So, the controversy persists! The article states clearly that these students were not randomly selected or randomly assigned to treatments, so the results of our t-tests are suspect. (The article did not report t-tests.) These analyses would be reasonable only if you can think of the students who showed up for the coaching program as somewhat like a random selection of students who take the exam.

Other variables, such as basic ability and motivation of the students, should be taken into account in a study such as this. In fact, it is very difficult to get data that will stand up to the assumptions of inference by looking at students after the fact (after they have already decided to enter a coaching program or not enter one). It would be much better to design an experiment with students randomly assigned to the two treatments (coached and not coached) and see what happens as they progress through the programs and the exams.

9.6 Paired Comparisons

Objectives

- to understand whether the data production process results in two independent samples or one sample of paired observations
- to learn to detect possible departures from normality both by studying the data and considering the population from which the data came
- to construct and interpret a confidence interval for the difference between means from paired comparisons
- to perform a significance test for the difference between means from paired comparisons
- to deepen the understanding of these terms in the context of comparing means: paired data, matched pairs design, repeated measures design, independent and dependent samples, transformations to normality, random sampling, and random assignment

Important Terms and Concepts

- paired data
- matched pairs design
- repeated measures design
- independent and dependent samples
- transformations to normality
- random sampling
- random assignment

Class Time
Five days

Materials
Rulers marked in millimeters for Activity 9.5

Suggested Assignments

Classwork		
Essential	**Recommended**	**Optional**
D38, D39, D41–D44, D47 P28, P29, P31	Activity 9.5 D40, D45, D46, D48 P30, P32, P33	

Homework		
Essential	**Recommended**	**Optional**
E33–E35	E36, E37	

Lesson Notes: One Sample or Two?

As you learned back in Chapter 4, paired data is a simple example of a randomized block design. The blocks might consist of two subjects matched on one or more characteristics related to the response of interest (as in the pulse rate study of Activity 4.5). Or, each subject might be his or her own block if each treatment can be measured on each subject. In agricultural experiments, blocks are often plots of land having similar soil conditions or plants paired according to their age and size. In industrial experiments, blocks are often segments of time when a process is operating under similar conditions (such as conditions of temperature and humidity or management style). The important point is that the pairing of experimental units must be designed into the study. It is incorrect to measure response first and then pair measurements that appear similar.

In order for a difference to be meaningful, the units must match. You can not take differences of pre- and post-test scores when the pre-test is scored as a percentage and the post-test as the number of correct answers out of 50 questions.

And not everything should be summarized by means. If you live close to a river you are probably more interested in its maximum height than its average height. Students studying their SAT scores might be more interested in the percentiles of the distribution of scores than in the mean. A designer of a bottle-filling machine may be more interested in the variation of the ounces of fill than in the mean because the mean is often easily controlled by the turn of a dial but the variation is much more difficult to control. Students should be taught to think broadly about data analysis so that they are not mislead into thinking that all problems must be turned into a question about means or proportions because that is all statisticians can analyze. Means and proportions do cover a lot of territory (which is the reason they are the mainstay of an introductory course), but students should recognize when they are not appropriate as well as when they are.

Random samples from a population or random assignment of treatments to experimental units are essential for statistical inference about that population or those treatments. Without randomness there can be no statistical inference about population parameters or about causal relationships among treatments! This point should be emphasized at every turn.

Activity 9.5: Handspans

1–2. A set of data on handspans from one statistics class is displayed here, along with the summary statistics. (The data were recorded in centimeters.)

Right	Left	R–L	Randomized Right	Randomized R–L
20.4	20.1	0.3	18.6	−1.5
23.5	22.9	0.6	20.3	−2.6
23.5	21.1	2.4	19.4	−1.7
19.6	19.0	0.6	19.0	0
21.5	22.1	−0.6	22.8	0.7
21.6	22.7	−1.1	16.5	−6.2
21.9	22.4	−0.5	21.6	−0.8
18.6	20.4	−1.8	24.0	3.6
16.5	17.1	−0.6	19.9	2.8
20.8	22.0	−1.2	21.5	−0.5
18.3	17.5	0.8	19.7	2.2
23.5	23.5	0	23.5	0
18.6	18.9	−0.3	21.9	3.0
24.4	24.6	−0.2	24.4	−0.2
19.0	18.4	0.6	20.4	2.0
19.2	19.3	−0.1	19.2	−0.1
19.4	19.1	0.3	23.1	4.0
20.3	19.8	0.5	23.5	3.7
19.7	19.8	−0.1	19.6	−0.2
19.9	20.6	−0.7	22.6	2.0
24.0	23.8	0.2	20.8	−3.0
22.8	23.2	−0.4	18.6	−4.6
23.1	22.8	0.3	18.3	−4.5
22.6	23.3	−0.7	23.5	0.2

	n	MEAN	STDEV	SEMEAN
Right	24	20.946	2.142	0.437
Left	24	21.017	2.131	0.435
R-L	24	-0.071	0.836	0.171
RandRight	24	20.946	2.142	0.437
RandR-L	24	-0.071	2.754	0.562

3–5. The differences from the paired data (repeated measures design) of step 2 yield a standard error of 0.171. The differences calculated after the right hand data is randomly ordered (step 3) yield a standard error of 0.562. Treating the data as two independent samples (step 4) yields a standard error of 0.617. Note that the differences taken after randomly ordering one set of the pairs (so that the data are no longer paired) gives about the same standard error as would two independent samples, one from right hands and one from left. The moral: Paired data can greatly reduce variation over independent samples and produce a much more sensitive test (or estimate) of the true mean difference. The reduction in variation will be greatest when there is considerable variation between individuals but little variation in the differences from pair to pair.

For these data it is not true that the right hand is bigger than the left, at least in terms of handspans. This phenomenon might hold for manual laborers, but does not appear to hold for students. (Perhaps work on a keyboard uses each hand more equally.)

6. You should expect that the left and right handspans for the same person from step 1 are highly correlated but that the randomly paired left and right handspans from step 3 would have no correlation. The reason is that your left hand tends to be about the same size as your right hand, but you wouldn't expect your left hand to be about the same size as the right hand of a randomly selected person. As you can see from these plots for the sample class, that is indeed the case. The correlations here are .923 and .169, respectively.

Step 1 Data

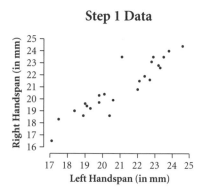

Step 3 Data

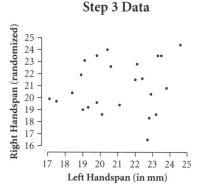

A Note on Randomization Tests for Completely Randomized, Matched Pairs and Repeated Measures Designs

As you have read and heard many times, randomization is the basis for inference because that is where probability comes into the picture. Students may see this point more clearly if they see an inference procedure that depends *only* on the randomization. Such procedures (paralleling those introduced in Chapter 8) are easily demonstrated for the completely randomized, matched pairs and repeated measures designs of the pulse rate study. The data are given on page 549 of the student text.

For the completely randomized design (CRD), the randomization separates the measurements into two groups. Under the hypothesis that which treatment a subject gets makes no difference in pulse rate, the observed difference of $77.71 - 74.86 = 2.85$ between the sample means should be due only to the randomization, that is, to which subjects just happened to get into each treatment group. To check this out, we rerandomize all 28 of the observed pulse rates into two groups and recompute the difference between the sample means. Doing this many times leads to a randomization distribution for the difference between the sample means. This plot shows such a distribution for 100 trials.

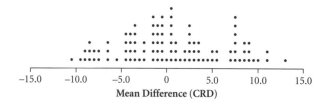

This randomization distribution shows that 30 out of 100 values of the difference in sample means exceed the observed difference of 2.85, for a simulated *P*-value of .30. When you use a *t*-procedure, the observed difference of 2.85 has a one-sided *P*-value of .31. Both procedures give approximately the same *P*-values, and both support the decision that there is not sufficient evidence to reject the null hypothesis. Historically, the *t*-test was developed as a mathematical approximation to the randomization test; randomization was the way R. A. Fisher thought about constructing tests of significance.

In the matched pairs and repeated measures designs, the only randomization is in the order in which a subject receives the treatments. In effect, then, the randomization is assigning only signs to the observed differences. The randomization distributions shown here were generated by randomly rearranging the signs of the observed differences, each time computing the mean difference under the new arrangement.

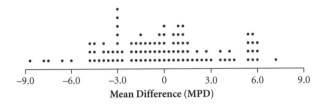

Mean Difference (MPD)

The observed mean difference for the matched pairs (MP) data is 3.714. In the randomization distribution shown here, 18 of 100 mean differences are larger than 3.714. Using a *t*-procedure to test the null hypothesis that the mean difference is 0 gives a *P*-value of .14, again pretty close to the simulated *P*-value from the randomization test.

With an observed mean difference of 8.357, the one-sided simulated *P*-value for the repeated measures (RM) data is virtually 0; we observe no sample means greater than 8.357 in the randomization distribution.

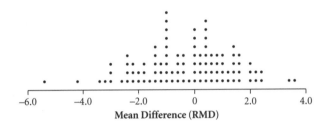

Mean Difference (RMD)

Lesson Note: Two Samples or Paired Data?

Discussion

D38. Completely randomized designs work well when there is relatively little variation among the experimental units before the treatments are applied. If there is a lot of variation among units, then pairing can help us see the differences due to the treatment more clearly. The success of a matched pairs design depends on the effectiveness of the matching. If units can be matched on a variable that is highly correlated with the response, then the differences recorded from the matched pairs should have less variation than the original measurements, allowing the treatment differences to show through. Of course, the most effective matching is to use the same

unit for both treatments (a repeated measures design). The differences recorded from the repeated measures generally have far less variation than the original measurements, making them very sensitive gauges of treatment differences. Unfortunately, repeated measures can not always be used because the treatments may destroy the units or have too much carry-over effect. In summary, matching pays big dividends in the analysis when the resulting differences between measurements have much less variation than the original measurements.

D39. **a.** The data come from two independent samples, so they can not be paired.

b. One way to gather matched pairs data for this type of experiment would be to have students work in teams of two, one randomly chosen to guess in feet and the other in meters. To gather repeated measures data, have each student guess in both feet and meters.

c. The matched pairs design may not have been used because students would have to have been matched on their ability to estimate distances and that would have taken some time to determine. Arbitrary matching may actually be worse than the completely randomized design that was used. Repeated measures might not be a true test of the different treatments because the student might simply change one guess to the other by multiplying by a constant.

d. This is not a meaningful comparison because one mean is in feet and the other in meters. So of course the means aren't going to be equal. Comparing means makes sense only if they are in the same scale. Further, the question asked was whether the students were as accurate in meters as in feet, and these data can't answer that question because we don't know what the true length was.

D40. **a.** This is a completely randomized design; the data are not paired. The two-sample *t*-procedure is an appropriate way to compare means. As in Section 9.5, random assignment of treatments to subjects allows the same analyses as random sampling from two different populations.

b. You might pair rooms, one with carpet and one without, that are near each other and have similar uses. This may be difficult, however, unless the experiment allows you to install carpet long before the data are collected. Alternatively, you could use a repeated measures design, giving each room both treatments. You need to randomize which eight rooms get the carpet first.

Practice

P28. **Completely Randomized Design.** A scatterplot of the data, as you might expect, shows little association between sit and stand measurements for the completely randomized design.

Check conditions. Boxplots show no reason to be concerned about non-normality here.

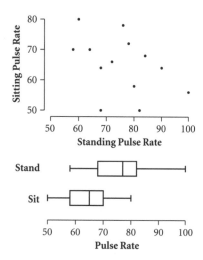

State your hypotheses. The null hypothesis is that the true difference between mean pulse rates for standing and sitting (for this group of subjects) is 0; the alternate is that standing increases the mean pulse rate.
H_0: $\mu(stand) - \mu(sit) = 0$
H_a: $\mu(stand) - \mu(sit) > 0$

Compute the test statistic and draw a sketch. The two-sample t-statistic is

$$t = \frac{(x_1 - x_2) - 0}{\sqrt{\dfrac{s_1^2}{n_1} + \dfrac{s_2^2}{n_2}}}$$

$$= \frac{(75.71 - 64.57) - 0}{\sqrt{\dfrac{11.68^2}{14} + \dfrac{9.33^2}{14}}}$$

$$= 2.788$$

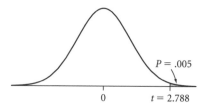

With 24.79 *df*, this produces a *P*-value of .005.

Write a conclusion in context. Reject H_0. There is sufficient evidence to conclude that standing does increase the mean pulse rate by more than would be expected by chance for this group of subjects.

Matched Pairs Design. The scatterplot of pairs from the matched pairs design shows a fairly strong positive association, so a one-sample test on the differences should be powerful.

Check Conditions. The boxplot of the differences shows a little skewness, but not enough to be a serious problem for this large a sample.

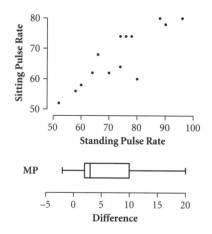

State your hypotheses.
H_0: $\mu_d = 0$, and H_a: $\mu_d > 0$, where μ_d is the mean difference in pulse rates if each treatment could have been assigned to each subject within each pair.

Compute the test statistic and draw a sketch. The one-sample t-statistic calculated from the 14 differences is

$$t = \frac{\bar{d} - \mu_d}{s_d/\sqrt{n}} = \frac{6.0 - 0}{6.563/\sqrt{14}} = 3.421$$

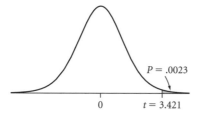

With 13 *df*, this leads to a *P*-value of .0023.

Write a conclusion in context. Reject H_0. Again, there is evidence to conclude that standing does increase the mean pulse rate by more than would be expected by chance, and the evidence is a little stronger (smaller *P*-value) than for the completely randomized design.

Repeated Measures Design. The scatterplot of pairs taken from the repeated measures design again shows a very strong positive trend.

Check conditions. The boxplot of the differences shows very little skewness.

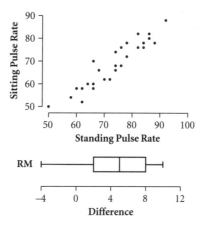

State your hypotheses.
H_0: $\mu_d = 0$, and H_a: $\mu_d > 0$ where μ_d is the mean difference in pulse rates if each treatment could have been given in both orders to each subject.

Do computations. The one-sample *t*-statistic calculated from the 28 differences is given by

$$t = \frac{\bar{d} - \mu_0}{s_d/\sqrt{n}} = \frac{4.643 - 0}{3.613/\sqrt{28}} = 6.800$$

With 27 *df*, the *P*-value is less than .0001. The test statistic is quite large and would be difficult to see in a sketch.

Write a conclusion in context. Reject H_0. Once again, here is evidence to conclude that standing does increase the mean pulse rate by more than would be expected by chance. The evidence is even stronger than in the matched pairs design.

In this study, all three designs produced statistically significant results, but the evidence in favor of the alternate increased as we reduced variation between pairs by first matching on base pulse rate and then using repeated measures. This is fairly typical of the performance of these three designs and is consistent with the results from Display 9.36.

Lesson Notes: What If Your Population Is Not Normal?

Discussion

D41. The order of transforming and taking differences may matter. Although the condition for the one-sample *t*-test is that the *differences* be normally distributed, statisticians typically transform the original data and then subtract. This usually does not result in the differences being normally distributed as well. The reason is that it is easier to interpret the difference of two similarly transformed variables than it is to interpret transformed differences. Further, the differences may produce negative numbers, which makes some of the common transformations (square roots, logs) impossible.

D42. ***Check conditions.*** The control group receiving this "treatment" was selected at random. The boxplots of the original data and the data transformed by square roots are shown next. The original data are not very skewed here, so they could be analyzed without transforming to a new scale. But the square root transformation does make the distribution of differences a little less skewed.

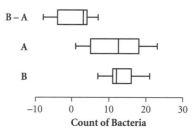

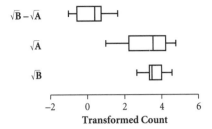

$\sqrt{B} - \sqrt{A}$

$\sqrt{A}$

$\sqrt{B}$

Transformed Count

Do computations. The differences on the square root scale produce the following 95% confidence interval:

$$\bar{d} \pm t^* \cdot \frac{s_d}{\sqrt{n}} \text{ or } 0.233 \pm 2.262 \cdot \frac{0.888}{\sqrt{10}}$$

or $(-0.40, 0.87)$. The differences between the original counts produce a 95% confidence interval of

$$-3.28 < \mu_d < 4.48$$

Write a conclusion in context. Because the confidence interval overlaps zero there is no statistically significant change in mean count after the "treatment" was applied. Thus, it looks as though the counts were not decreasing over this time interval in any significant way. This evidence gives more credence to the conclusion that the real treatment was effective in reducing the bacilli.

Practice

P29. **a.** The boxplot of the differences on the miles-per-gallon scale shows some skewness toward the larger values, but no outliers are present.

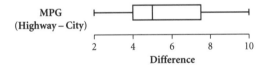

MPG
(Highway – City)

Difference

b. The boxplot of the differences on the gallons-per-mile scale shows greater symmetry, although there is now a hint of skewness toward the smaller values.

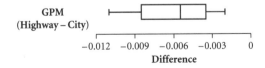

GPM
(Highway – City)

Difference

c. The gallons-per-mile scale better meets the conditions of the *t*-procedures. The resulting 95% confidence interval for the

difference between means for highway and city driving is

$$\bar{d} \pm t^* \cdot \frac{s_d}{\sqrt{n}} \text{ or } -0.006 \pm 2.093 \cdot \frac{0.003}{\sqrt{20}}$$

or $(-0.0074, -0.0046)$.

The corresponding two-sided *t*-test is presented next.

State your hypotheses.
H_0: $\mu_d = 0$, and H_a: $\mu_d \neq 0$, where μ_d is the mean difference in highway and city gpm for all small car models.

Do computations. The *t*-statistic is

$$t = \frac{\bar{d} - \mu_0}{s_d/\sqrt{n}} = \frac{-.006 - 0.0}{0.003/\sqrt{20}} \approx -8.94$$

or $t \approx -8.670$ with no rounding. With 19 *df*, the *P*-value is less than 0.0001.

Write a conclusion in context. Reject H_0. The confidence interval does not overlap zero, and the test of significance produces a very small *P*-value. By either method there is ample evidence to say that highway driving produces significantly greater fuel economy than city driving. We are 95% confident that highway driving saves between 0.005 and 0.007 gallons per mile, on the average.

P30. **a.** ***Check conditions.*** The brain weights are rather skewed and can be drawn closer to normality through the log transformation, as can be seen in the boxplots.

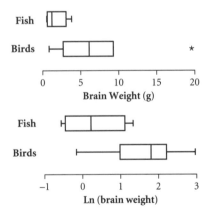

Fish

Birds

Brain Weight (g)

Fish

Birds

Ln (brain weight)

These data are not paired, and the two-sample *t*-test on comparing the means of the log brain weights yields the following results.

State your hypotheses.
H_0: $\mu(LnBrain{:}B) - \mu(LnBrain{:}F) = 0$
H_a: $\mu(LnBrain{:}B) - \mu(LnBrain{:}F) \neq 0$

Compute the test statistic and draw a sketch.
The *t*-statistic is

$$t = \frac{(\bar{x}_1 - \bar{x}_2) - 0}{\sqrt{\dfrac{s_1^2}{n_1} + \dfrac{s_2^2}{n_2}}}$$

$$= \frac{(1.589 - 0.359) - 0}{\sqrt{\dfrac{1.018^2}{7} + \dfrac{0.726^2}{7}}}$$

$$= 2.604$$

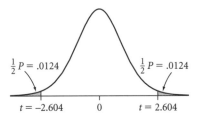

$\frac{1}{2}P = .0124$ $\frac{1}{2}P = .0124$

$t = -2.604$ 0 $t = 2.604$

With 10.85 *df*, the *P*-value is .0248.

Write a conclusion in context. Reject H_0. There is evidence to conclude that the mean brain weights of species of birds and species of fish differ. (A one-sided test would conclude that species of birds have the larger brains.)

b. Analysis of the body weights presents a problem. The birds have a very large (vulture) and a very small (canary) species in their sample, relative to the others. The vulture is an outlier on the *gram* scale, and the canary is an outlier on the ln(*gram*) scale. In fact, it would be hard to find a transformation that will bring these data close to symmetry.

A *t*-test on the difference in mean body weights based on the original data gives $t = 1.61$, which is not close to showing a significant difference in means. Using the log-transformed data, $t = 1.70$, which is still not significant. If the vulture is dropped out of the original data set, then the untransformed data yields a $t = 2.765$, which is significant at the 5% level. So, we have a problem! The comparison between fish and bird body weights is difficult to make using these basic procedures; we either need higher level statistical procedures or need to stratify the species into more homogeneous groups before making comparisons.

Lesson Notes: Is It Meaningful to Compare Means?

Discussion

D43. **a.** Comparing means would be appropriate if it is reasonable to assume that the students have a somewhat random or else representative set of eruptions. There appears to be no obvious reason why this would not be the case. Note that the data for analysis are the times between eruptions. It turns out that there is a substantial difference: After eruptions that last less than three minutes, the average waiting time is 54 minutes, with a standard deviation of 6.3; after eruptions that last longer than 3 minutes, the average waiting time is 78 minutes, with a standard deviation of 6.9 minutes. For the data, see Sanford Weisberg, *Applied Linear Regression*, 2nd ed. (New York: John Wiley and Sons, 1985). For an analysis of the bimodality, see Samprit Chatterjee et al., *A Casebook for a First Course in Statistics and Data Analysis* (New York: John Wiley and Sons, 1995), pp. 5–12. The data can also be found in Statlib at www.stat.cmu.edu.

b. The intereruption times are unpaired measurements.

D44. In a literal sense, comparing means is meaningful, but in a practical sense it's a waste of time. You don't need statistics to know that hens' eggs are longer than they are wide. (The reason Dempster collected the data was to test the fit of an ellipsoidal model for the volume. In the logarithmic scale, the volume is a weighted sum of the length and width.)

D45. Taken together, questions D39–D44 illustrate various situations for which the comparison of means may or may not be appropriate. It is appropriate to compare means in D40 (Hospital carpets) and D43 (Old Faithful). D39 (Guessing distances) represents a situation where it is possible to compare means, but only after the data have been put in comparable scales. The design that underlies D41 and D42 allow the comparison of means by looking at the differences of paired data, but only after a transformation is made so that the data are more nearly normal. D44 (Hens' eggs) represents a situation where it is meaningful but not useful to compare means.

Practice

P31. The goal here is good mixing, which implies that the proportions of the components (A, B, etc.) would be nearly the same across the samples taken from various parts of the mixture. A comparison of means would not answer the question about mixing because the means of the proportions tell you nothing about the variability in the proportions. For measuring the degree of mixing, you would be better off to study the standard deviation of the proportions for each of the components of the mixture. For good mixing, these standard deviations should be smaller than some acceptable standard. Note that the proportions here are continuous measurements, as opposed to proportions based on binomial counts, so that the standard deviation would be estimated by s.

P32. For this situation, it is not the center but the variability that is of interest. Comparing means might be relevant to make sure that the new settings gave the same mean as the old settings, but that's not what this question is about. (Reducing the variability is very often the main challenge in statistical quality control, just as it often is in design of experiments.)

Lesson Notes: Does Your Inference Have a Chance?

Discussion

D46. (See D40 on hospital carpets). This is a straightforward example of a randomized controlled experiment. Inference is appropriate. (However, as with any inference, it would be important to check the actual data for possible violations of conditions before going ahead with a statistical test.)

D47. Inference for the comparison of means requires two independent random samples or one random sample of paired data. Collecting a single sample and then splitting it into two groups based on the size of the data values is *not* an appropriate way to generate

two independent samples. Data divided this way will almost always produce a "significant" difference, but the comparison is meaningless.

D48. As stated in the solution to D47, inference for the comparison of means requires two independent random samples or one random sample of paired data. In experiments, the samples can come from completely randomized or paired designs, but the key is randomization. Thus, the main way data fall short of the requirements for inference is through lack of randomization. For the procedures of this chapter to work, the data also must come from approximately normal distributions unless the sample size is quite large, which may mean that a transformation is in order before inference can proceed. Many questions that arise in investigations can not be answered by means, so the analysis of means (although possibly correct) is irrelevant.

Practice

P33. **a.** No. Asking for volunteers is a useful way of obtaining subjects for an experiment; that is essentially what is done in medical experiments, for example. The main difficulty here is that there is no random assignment into treatment groups. This is an observational study, so you can not attribute any difference in scores to the effect of the music.
b. This is better than the design in part a because it partially accounts for the abilities of the students and can reduce student-to-student variability in the results by looking at differences between pairs. But there still is no random assignment of treatments to subjects.
c. A good design would require a group of students (volunteer or otherwise selected) to be randomly divided between the two treatment groups ("radio on" and "radio off") and then followed over a period of time to see that they were staying on the treatment. Scores on an exam taken at the end of the time period could be used for assessing the treatment effect. The students could be paired on the basis of past performance in the course.

Exercises

E33. *Check conditions.* These are paired data, so the analyses will be done using one-sample techniques. The problem states that the drugs were assigned in random order. The first step of a good analysis is to take a careful look at the data. The boxplots of the differences show one outlier in the values of A − C. Other than that, there is no reason to suspect that these differences could not have come from normally distributed populations.

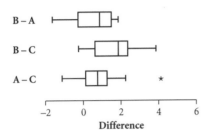

a. *State your hypotheses.* If A causes more drowsiness than B, then the mean for A should be smaller than the mean for B. That is, the mean difference, with A subtracted from B, should be greater than 0. Thus, the test of significance proceeds as follows:

H_0: $\mu(B - A) = 0$
H_a: $\mu(B - A) > 0$

Do computations. The t-statistic is

$$t = \frac{\bar{d} - \mu_d}{s_d/\sqrt{n}} = \frac{0.610 - 0}{1.211/\sqrt{9}} = 1.511$$

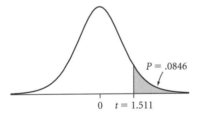

$P = .0846$

$0 \quad t = 1.511$

With 8 *df*, the *P*-value is .0846.

Write a conclusion in context. With a *P*-value this large, there is insufficient evidence to reject the null hypothesis that there is no difference between the true mean responses for drugs A and B.

b. The 95% confidence for the mean of B − C is

$$\bar{d} \pm t^* \cdot \frac{s_d}{\sqrt{n}} \text{ or } 1.613 \pm 2.306 \cdot \frac{1.274}{\sqrt{9}}$$

or (0.63, 2.59).

Because this interval does not overlap zero, there is evidence to say that the mean flicker frequency for Treatment B differs from that for Treatment C, in the direction indicating that C causes more drowsiness.

c. The 95% confidence for the mean of A − C is

$$\bar{d} \pm t^* \cdot \frac{s_d}{\sqrt{n}} \text{ or } 1.003 \pm 2.306 \cdot \frac{1.500}{\sqrt{9}}$$

or (−0.15, 2.16).

This indicates no significant difference between the mean flicker frequencies for Treatments A and C, because the interval overlaps zero. These are the differences with the outlier, so it is appropriate to check its influence by doing the analysis without the outlier. The resulting 95% confidence interval is

$$-0.22 < \mu(A - C) < 1.45$$

which is slightly narrower than the first interval but still shows no significant difference between the means for A and C.

d. Taking the above analyses together, we can say that C appears to cause more drowsiness than the placebo B, but none of the other differences shows up as significant. Here we see an example of the commonly occurring bind we get into when comparing more than two means. It looks like B beats C and A is not different from B, but A does not beat C. In general, it is impossible to place more than two means in a complete ordering by a series of tests of significance. There are special procedures to compare three or more means, but they are beyond the scope of this book.

E34. The fact is, for the years 1980 through 1984, more jeans were sold in June than in January. No inference—paired or otherwise—is needed to establish this fact. These are population data for a selected group of years; there is no randomization in either the selection of years or months, or in the way the pairing is done. In addition, these are time series data, which implies that the values will be correlated with one another (even if we take the differences for each year) as opposed to being independently selected measurements.

However, the small *P*-value does tell us that such differences are unlikely to be produced by chance alone.

E35. **a.** The two most striking features of this data set are clear from this scatterplot.

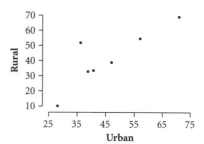

First, points for six of the seven twin pairs fall close to a line, a pattern that strongly suggests that some combination of heredity and early childhood environment is a major determining factor in the rate of tracheobronchial clearance. Second, one twin pair is a clear outlier, as can be seen in the next plot.

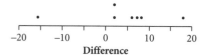

The summary statistics with and without the outlying pair are shown at the bottom of the page.

It is worth taking time to help students recognize that for the rural readings in isolation, or the urban readings in isolation, removing the outlier has only a modest effect on the summaries. The place where excluding the outlier has the biggest effect is the *SD* for the differences, which goes from over 10 to under 6.

Are the formal tests justified here? There is certainly no randomization. Conditions were not assigned, and so could not be randomized; nor were the twin pairs randomly selected from some population. Indeed, it is hard to specify the population that would be a reasonable target for the inferences: the set of all twin pairs with one twin living in each environment and both twins willing to inhale radioactive Teflon? (Surely not a large or representative component of society!)

Overall, there are many reasons not to take the probability calculations at face value. Nevertheless, the result can not be explained by chance variation. One of the alternative possible explanations is that where you live has an effect on how efficiently your lungs clear, with rural environments somewhat healthier, on average. But another possible explanation is that the healthier twin tends to choose to live in the country for some reason. None of this is exactly headline-making news! Perhaps the more interesting results come not from comparing means but from the pattern in the scatterplot.

b. Independent samples would require the independent selection of random samples from clearly defined rural and urban populations of interest. Then, each subject would agree to breathe Teflon particles. Clearance rates could then be measured and the means compared by a two-sample procedure.

c. A paired study is probably the better design here, because the analysis of differences reduces the person-to-person variation. In general, the pairs would have to be matched on some other criterion related to breathing capacity.

d. The main advantage of using two independent samples is that you would not have to find a criterion on which to pair the subjects. In addition, the two-sample design could be better if there is little person-to-person variability in clearance rates. Twins might be difficult to find for most studies.

Lesson 9.6, E35a

	Rural	Urban	Diff.	Outlier Excluded Rural	Outlier Excluded Urban	Outlier Excluded Diff.
Mean	41.5	45.5	4.03	39.8	47.1	7.30
SD	19.0	14.4	10.15	20.2	15.1	5.82
t			1.05			3.07
P-value			.33			.028

E36. An exploratory analysis might begin with a back-to-back stemplot of the data as well as of the differences, because the data come in pairs defined by the occasion.

```
Previously
Stung          Fresh
      94 |0| 69
         |1| 05569
     721 |2| 1
     333 |3|
         |4|
         |5|
         |6|
       0 |7|
```

```
Stem-and-leaf of P - F
Leaf Unit = 1.0

 -0 |62
  0 |026
  1 |288
  2 |
  3 |
  4 |
  5 |
  6 |0
```

The data are consistent with the predictions of the theory: On average, the bees left fewer stingers in the fresh cotton balls than in those that had been previously stung. The numbers for *Fresh* look well-behaved, with no outliers or gross asymmetries and a fairly small spread. (These characteristics are especially welcome because the sample size is so small.) The numbers for *Stung* are not quite so "cooperative." There is one outlier (70), and a somewhat greater spread. This outlier produces an outlier among the differences as well.

Because the numbers come in pairs, a scatterplot is indicated. This plot confirms that Occasion 9 is an outlier, although there is a mild suggestion of a wedge shape, nar-rower toward the lower left, hinting that a change of scale might be useful.

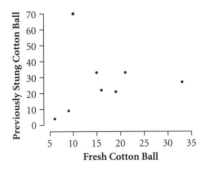

It is reasonable to regard the nine occasions as a representative and possibly quasi-random sample of some vaguely defined larger population of occasions, and the careful 4×4 arrangement of cotton balls of the two types offers a near guarantee that the bees are not choosing one kind over the other on the basis of location.

Let $d_i = Stung - Fresh$ for occasion i, and let μ_d be the underlying mean difference. The hypothesis that bees have no preference can be written $H_0: \mu_d = 0$. An argument can be made for a one-sided alternate, that bees are more likely to sting the balls that had been previously stung ($H_a: \mu_d > 0$), although a two-sided alternate is not wrong.

Because of the outlier, it is worth doing two sets of tests, with the complete data set and with the outlier excluded. See the table at the bottom of the page.

Removing the outlier cuts the mean difference in half, from 12 to 6 stings, but

Lesson 9.6, E36

	All 9 Occasions			Outlier Excluded		
	Prev. Stung	Fresh	Diff.	Prev. Stung	Fresh	Diff.
Mean	28	16	12	22.75	16.75	6.0
SD	18.9	8.0	19.9	11.2	8.2	9.13
t			1.807			1.858
P-value (one-tailed)			.0542			.0528
P-value (two-tailed)			.1084			.1055

cuts the standard deviation in half also, so the *t*-statistic is virtually unchanged. The evidence can hardly be taken as conclusive because the *P*-values are borderline at best (for one-tailed tests). The data do tend to confirm the theory that smoke masks some odor that a bee leaves behind, along with its stinger, in order to tell other bees to "sting here," but the evidence is not overwhelming.

E37. **a.** The distributions of differences with the 0's and without (the latter called the adjusted differences) are shown in the next two boxplots.

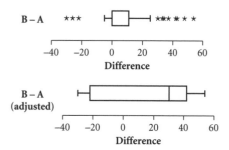

The original data show many outliers because the variability is so small (due to the many 0's) that otherwise ordinary values show up as being far away from the mean. The adjusted data look much better for inference based on *t*-procedures. For comparison purposes, the summary statistics and both 95% confidence intervals are shown here.

	B − A	(B − A) Adjusted
Count	40	15
Mean	6.38	17
Median	0	30
SD	20.14	30.60
Std Error	3.18	7.90

$$-0.06 < \mu(B - A) < 12.82$$
$$0.06 < \mu((B - A) \text{ adj}) < 33.94$$

Note that the first interval would lead to a conclusion that the two population means do not differ and the second would lead to a conclusion that they do. The second interval is much longer because of the increased variation and smaller sample size. However, the method that produced the second interval will have nearly the correct capture rate,

whereas because of the outliers, the method of the first interval will have a capture rate that is too low.

b. You are really estimating two different means here; the first is the mean difference for all accounts, and the second is the mean difference for only the accounts with nonzero differences. The latter is the more reliable estimate because the conditions of the *t*-procedure are better met for the adjusted data. How, then, can you turn this into an estimate of the total discrepancy for all accounts? The answer lies in the fact that you have another piece of information in the sample, an estimate of the proportion of accounts that have zero differences. This turns out to be $\left(\frac{25}{40}\right) = .625$. If the firm has 1000 accounts, you would expect about 625 of them to show no difference between the book and audit values, and the other 375 to show some difference. Roughly speaking, the interval based on the adjusted data estimates the mean difference for the 375 accounts.

You can estimate the total, then, by simply multiplying both ends of the interval by 375 to obtain (22.5, 12,727.5). This is a huge interval—so huge, in fact, that it is practically meaningless. You need a much bigger sample to estimate the total precisely, especially if a large portion of the sample is going to yield 0's.

Review

Review Exercises

E38. *Check conditions.* The countries were randomly selected, and the measurements are paired by country, so the differences can be analyzed as a single random sample. The boxplot of the differences, with the male measurements subtracted from the female, shows one outlier (Mauritius with a difference of 8 years). No simple transformation will work well here, so it is better to analyze the data both with and without the outlier to see its effect.

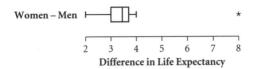

Do computations. The 95% confidence interval using all the data is

$$\bar{d} \pm t^* \cdot \frac{s_d}{\sqrt{n}} \text{ or } 3.64 \pm 2.262 \cdot \frac{1.673}{\sqrt{10}}$$

or (2.44, 4.84).

The 95% interval without the outlier is

$$2.61 < \mu_d < 3.705$$

which is a little narrower because of the smaller sample standard deviation. The influence of the outlier is not as much as we may have suspected.

Write a conclusion in context. There is evidence to say that the difference between the means is positive, which implies that the population mean life expectancy for females is larger than that for males.

E39. **a.** The study was motivated in part by the expectation, based on theory, that concentrations would be higher near the river bottom than at mid-depth. Thus, a one-sided alternate is appropriate here. The null hypothesis is that the mean aldrin concentration at the bottom equals the mean concentration at mid-depth; the alternate is that the mean concentration is higher at the bottom. If you define μ_M and μ_B as the mean concentrations at mid-depth and bottom, these hypotheses may be written as $H_0: \mu_M = \mu_B$ and $H_a: \mu_M < \mu_B$.
b. There is no explicit randomization, and so caution is in order. However, it is reasonable to think of the sampling process as inheriting a kind of quasi-randomness due to the river current.
c. The following figure shows boxplots for the aldrin concentrations.

Center: Concentrations tend to be somewhat higher for samples taken near the bottom, just as predicted by the theory.

Spread: The bottom concentrations are a bit more spread out than the mid-depth concentrations. Note that it is the group

with the higher values that shows the greater spread. This is typical of concentrations, which often behave "better" after transforming to a new scale. (Remember that pH is the logarithm of a concentration, so this might be a good transformation to try.)

Symmetry/Skewness: The distribution of concentrations from bottom samples is slightly skewed toward larger values, but not enough to have a major affect on the *t*-procedures. This pattern is another consequence of a tendency for larger values to show larger spreads.

Outliers: None.

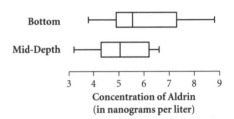

d. A two-sample *t*-test on the difference between population means without transforming the data gives the following results:

State your hypotheses.
$H_0: \mu_M - \mu_B = 0$
$H_a: \mu_M - \mu_B < 0$

Compute the test statistic and draw a sketch. The test statistic is

$$t = \frac{(\bar{x}_1 - \bar{x}_2) - 0}{\sqrt{\dfrac{s_1^2}{n_1} + \dfrac{s_2^2}{n_2}}}$$

$$= \frac{(5.05 - 6.04) - 0}{\sqrt{\dfrac{1.10^2}{10} + \dfrac{1.58^2}{10}}}$$

$$\approx -1.625$$

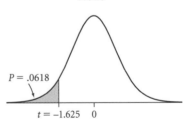

With approximately 16 degrees of freedom, the *P*-value is .0618.

Write a conclusion in context. The *P*-value of .06 leads to the decision that we can not reject the null hypothesis at the .05

significance level. This is a small *P*-value, however, so it does provide some evidence in favor of the alternate of differing means—perhaps enough evidence to suggest that the experimenter should repeat the study in order to obtain more data.

The two-sided test done in the example on pages 538 and 539 of the student text shows little evidence in favor of the alternate, and the decision made there was not to reject the null hypothesis. One-sided tests often lead to different conclusions than those coming from two-sided tests using the same data, so it is important to specifying the alternate of interest *before* looking at the data.

e. The borderline results do cast suspicion on H_0, but the conclusion here is limited not so much by the *P*-value as by a lack of support for generalizing. The analysis has looked only at one pollutant, aldrin, at only one site on only one river. For the evidence to be strong enough to argue for a change in the EPA's measurement protocol, you would need additional studies. In this context, it doesn't really matter much whether the *P*-value in part d is .06 or .01.

E40. **a.** The null hypothesis is that the mean time until the next eruption is the same for the two groups, short (following an eruption of 3 minutes or less) and long (following an eruption of more than 3 minutes). The alternate hypothesis is that the means are unequal. You could also argue that a one-sided alternate is appropriate here, because theory predicts a shorter waiting time following a shorter eruption, and vice-versa. If μ_S and μ_L are the mean waiting times following short and long eruptions, the hypotheses are H_0: $\mu_S = \mu_L$ versus either H_a: $\mu_S \neq \mu_L$ or H_a: $\mu_S < \mu_L$.

b. There is no explicit randomization here. Samples were not chosen using a chance device, and the conditions of interest (long or short eruptions) could not be assigned, and so could not be randomly assigned. Moreover, the measurements come from a time series, and it is reasonable to expect the conditions affecting the duration of an eruption or time to the next eruption to be closely related to the conditions affecting the duration of the following eruption and time

until the eruption after that. In short, it is almost certain that the data do not satisfy the independence assumption.

c. The standard deviations for the two distributions are quite close, and the distributions are roughly symmetric. (Because of the large sample sizes, the slight skewness in the short group is not an issue.) There are a few outliers, but here, too, the large sample sizes provide reassurance. Note also that removing the four outliers shown in the plot will strengthen the already strong evidence of a difference.

d. After eruptions that last less than 3 minutes ($n = 67$), the average waiting time is 54.46 minutes, with a standard deviation of 6.3; after eruptions that last longer than 3 minutes ($n = 155$), the average waiting time is 78.16 minutes, with a standard deviation of 6.89 minutes. A two-sample *t*-statistic computed from the summary statistics is huge ($t = 25.0$ with 136.3 degrees of freedom and *P*-value essentially 0), and H_0 is rejected.

e. The *P*-value is so extremely small that issues of one-sided versus two-sided alternates and some adjustment for observations that are correlated in time are of no concern. You don't need a statistical test to conclude that there is a "real" difference in waiting times for the two groups of eruptions.

Note that this is an example where it would be hard to satisfy the independent random sampling that the *t*-test needs in order to be valid, but the evidence is so clear cut that you don't need fine-tuned statistics to decide that the difference is real.

E41. **a.** *Check conditions.* The batting averages are selected from a population that is approximately normal. It is assumed in the hypotheses that the batting averages of the 15 regular players on a team are randomly selected, although this is obviously not the case in practice. Here you are checking to see whether the team average (for a team selected for particular skills) is really better than one selected at random.

State your hypotheses. The null hypothesis is that 15 players are randomly selected from a population with mean of 250. The alternate is that this is not the case.

Compute the test statistic and draw a sketch.
Because σ is known, the test statistic is

$$z = \frac{\bar{x} - \mu_0}{\sigma/\sqrt{n}} = \frac{267 - 250}{50/\sqrt{15}} \approx 1.32$$

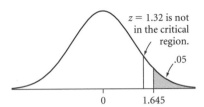

z = 1.32 is not in the critical region.

.05

0   1.645

Write a conclusion in context. The *z*-statistic for the observed sample mean is only 1.32, which implies that the null hypothesis can not be rejected at the 5% level ($z^{\star} = 1.645$). There is no evidence to suggest that the batting average of the New York Yankees is any better than one that would be obtained from 15 players selected at random.

b. *Check conditions.* Same as part a.

State your hypotheses. Same as part a.

Compute the test statistic and draw a sketch.
The test statistic is

$$z = \frac{\bar{x} - \mu_0}{\sigma/\sqrt{n}} = \frac{288 - 250}{50/\sqrt{15}} \approx 2.94$$

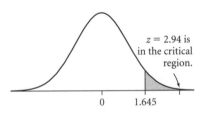

z = 2.94 is in the critical region.

0   1.645

Write a conclusion in context. The *z*-statistic for the observed sample mean is 2.94, which implies that the null hypothesis can be rejected at the 5% level ($z^{\star} = 1.645$). There is sufficient evidence to suggest that the batting average of the Seattle Mariners is better than one that would be obtained from 15 players selected at random.

E42. a. You have paired data: There is one sample of eight brands, with two measurements, sidestream and mainstream, on each brand.
b. Good estimates for the *P*-value would be .001 or .01. The evidence of a difference is very strong, and students should be able to see that and recognize that the *P*-value will be correspondingly low.
c. There is little justification for regarding the eight brands as a random sample

chosen from all brands. For any given brand, cigarettes are uniform enough that it is reasonable to regard the values in the data as typical of all cigarettes of that brand, but the justification comes from the consistent pattern, not from the logic of random samples. Moreover, because the message from the numbers is so overwhelmingly clear, it is reasonable to expect the pattern to generalize to other brands, but here, also, the justification does not come from the logic of random samples.

The two "conditions" being compared, sidestream versus mainstream, can not be assigned as in a true experiment, so inference about cause, of the sort that you can make from experimental data, is not possible here.

The only statistical inference you can make here is to rule out a pattern caused just by chance: Is the observed difference too big to have occurred just by chance? In this kind of inference, you use *P*-values as a kind of ruler for measuring the size of the observed difference.

d. A scatterplot shows no evidence of a positive correlation (between sidestream and mainstream readings) of the sort that indicates that a paired *t*-test will give much lower *P*-values than a two-sample *t*-test. Brand H stands out because of its high sidestream and low mainstream carbon monoxide.

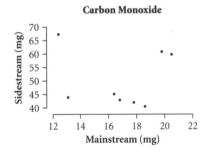

Carbon Monoxide

e. A stemplot for the differences is strongly skewed toward high values.

```
2| 19 42 61 87      Key: 2|19 = 21.9
3| 08 93
4| 10
5| 49
```

Because the sample size is only 8, you should expect the skewness to lead to a capture rate that is less than advertised. It follows that the *P*-value will be artificially (and incorrectly) low.

f. Here are summaries.

	Sidestream	Mainstream	Side − Main
n	8	8	8
$\bar{y}$	50.29	16.93	33.36
s	10.54	2.93	11.04

The paired *t*-statistic is $t = 8.54$ on 7 *df*, which gives a two-tailed *P*-value far below .001.

The two-sample *t*-statistic is $t = 8.629$ on 8.1 degrees of freedom, with a *P*-value far below .001. The *P*-values of $< .001$ are similar, which was what was predicted in parts b and d.

g. Here the evidence is so strong, "you don't need a weatherman to know which way the wind blows." For the eight brands tested, the carbon monoxide levels in sidestream smoke are much higher than the levels in mainstream smoke. A difference this large can not be reasonably attributed to chance.

E43. a. A scatterplot shows little evidence of correlation and in other respects is not very informative. A side-by-side boxplot, however, shows how strikingly different the two sets of nicotine levels are. For sidestream smoke, the yields are large, and the spread is also large. For mainstream smoke, the yields are less than one-third as high and show hardly any variation. (Note that here, even more than for the pesticide concentrations, center and spread are related, with large values showing large spread, and vice versa.)

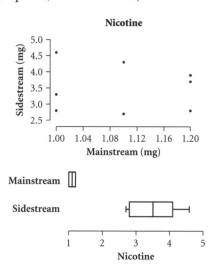

b. A stemplot of the differences shows none of the skewness that characterizes the carbon monoxide readings.

```
1| 6 6 8    Key: 1|6 = 1.6
2| 3 5 7
3| 2 6
```

There is nothing in this plot to raise concerns about a *t*-test.

c. The null hypothesis is that the mean difference in nicotine yields is zero:
H_0: $\mu(side - main) = 0$.
The alternate is that the yields are unequal:
H_a: $\mu(side - main) \neq 0$.

	Sidestream	Mainstream	Side − Main
n	8	8	8
$\bar{y}$	3.51	1.1	2.41
s	0.73	0.09	0.74

The test statistic is

$$t = \frac{2.41 - 0}{0.74/\sqrt{8}} \approx 9.211$$

on 7 *df*. Computing directly from the data, $t \approx 9.226$. The corresponding *P*-value is approximately 0, resulting in a decision to reject H_0.

d. For these eight brands, the evidence is overwhelming: Sidestream smoke contains higher levels of nicotine than does main-stream smoke. A difference this large could not be attributed to chance alone.

E44. A scatterplot shows a weak negative relation-ship: Brands with higher levels of sidestream tar tend to have lower levels of mainstream tar, and vice versa. Side-by-side boxplots show two distributions whose spreads are roughly equal and whose shapes are only mildly skewed, with no outliers.

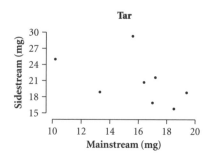

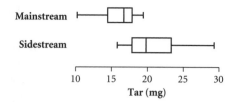

A stemplot of the differences shows nothing remarkable.

```
Differences: -2.7, -0.6, -0.1, 4.3, 4.4, 5.6,
13.7, 14.8
-0|01 06 27      Key:  -0|01 = -0.1
 0|43 44 56            0|43 =  4.3
 1|37 48              1|37 = 13.7
```

Here are summary statistics.

	Sidestream	Mainstream	Side − Main
n	8	8	8
$\bar{y}$	20.88	15.95	4.93
s	4.45	2.96	6.43

The test statistic (paired t) is

$$t = \frac{4.93 - 0}{6.43/\sqrt{8}} \approx 2.169$$

on 7 *df*, with a two-sided *P*-value of .07.

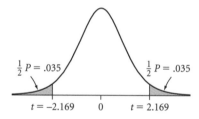

The evidence here is much less strong than for carbon monoxide or nicotine. For three of the eight brands, tar levels were actually higher in mainstream smoke. Although the test, if taken at face value, tends to confirm what is apparent just from inspection of the data, the test's main value here is to quantify how much weaker the evidence is for tar than for carbon monoxide or nicotine. The differences for tar could be due to chance alone.

E45. a. As the description makes clear, there is one set (sample) of subjects, with two measurements on each subject—control and alcohol.

b. A scatterplot shows one clear outlier, Subject 10, with readings of 900 and 900: an endurance champion as well as an outlier.

The remaining nine points lie scattered about a line with slope near zero, with no evidence of any association, positive or negative. Side-by-side boxplots confirm the presence of the outlier; what makes Subject 10 unusual is the long period of useful consciousness after drinking whiskey.

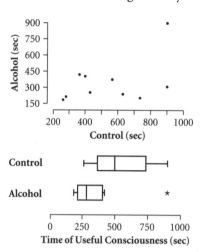

The two distributions are roughly symmetric, with only a slight skewness toward high values. However, the spreads are unequal, with the larger spread belonging to the group with the larger values, as is so often the case for waiting-time data.

A stemplot of the differences shows a distribution skewed toward the high values:

```
-0| 05 55
 0| 00 65 76
 1| 75 90
 2|
 3| 90
 4|
 5| 30 90
```

Notice that the outlying Subject 10 contributes a difference of 0, which falls in the middle part of the data: Removing the outlier won't have much effect on the *P*-value.

Here the null hypothesis is that alcohol has no effect on the mean duration of useful consciousness. On the basis of physiology, you can rule out the possibility that alcohol increases the mean duration, which leaves as the alternate hypothesis H_a: $\mu_A < \mu_C$, where μ_A and μ_C are the mean durations after alcohol and under the control conditions, respectively. This is the same as saying the mean of the differences, μ_{C-A}, is greater than zero.

c. The summary statistics for these data are shown next.

	Control	Alcohol	C − A
n	10	10	10
$\bar{y}$	546.6	351.0	195.6
s	238.81	210.88	230.53

The 95% confidence interval for μ_{C-A} is

$$\bar{d} \pm t^* \cdot \frac{s_d}{\sqrt{n}} \text{ or } 195.6 \pm 2.262 \cdot \frac{230.53}{\sqrt{10}}$$

or (30.69, 360.51).

As usual μ_{C-A} refers to a "true" mean of differences, here the difference in duration of useful consciousness, but because there is no explicit randomization, you can't pin down to what "true difference" refers. Because the subjects are not a random sample from a population, there is no straightforward way to figure out to whom, other than the subjects themselves, the results apply. Moreover, all the subjects received the control conditions first, treatment second, so the observed difference could, in principle, be due to something other than alcohol that was linked to the order, although this seems doubtful. A reasonable conclusion is that alcohol appears to reduce the duration of useful consciousness at high altitude, but that it remains to be established how true this is in general.

E46. Using $z^* = 2$ for an approximate 95% confidence interval, the required sample sizes are as follows.

a. $n = \left(\dfrac{z^* \cdot \sigma}{E}\right)^2 = \left(\dfrac{2 \cdot 2.5}{2}\right)^2 = 6.25$ or 7

b. $n = \left(\dfrac{z^* \cdot \sigma}{E}\right)^2 = \left(\dfrac{2 \cdot 2.5}{1}\right)^2 = 25$

c. $n = \left(\dfrac{z^* \cdot \sigma}{E}\right)^2 = \left(\dfrac{2 \cdot 2.5}{0.5}\right)^2 = 100$

Using $z^* = 1.96$, the sample sizes are 6.0025 or 7, 24.01 or 25, and 96.04 or 97, respectively.

E47. a. Here the alternate hypothesis is that the special course raises scores by more than 30 points or, more formally, that the mean score for those assigned to take the course is more than 30 points higher than the mean

for those assigned to the control group. In symbols, H_a: $\mu_{course} > 30 + \mu_{control}$.

The null hypothesis is conventionally stated as H_0: $\mu_{course} = 30 + \mu_{control}$, although, informally, you can think of the null hypothesis as the "opposite" of the alternate, namely, that the special course does not raise scores by more than 30 points, or H_0: $\mu_{course} \leq 30 + \mu_{control}$. This is equivalent to H_0: $\mu_{course} - \mu_{control} \leq 30$. (Does it matter whether $\mu_{course} = 30 + \mu_{control}$ is part of the null hypothesis or part of the alternate? Not really, but the usual convention is to place the equality in the null hypothesis so that it provides a constant as a standard against which to compare the observed sample mean in the test statistic. If we reject the hypothesis that a population mean is equal to a specified constant in favor of an alternative that is larger, then we would certainly reject any smaller hypothesized value of the population mean as well.)

b. You reject H_0 if the confidence interval for $(\mu_{course} - \mu_{control})$ falls to the right of 30.

c. The t-statistic is given by

$$t = \frac{(\bar{x}_1 - \bar{x}_2) - (\mu_1 - \mu_2)_0}{\sqrt{\dfrac{s_1^2}{n_1} + \dfrac{s_2^2}{n_2}}}$$

$$= \frac{(1100 - 1060) - 30}{\sqrt{\dfrac{100^2}{16} + \dfrac{80^2}{16}}}$$

$$\approx 0.312$$

which is not close to being significant at any reasonable level.

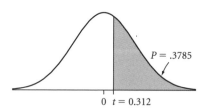

$P = .3785$

$0 \quad t = 0.312$

The 95% confidence interval for the difference of means runs from −25.5 to 105.5. Because 30 is well within this interval, the evidence, again, is not strong enough to reject H_0.

E48. From E43, the observed mean difference is 2.41, with the standard deviation of differences equal to 0.74. The null hypothesis is that the mean difference is 2 mg, and the alternate hypothesis is that the mean difference is greater than 2 mg. The t-statistic is

$$t = \frac{\bar{d} - \mu_{do}}{s/\sqrt{n}} = \frac{2.41 - 2}{0.74/\sqrt{8}} = \frac{0.41}{.261} \approx 1.57$$

With 7 degrees of freedom, a one-sided P-value is .0805. (Computing directly from the data gives $t \approx 1.578$ and P-value .0793.)

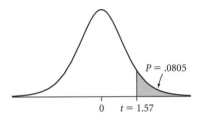

$P = .0805$

$0 \quad t = 1.57$

A 95% confidence interval for the true mean difference is

$$2.41 \pm (2.365)(.261) \text{ or } (1.79 \text{ to } 3.03)$$

Because the P-value for the test is fairly large, or because the confidence interval contains the null value of 2.0, we do not reject H_0. In other words, the evidence, though suggestive, is not strong enough to rule out the possibility that the true difference is 2 or less.

All this assumes that "true difference" has a clear meaning related to the observed data by way of a probability model for the data production process. As discussed in the solution to E42, part c, such an assumption has little basis in fact.

E49. Assuming a random sample when there really was no randomness in the data collection process will not cut it, so to speak. The techniques of inference will not work without randomness, and imagining randomness is about as effective as imagining that you have a can opener. It is better to refer to random sampling or random assignment of treatment as required conditions for an inference procedure to work rather than as something you "assume."

E50. **a.** The data are severely skewed toward the larger values, so a transformation is in order to bring the data closer to normal. It would seem natural to try a logarithmic transformation on these skewed distributions, but there are zeros in the data and log 0 is undefined. As logs are similar to power transformations with powers less than one, a square root or cube root might work. You

can see in the three boxplots here that the cube root transformation does quite well in bringing the data for the two treatments into symmetry with no outliers but does not do quite as well with the placebo data. In fact, no transformation will make the placebo data symmetric because so many of the data points pile up at zero.

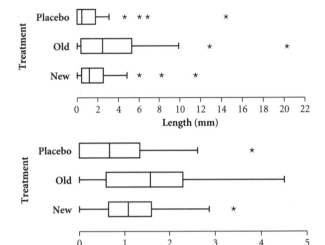

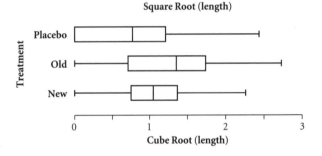

b. The estimate of the difference in means should be made on the cube root scale, but analyses for both the transformed and original scales will be presented for comparison.

With 90% confidence, $0.205 < \mu(old{:}cube\ rt) - \mu(placebo{:}cube\ rt) < 0.785$.

With 90% confidence, $0.586 < \mu(old{:}length) - \mu(placebo{:}length) < 3.757$.

c. Again, both the transformed and untransformed versions will be supplied. With 90% confidence, $0.039 < \mu(new{:}cube\ rt) - \mu(placebo{:}cube\ rt) < 0.545$.

With 90% confidence, $-0.634 < \mu(new{:}length) - \mu(placebo{:}length) < 1.587$.

d. Again, both versions will be presented.

With 90% confidence, $-0.064 < \mu(old{:}cube\ rt) - \mu(new{:}cube\ rt) < 0.469$.

With 90% confidence, $0.167 < \mu(old{:}length) - \mu(new{:}length) < 3.224$.

e. There is sufficient evidence (90% confidence) to say that the old treatment produces longer mean lengths than the placebo; both the original and transformed data tell the same story here. As to the comparisons between the new treatment and the placebo and between the old and new treatments, the two analyses produce conflicting results. The conflict should be settled by having the analyses based on the transformed data take precedence. Thus, the new treatment produces longer mean lengths than the placebo, but the old and the new treatments do not differ significantly with regard to mean lesion length.

Overall, the new treatment is closer to the placebo than the old, and that is good news for the producers of the new treatment. However, more data needs to be collected before it can be stated confidently that the new is better than the old.

10

CHI-SQUARE TESTS

Overview

This chapter describes three types of chi-square tests: a goodness-of-fit test, a test of homogeneity, and a test of independence. We will begin with the goodness-of-fit test, which is the easiest for most students to understand, and we will use it to introduce the principles and mechanics of chi-square tests. The test of homogeneity and test of independence then follow easily and naturally.

Goals

In this chapter, students should learn

- to recognize, conduct, and understand the chi-square test for goodness-of-fit and to see that it is an extension of a significance test on a single proportion
- to recognize, conduct, and understand the chi-square test for homogeneity and to see that it is an extension of the significance test of equality of two population proportions
- to recognize, conduct, and understand the chi-square test of independence and to see that the notion of statistical independence of two variables measured on the same subjects is new, that this test is not an extension of any that have come before, even though it looks similar to the test for homogeneity (This idea can help set the stage for regression analysis, which is presented in the next chapter.)
- to see connections between analysis of counts and interpretations of the results based on sample proportions

Content Overview

For students who are already familiar with the basics of statistical inference, this chapter should require only about nine class periods for thorough coverage, three for each section.

In Section 10.1, students will be using the data given in the introduction about the die that was rolled 60 times. If you prefer, you can bring in your own die, have a student roll it 60 times, and use that data. Some teachers have "loaded" a die so that it actually is unfair. Another possibility is to ask a student who has the tools to make a small die out of wood and then have the class test to see how fair it is.

Time Required

Traditional Schedule			Block	4 x 4 Block
Section 10.1				
2–3 days	Day 1	Test statistic for chi-square tests, distribution of chi-square, Activity 10.1	3 days	2 long
	Day 2	Using a table of chi-square values, chi-square goodness-of-fit test		
	Day 3	Expected value, chi-square test versus the z-test, summary, exercises		
Section 10.2				
2–3 days	Day 1	Categorical data with two variables, computing expected counts	3 days	2 long
	Day 2	Computing the chi-square statistic, procedure for chi-square test of homogeneity		
	Day 3	Multiple z-tests versus one chi-square test, degrees of freedom, summary, exercises		
Section 10.3				
3–4 days	Day 1	Independence, Activity 10.2, graphical display of data, expected values	3 days	2 long, 1 short
	Day 2	Procedure for chi-square test of independence, homogeneity versus independence		
	Day 3	Strength of association and sample size, summary, exercises		
Review				
1 day			1 day	1 day

Materials

Section 10.1: For Activity 10.1, one die for each group of students. If you do the suggested activity Counting Peanut M&M's, on page 194 of this Instructor's Guide, you will need a one-pound bag of peanut M&M's.

Section 10.2: None. If you do the suggested activity Paper Towel Experiment, on page 204 of this Instructor's Guide, you will need one roll each of three brands of paper towels and a golf ball and ruler for each group of students.

Section 10.3: None

Suggested Assignments

Classwork			
Section	**Essential**	**Recommended**	**Optional**
10.1	Activity 10.1 D1–D14 P1–P6	D15, D16 P7	
10.2	D17–D20 P8–P10		
10.3	Activity 10.2 D21, D23, D26–D31, D33, D34 P12–P15	D22, D25, D32 P11, P16	D24

Homework			
Section	**Essential**	**Recommended**	**Optional**
10.1	E1–E3	E4–E6	E7–E11
10.2	E12, E13, E15, E17	E16, E19, E20	E14, E18
10.3	E21–E23	E24, E25	
Review	E27–E29, E31, E35	E26, E30, E32, E34, E36	E33, E37

10.1 Testing a Probability Model: The Chi-Square Goodness-of-Fit Test

Objectives

- to become familiar with the chi-square statistic, χ^2, and with how its distribution changes as the degrees of freedom change
- to find expected values and degrees of freedom
- to recognize when to use a chi-square goodness-of-fit test
- to perform a chi-square goodness-of-fit test and to understand that it answers the question "Does this look like a random sample from a population in which the proportions that fall into these categories are the same as those hypothesized?"
- to see that the chi-square goodness-of-fit test is an extension of the significance test for a single proportion

Important Terms and Concepts

- goodness-of-fit test
- chi-square statistic
- chi-square distribution
- degrees of freedom (df)

Lesson Planning

Class Time

Two to three days

Materials

For Activity 10.1, one die for each group of students. If you do the suggested activity Counting Peanut M&M's, on page 194 of this Instructor's Guide, you will need a one-pound bag of peanut M&M's.

Suggested Assignments

Classwork		
Essential	**Recommended**	**Optional**
Activity 10.1	D15, D16	
D1–D14	P7	
P1–P6		

Homework		
Essential	**Recommended**	**Optional**
E1–E3	E4–E6	E7–E11

All of the Discussion questions should be covered in class. You can do this in at least three ways as you come to each question in the material.

1. Lead your class in a discussion.
2. Have groups of students discuss the question. To bring the class together at the end, you may want to ask a group to present its solution to the class.
3. Incorporate the answers to discussion questions in your presentation of the material.

Lesson Notes: A Test Statistic

Introducing a Chi-Square Goodness-of-Fit Test

Here is an example you can use in your class to introduce the chi-square goodness-of-fit test.

Chi-square tests compare the number of items in a sample that fall into different categories with the number of items that you would expect to fall into the categories under a given probability model. For example, suppose 25 balls are thrown into 5 bins. If the balls are no more likely to go into one bin than another, you would expect the following "ideal" result:

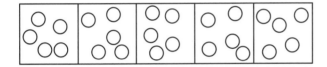

Suppose that the following result is observed from the sample:

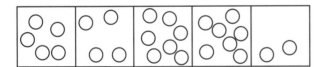

Is this a reasonably likely result if a ball is equally likely to go into any bin? Or is the result from the sample so different from the expected result that you have to assume that you have the wrong probability model?

Lesson Notes: Toward a Test Statistic

The Test Statistic

Test statistics that students have encountered previously have been of the form

$$\frac{estimate - parameter}{standard\ deviation\ of\ the\ estimate}$$

The χ^2 statistic is a bit different and is of the form

$$\sum \frac{(estimate - parameter)^2}{parameter}$$

where "estimate" is the observed frequency and "parameter" is the expected frequency.

Discussion

D1. The null hypothesis is that the die is fair or, in other words, the probability that each face will come up is $\frac{1}{6}$. The alternate hypothesis is that the die is not fair.

D2. **a.** $\sum(O - E) = 2 + (-1) + 0 + (-4) + 1 + 2 = 0$

b. Yes, the sum of the values $(O - E)$ is always 0:

$$\sum(O - E) = \sum O - \sum E$$
$$= 0$$

because the sum of the observed frequencies must equal the sample size, as must the sum of the expected frequencies.

c. No, because it gives the same value, 0, for every sample.

D3. The sum of the deviations from the mean is always 0. The sum of the residuals from the least-squares regression line is always 0. In both cases, to get a measure of distance we squared the deviations before adding them.

D4. **a.** $\sum(O - E)^2 = 4 + 1 + 0 + 16 + 1 + 4 = 26$

b. Die A appears more likely to be unfair. For each outcome, the two tables have exactly the same value of $(O - E)$, but the percentages are different. For example, for Die A, a 1 occurs only about 8% of the time, whereas a 3 occurs 30% of the time. However, for Die B, each outcome occurs close to $\frac{1}{6} \approx 16.7\%$ of the time, which is what we expect from a fair die. Because Die B does so well with such a large sample size, we don't have any evidence that it is unfair.

Even though we expect more variability in the percentages when the sample size is small, the percentages from Die A are far enough from 16.7% that we will have to select it as the more likely to be the unfair die.

c. Because the two tables have exactly the same values of $(O - E)$ for each possible outcome, the values of $\Sigma(O - E)^2$ are also the same,

$$25 + 36 + 64 + 36 + 25 + 4 = 190$$

This does not appear to be a reasonable test statistic because it gives the same value for Die A, which we suspect may not be fair, and Die B, which certainly appears to be fair.

Lesson Notes: A Test Statistic

Discussion

D5. You reject the null hypothesis that the die is fair if χ^2 is relatively large. Roll a die that you know is fair 60 times and compute χ^2. Repeat this many times until you find out whether a value of 2.6 or larger is a rare event with a fair die.

D6. For Die A,

$$\chi^2 = \Sigma\frac{(O - E)^2}{E}$$

$$= \frac{(-5)^2}{10} + \frac{6^2}{10} + \frac{8^2}{10} + \frac{(-6)^2}{10} + \frac{(-5)^2}{10} + \frac{2^2}{10}$$

$$= \frac{190}{10}$$

$$= 19.0$$

For Die B, see the equation at the bottom of the page. Yes, the larger value of χ^2 corresponds to the die that looks more unfair.

Dividing by E prevents the categories with large expected values from dominating the

value of χ^2. In other words, dividing by E gives us a relative squared error. With larger sample sizes, we expect the values of $(O - E)$ to be larger than they are with smaller sample sizes even though the observed proportions may be relatively close to the expected proportions in each category. Dividing by E means that, essentially, we are adding the differences in the proportions, not just the differences in the actual numbers.

D7. Add the observed frequencies to get the sample size n. Then multiply n by each hypothesized proportion to get the expected frequencies.

D8. A sum of squared differences appears in the formula for the standard deviation. Minimizing the SSE, or sum of squared errors, is the criterion for the least squares regression line.

Practice

P1. For a tetrahedral die, we'd expect each face to come up one-fourth of the time, so we'd expect in each category to have a count of $\frac{50}{4}$, or 12.5. The value of χ^2 would be as shown at the bottom of page 193.

P2. 0

Lesson Notes: The Distribution of Chi-Square

In the following activity, students will use simulation to generate a χ^2 distribution with 5 degrees of freedom. They will then be able to compare the value of $\chi^2 = 2.6$ for the die in the *Fair Die* example with this distribution to see whether $\chi^2 = 2.6$ is a rare event for a fair die.

Lesson 10.1, D6

$$\chi^2 = \Sigma\frac{(O - E)^2}{E}$$

$$= \frac{(-5)^2}{1000} + \frac{6^2}{1000} + \frac{8^2}{1000} + \frac{(-6)^2}{1000} + \frac{(-5)^2}{1000} + \frac{2^2}{1000}$$

$$= \frac{190}{1000}$$

$$= 0.190$$

Activity 10.1: Generating the Chi-Square Distribution

1. Make sure you have enough dice for every group to have one or two. Values of χ^2 will vary depending on the results the class gets.

2. On a TI-83, enter randInt(1,6,60). To get the randInt(command, press [MATH] PRB 5:RandInt(.

3. Enter randInt(1,6,60)→L1 to store the results in list L1. Then sort the list (or make a histogram with Xmin = 0.5, Xmax = 6.5, and Xscl = 1) and count the number of 1's, 2's, 3's, 4's, 5's, and 6's. Place these observed frequencies in list L2. In list L3, place the expected frequencies of 10, 10, 10, 10, 10, and 10. On the homescreen, compute

$$\chi^2 = \Sigma \frac{(O-E)^2}{E}$$

by entering sum((L2 − L3)²/L3). To get the sum(command, press [2nd] [LIST] MATH 5:sum(.

4. Here's a sample histogram for 200 trials of rolling a die 60 times each and computing χ^2. The histogram is skewed right.

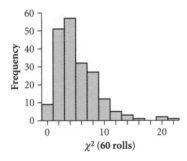

5. This should be a one-tailed test because an unfair die results in a value of χ^2 that is far from 0. From the histogram in step 4, the estimated P-value for $\chi^2 = 2.6$ is about $\frac{150}{200}$, or .75. There is about a 75% chance of getting a value of χ^2 of 2.6 or greater if a fair die is rolled 60 times, so $\chi^2 = 2.6$ is a reasonably likely outcome.

The Chi-Square Distribution

The χ^2 distribution, like the normal distribution, is a continuous distribution. As the number of categories increases, the χ^2 distribution approaches a normal distribution. For example, here is the histogram of 5000 values of χ^2 taken from a distribution with 100 categories or 99 degrees of freedom.

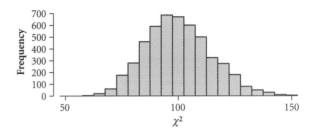

Be sure that students understand what the histograms on page 582 of the student text represent. For the tetrahedral die, for example, the computer simulated rolling a fair tetrahedral die 60 times and χ^2 was computed. This procedure was repeated until there were 5000 values of χ^2. These 5000 values were then plotted in the histogram.

Students may notice that the mean of these distributions lies at the number of categories minus 1, which is called the degrees of freedom, *df*. That is, $\mu = df$. The variance of a χ^2 distribution is $\sigma^2 = 2 \cdot df$.

Discussion

D9. As the number of categories increases, the distribution stretches out and moves to the right. That is, the mean and standard deviation increase. The shape gradually becomes less skewed and more mound-shaped.

D10. Icosahedral die; tetrahedral die. More categories means more variation.

D11. Because 5% of 5000 is 250, we are looking for the value that cuts off about 250 values in the upper tail.

Tetrahedral die: about 8
Regular die: about 11
Octahedral die: about 14
Dodecahedral die: about 19 or 20
Icosahedral die: about 30

Lesson 10.1, P1

$$\chi^2 = \frac{\Sigma(O-E)^2}{E} = \frac{(14-12.5)^2}{12.5} + \frac{(17-12.5)^2}{12.5} + \frac{(9-12.5)^2}{12.5} + \frac{(10-12.5)^2}{12.5}$$

$$= 3.28$$

Lesson Notes: Using a Table of Chi-Square Values

Finding the *P*-Value on a TI-83

To find the upper-tail *P*-value for a computed value of χ^2, use the χ^2cdf(command. You get the command by pressing 2nd [DISTR] 7:χ^2cdf(, and you enter the command in the form χ^2cdf(computed value of χ^2, a very large number, *df*). You can use any very large number, for example 999,999,999,999. The command finds the area under the χ^2 distribution curve between the computed value of χ^2 and the very large number.

Practice

P3. For a 12-sided die, *df* = 11. So, from the table, the *P*-value is about .025. Reject the null hypothesis at $\alpha = .05$. Do not reject the null hypothesis at $\alpha = .01$.

P4. From the table with *df* = 7, the *P*-value is between .0025 and .005. Reject the null hypothesis at $\alpha = .05$. Reject the null hypothesis at $\alpha = .01$.

P5. **a.** .7614
  b. .0304

Lesson Notes: The Chi-Square Goodness-of-Fit Test

Criteria for a Chi-Square Goodness-of-Fit Test

There are two situations in which a chi-square goodness-of-fit test is used. Here are examples.

A. The *Plain Versus Peanut* example on page 585 in the student text is a test of whether peanut M&M's have the same distribution of colors that is known to be the case for plain M&M's. In the example on page 585, we take a random sample of peanut M&M's and find that the distribution of colors in the sample is unlikely to have occurred if peanut M&M's have the same distribution of colors as plain M&M's. In this situation, we have a random sample. So we reject the hypothesis that peanut M&M's have the same distribution of colors as plain M&M's. (If your students would like to do their own test of this situation, the activity is described in the next section.)

B. In P6, students will be given a table of the ages of all people on grand juries in Alameda County, California. They will compare the ages of grand jurors to the ages of all adults in the county. There is no random sample here. The question is whether

the distribution of ages of the grand jurors looks like it could be a random sample from people in the county. It turns out that if you take a random sample from adults in the county, then it would be very unusual to get a group that has an age distribution as old as that of the grand jurors given in P6. We reject the hypothesis that the grand jurors' ages look like a random sample from the population of all adults in the county. Thus some factor must be in operation that makes grand jurors more likely to be older than adults in general.

To incorporate these two situations, the null hypothesis for a chi-square goodness-of-fit test is

H_0: The sample is a random selection from a population with the specified distribution.

These examples show the two ways that this null hypothesis can be rejected:

A. The sample is a random selection from a population with some other distribution than the one hypothesized.

B. The sample is a nonrandom selection from a population with the specified distribution.

Suggested Activity: Counting Peanut M&M's

To turn the example on page 585 of the student text into an activity, you will need a one-pound bag of peanut M&M's.

The way that the M&M's are put into the bags makes each bag a random sample of all M&M's of that type. The M&M's, with colors already on them, are mixed in the proportions below in a very big vat. The M&M's then have the little M stamped on them and go into the bags.

According to the company that makes them, 20% of plain M&M's are red, 20% are yellow, 10% are green, 10% are orange, 30% are brown, and 10% are blue. Do these same percentages apply to peanut M&M's?

1. State how this scenario meets the criteria for a chi-square goodness-of-fit test.

2. State the null and alternate hypotheses.

3. Take a sample of 75 peanut M&M's and count the number of each color.

4. Make a table of the observed number of peanut M&M's of each color.

5. Calculate the expected number of peanut M&M's of each color.

6. Calculate the χ^2 test statistic and refer to the χ^2 table for the corresponding *P*-value.

7. State your conclusion at the .05 and the .01 levels.

A Note on Degrees of Freedom

Degrees of freedom in a chi-square test refers to the number of hypotheses that would have to be tested if you were doing them one at a time. In the case of a six-sided die, you would have to test five of the outcomes to see whether $\frac{1}{6}$ is a plausible value for their probability. Once you determine plausible values for five of the outcomes, the sixth is determined by the fact that the proportions must add to one. (In that case, you may wonder why the table doesn't just use the number of categories rather than the number of categories minus one. It could, but then it wouldn't be as useful for other situations.)

Look at Proportions as Well as Counts

When conducting tests based on counts, it is always good policy also to investigate the relevant proportions to see what pattern these sample proportions might suggest.

Discussion

D12. The expected number for each category is 100. The value of χ^2 is 0.16 with $df = 5$. On a TI-83, the probability of getting a value of χ^2 this close or closer to 0 is

$$\chi^2\text{cdf}(0, 0.16, 5) \approx .000515$$

We reject the hypothesis that these data came from actually rolling a die. It looks as though the student fabricated the data.

D13. **A.** True. The order of the categories does not matter.

B. True, because observed frequencies are counts.

C. False. For example, if you roll a fair die 15 times, the expected number of 1's is $\frac{15}{6}$.

D. False. The number of degrees of freedom is one less than the number of categories.

E. False. It indicates a large difference between the observed frequencies and expected frequencies.

D14. Typically, in a chi-square goodness-of-fit test, you are testing the null hypothesis that the distribution in your sample is consistent with a given hypothesized distribution or probability model. So you reject the null hypothesis if there is a big relative difference between the observed and expected frequencies (which makes χ^2 relatively large and far out in the tail of the distribution). In the case when you are concerned that χ^2 may be *too* close to 0 (as in D12 on page 587 of the student text), you still use a one-tailed test but the critical region is in the left tail.

Practice

P6. We will perform a chi-square goodness-of-fit test on the data shown in the table at the bottom of the page.

Check conditions. This situation meets the criteria for a chi-square goodness-of-fit test. There were 66 jurors selected, but as usual we can't be sure they were independently or randomly selected. This isn't a problem because this is essentially what we want to test. Each juror falls into exactly one of the age groups. We have a model that gives the hypothesized proportion of outcomes in the population that fall into each category. The expected frequency in each category is 5 or greater.

Lesson 10.1, P6

Age	Countrywide Percentage	Observed Number of Grand Jurors	Expected Number of Grand Jurors
21–40	42	5	.42(66), or 27.72
41–50	23	9	.23(66), or 15.18
51–60	16	19	.16(66), or 10.56
61 or older	19	33	.19(66), or 12.54
Total	**100**	**66**	**66**

State your hypotheses.

H_0: The distribution of the ages of the grand jurors looks like a typical random sample from the ages of all adults in this county.

H_a: The distribution of ages of the grand jurors doesn't look like a typical random sample from the ages of all adults in this county.

Compute the test statistic and draw a sketch.

The test statistic is

$$\chi^2 = \Sigma \frac{(O - E)^2}{E}$$

$$\approx 61.27$$

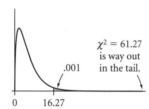

Comparing the test statistic to the χ^2 distribution with $4 - 1 = 3$ degrees of freedom, we find that the value of χ^2 from the sample, 61.27, is very far out in the tail. The *P*-value is 3.15×10^{-13}, or .000000000000315.

Write a conclusion in context. We reject the null hypothesis. We can not attribute the differences to random sampling. A value of χ^2 this large is extremely unlikely to occur if grand jurors are selected without regard to age. Either older people are more likely to be available for grand juries or they are deliberately selected.

P7. **a.** Each digit should occur $\frac{1}{10}$ of the time.

b. We will perform a chi-square goodness-of-fit test on the data. Each expected frequency is $.1(104) = 10.4$.

Check conditions. This situation meets the criteria for a chi-square goodness-of-fit test. There are 104 measurements of the lengths of rivers, presumably independent measurements. However, note that the rivers were not randomly selected—they are 104 of the most important rivers. Perhaps we can view their final digits, however, as a random sample. Each measurement ends in exactly one of the digits. We have a model that gives the hypothesized proportion of outcomes in the population that fall into each category.

The expected frequency in each category is at least 5.

State your hypotheses.

H_0: The probability that the length of a river ends in any given digit is $\frac{1}{10}$.

H_a: The probability is not $\frac{1}{10}$ for all of the digits.

Compute the test statistic and draw a sketch.

The test statistic is

$$\chi^2 = \Sigma \frac{(O - E)^2}{E}$$

$$\approx 131.77$$

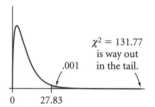

Comparing the test statistic to the χ^2 distribution with $10 - 1 = 9$ degrees of freedom, we find that the value of χ^2 from the sample, 131.77, is very far out in the tail. The *P*-value is 5.13×10^{-24}.

Write a conclusion in context. We reject the null hypothesis. We can not attribute the differences to chance variation. A value of χ^2 this large is extremely unlikely to occur if rivers are accurately measured to the nearest mile and each digit is equally likely to be the final digit. It appears that the measurements were approximated in some cases and not measured to the nearest mile, as there are too many that end in 0 and in 5.

Lesson Notes: Chi-Square Test Versus the *z*-Test

Discussion

D15. In the goodness-of-fit situation, the null hypothesis specifies a probability for each category. If there are only two categories (two possible outcomes) and you specify one probability, the other is determined. Thus, the two-category chi-square test is equivalent to a *z*-test on a single binomial proportion. For the binomial case, comparing the observed count to the expected count is the same as comparing the sample proportion to the hypothesized probability of success.

D16. The responses can be recorded in three categories, and probabilities are specified for each of these categories. A goodness-of-fit test with three categories could be used. However, the claim to be checked involves only those eating off campus versus those not eating off campus. For this test it would be better to conduct a goodness-of-fit test with two categories (off campus and not off campus), which is equivalent to a z-test on the single proportion involving the off-campus eating. The two- and three-category tests are not equivalent; it is better to use the smaller number of categories so as to increase the number of observations per category. Remember that the chi-square procedure is a large sample approximation, as is the z procedure.

Exercises

E1. **a.** The technique in Chapter 8 would be a test of significance of a proportion.

Check conditions. This is a random sample from a potentially infinite population.

State your hypotheses.
H_0: This coin is fair; that is, the probability of getting a head with this coin is .5.
H_a: The coin is not fair.

Compute the test statistic and draw a sketch. The test statistic is $z = 2.8$.

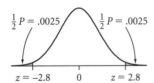

The P-value for a two-tailed test is .005.

Write a conclusion in context. We reject the null hypothesis that the coin is fair. It seems to favor heads.

b. To use a chi-square goodness-of-fit test, we set up this table.

Outcome	Observed	Expected
Heads	64	50
Tails	36	50
Total	100	100

Check conditions. This situation meets the criteria for a chi-square goodness-of-fit test. There were 100 independent coin flips. Each coin flip is either a head or a tail. We have a model that gives the hypothesized proportion of outcomes in the population that fall into each category. The expected frequency in each category is 5 or greater.

State your hypotheses.
H_0: The coin is fair; that is, the probability the coin lands heads is .5, and the probability it lands tails is .5.
H_a: The coin is not fair.

Compute the test statistic and draw a sketch. The test statistic is

$$\chi^2 = \Sigma \frac{(O - E)^2}{E}$$

$$= 7.84$$

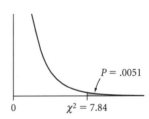

Comparing the test statistic to the χ^2 distribution with $2 - 1 = 1$ degree of freedom, we find that the value of χ^2 from the sample, 7.84, is far out in the tail. The P-value from the table is about .005.

Write a conclusion in context. We reject the null hypothesis. We can not attribute the differences to random variation. A value of χ^2 this large is extremely unlikely to occur if the coin is fair. This coin appears to favor heads.

c. The P-values for the two different techniques are the same. Also, note that the test statistic $z = 2.8$ and $\chi^2 = 7.84$ are related in the following way: $z^2 = \chi^2$. This is always the case and is not hard to prove algebraically.

E2. To use a chi-square goodness-of-fit test, set up the table shown at the bottom of the page.

Check conditions. This situation meets the criteria for a chi-square goodness-of-fit test. There were 20,000 independent rolls. Each roll is a 1, 2, 3, 4, 5, or 6. We have a model that gives the hypothesized proportion of outcomes in the population that fall into each category from which the expected frequencies can be derived. The expected frequency in each category is 5 or greater.

State your hypotheses.

H_0: The die is fair; that is, the probability the die lands on each face is $\frac{1}{6}$.

H_a: The die is not fair.

Compute the test statistic and draw a sketch.
The test statistic is

$$\chi^2 = \sum \frac{(O-E)^2}{E}$$

$$\approx 94.19$$

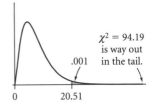

Comparing the test statistic to the χ^2 distribution with $6 - 1 = 5$ degrees of freedom, we find that the value of χ^2 from the sample, 94.19, is very far out in the tail. The P-value from the calculator is 8.841×10^{-19}.

Write a conclusion in context. We reject the null hypothesis. We can not attribute the differences to random variation. A value of χ^2 this large is extremely unlikely to occur if the die is fair. This die (or the method of tossing or recording the results) appears to avoid 4's and favor 2's.

E3. To use a chi-square goodness-of-fit test, we set up the table shown at the bottom of the page.

Check conditions. The sample consists of 200 outcomes, but we aren't told the sample was randomly selected. Each person is classified into exactly one of four categories. We have a model that gives the hypothesized proportion of outcomes in the population that fall into each category. The expected frequency in each category is 5 or greater.

State your hypotheses.

H_0: Admissions are unrelated to birthday. Specifically, the number of people admitted in each time period is proportional to the length of that time period.

Lesson 10.1, E2

	Outcome					
	1	2	3	4	5	6
Observed Frequency	3407	3631	3176	2916	3448	3422
Expected Frequency	3333.3	3333.3	3333.3	3333.3	3333.3	3333.3

Lesson 10.1, E3

Proximity of Birthday	Observed Admissions	Expected Admissions
Within 7 Days	11	$(15/365)200 \approx 8.219$
8–30 Days	24	$(46/365)200 \approx 25.205$
31–90 Days	69	$(120/365)200 \approx 65.753$
More Than 90 Days	96	$(184/365)200 \approx 100.82$
Total	**200**	**200**

H_a: People are more likely to be admitted on days that fall in some time periods than on days that fall in others.

Compute the test statistic and draw a sketch.
The test statistic is

$$\chi^2 = \Sigma \frac{(O - E)^2}{E}$$

$$\approx 1.39$$

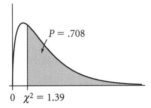

Comparing the test statistic to the χ^2 distribution with $4 - 1 = 3$ degrees of freedom, we find that the value of χ^2 from the sample, 1.39, isn't out in the tail. The P-value is .708.

Write a conclusion in context. We can not reject the null hypothesis that the number of people admitted in each time period is proportional to the length of that time period. The observed differences in admissions can easily be attributed to random variation. However, we don't know whether the admissions were randomly or independently selected. We are told only that they are a "sample." So we should consider this an exploratory test only.

E4. To use a chi-square goodness-of-fit test, we set up this table.

Type of Pea	Observed	Expected
Smooth Yellow	315	$(9/16)556 \approx 312.75$
Wrinkled Yellow	101	$(3/16)556 \approx 104.25$
Smooth Green	108	$(3/16)556 \approx 104.25$
Wrinkled Green	32	$(1/16)556 \approx 34.75$
Total	556	556

Check conditions. We have a sample of 556 peas. Each pea is classified into exactly one of four categories. We have a model that gives the hypothesized proportion of outcomes in the population that fall into each category. The expected frequency in each category is 5 or greater.

State your hypotheses.
H_0: Peas are produced so that $\frac{9}{16}$ are smooth yellow, $\frac{3}{16}$ are wrinkled yellow, $\frac{3}{16}$ are smooth green, and $\frac{1}{16}$ are wrinkled green.
H_a: Peas are produced in some other ratio.

Compute the test statistic and draw a sketch.
The test statistic is

$$\chi^2 = \Sigma \frac{(O - E)^2}{E}$$

$$\approx 0.47$$

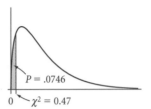

Comparing the test statistic to the χ^2 distribution with $4 - 1 = 3$ degrees of freedom, we find that the value of χ^2 from the sample, 0.47, is close to 0. The probability of getting a P-value this close or even closer to 0 is only .0746.

Write a conclusion in context. This P-value in and of itself is a bit suspicious, but not conclusive. However, Mendel performed several such experiments and in each case, the P-value was suspiciously low, leading statisticians to believe that the data may have been "fudged" to fit his theory. In other words, the results are too close to Mendel's theory to look like a random sample.

E5. Because these data are tied to months of the year, we should first look at a plot over time of the number of births.

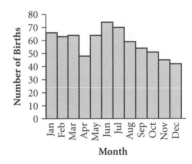

The number of births generally decreases throughout the year, with the most births in the late spring/early summer.

To use a chi-square goodness-of-fit test, we set up this table.

Month	Observed Number of Births	Expected Number of Births
January	66	$(31/365)700 \approx 59.452$
February	63	$(28/365)700 \approx 53.699$
March	64	$(31/365)700 \approx 59.452$
April	48	$(30/365)700 \approx 57.534$
May	64	$(31/365)700 \approx 59.452$
June	74	$(30/365)700 \approx 57.534$
July	70	$(31/365)700 \approx 59.452$
August	59	$(31/365)700 \approx 59.452$
September	54	$(30/365)700 \approx 57.534$
October	51	$(31/365)700 \approx 59.452$
November	45	$(30/365)700 \approx 57.534$
December	42	$(31/365)700 \approx 59.452$
Total	**700**	**700**

Check conditions. There were 700 births, but they all were in one hospital during one particular year. Each birth is classified into exactly 1 of 12 categories. We have a model that gives the hypothesized proportion of outcomes in the population that fall into each category. The expected frequency in each category is 5 or greater.

State your hypotheses.

H_0: The number of births in a month is proportional to the number of days in the month.

H_a: The number of births in a month is not proportional to the number of days in the month for at least one month.

Compute the test statistic and draw a sketch.
The test statistic is

$$\chi^2 = \Sigma \frac{(O - E)^2}{E}$$

$$\approx 20.468$$

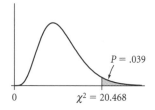

Comparing the test statistic to the χ^2 distribution with $12 - 1 = 11$ degrees of freedom, we find that $\chi^2 = 20.468$ gives a P-value of .039.

Write a conclusion in context. We can reject the null hypothesis if $\alpha = .05$ but not if $\alpha = .01$. It would be a rare event (with $\alpha = .05$) to get a value of χ^2 this large if the number of births in a month is proportional to the number of days in the month. The differences between the observed values and expected values can not easily be attributed to chance variation in the timing of births.

Apparently, there are more births in the late spring/early summer and in the first months of the year. However, we have to be suspicious of the conclusion that the number of births varies by season because we don't have a random sample of births—we have all the births in this particular year for this particular hospital. Births appear generally to decrease over the year, but perhaps women were leaving this part of Switzerland or perhaps a new hospital opened and women started going to it; or there may be some other explanation why the decrease occurred in this hospital at this time.

Students may or may not take into consideration that the months have different lengths. If they assume that the probability of a birth being in any given month is $\frac{1}{12}$, then $\chi^2 = 19.726$ and the P-value is .0492.

E6. A chi-square goodness-of-fit test should not be used on these data as given, as students will discover if they try a chi-square test in pounds and then in ounces. Converting to ounces makes it appear that the sample size is different. We are given the expected percentage of nuts in each category, but have no way of computing the expected frequency or number of nuts in each category.

E7. **a.** As the sample size increases, the value of sample statistics such as the mean of the sample or the proportion of successes in the sample tend to get closer to the mean of the population or the proportion in the population. This property gives a test of significance more power to reject a false null hypothesis. We have seen test statistics of the form

$$\frac{estimate - parameter}{standard\ deviation\ of\ the\ estimate}$$

If the difference between the estimate and the parameter stays the same as the sample size n increases, the standard deviation of the estimate will decrease (because usually it has $\sqrt{n}$ in its denominator). Thus, the test statistic will increase, resulting in a lower P-value.

b. Yes, although this is difficult to see with the chi-square goodness-of-fit test because the table of P-values uses only the number of categories, not the sample size. However, the value of χ^2 itself does depend on the sample size.

The terms in the χ^2 goodness-of-fit statistic are of the form

$$\frac{(O - E)^2}{E} = \frac{(O - np)^2}{np}$$

$$= \frac{n\left(\frac{O}{n} - p\right)^2}{p}$$

$$= \frac{n(\hat{p} - p)^2}{p}$$

If the null hypothesis is false, then at least one sample proportion is converging to something other than the hypothesized p, and the test statistic will increase as n increases.

E8. As the number of degrees of freedom increases, the distribution becomes more mound-shaped, spreads out, and moves to the right. Specifically, the mean increases, the standard deviation increases, and the shape becomes more approximately normal.

E9. Students might answer these questions:

- Are all possible single digits equally likely to occur?

- Are all possible pairs of digits equally likely to occur?

- Are all possible triples of digits equally likely to occur?

E10. Another possible project idea is to look at the last digit of the years on a sample of pennies to see whether they are uniformly distributed. This probably won't be the case because the final digit on this year's and last year's pennies will be more frequent.

E11. a.

Digit k	$\log_{10}(1 + 1/k)$
1	0.301
2	0.176
3	0.125
4	0.097
5	0.079
6	0.067
7	0.058
8	0.051
9	0.046
Total	1.00

b. See equation at the bottom of the page.

c. Many tables of real data follow Benford's Law. It has been hypothesized that this is because many sets of data come from the product of two uniformly distributed variables and such a product approximately follows Benford's Law. For example, the area of a lake may be approximated by measuring the width a and the length b and using the formula for the area of an ellipse: πab.

Lesson 10.1, E11b

$$\log_{10}\left(\frac{1 + 1}{1}\right) + \log_{10}\left(\frac{2 + 1}{2}\right) + \log_{10}\left(\frac{3 + 1}{3}\right) + \cdots + \log_{10}\left(\frac{9 + 1}{9}\right)$$

$$= \log_{10}\left(\frac{2}{1}\right) + \log_{10}\left(\frac{3}{2}\right) + \log_{10}\left(\frac{4}{3}\right) + \cdots + \log_{10}\left(\frac{10}{9}\right)$$

$$= \log_{10}\left(\frac{2}{1} \cdot \frac{3}{2} \cdot \frac{4}{3} \cdot \ldots \cdot \frac{10}{9}\right)$$

$$= \log_{10}10$$

$$= 1$$

Additional Project Ideas

As in the jury example of P6, chi-square tests are often used to determine whether the gender, age, or ethnic distribution of a jury, a work force, or a student body can reasonably be said to reflect the composition of the population at large. There may be an opportunity for your students to collect data on such an issue. Does the ethnic composition of the football team reflect the composition of the entire student body? Does the gender composition of the academic honor society reflect the composition of the entire student body?

However, be sure that your students understand that the chi-square test tells us only whether the result from the sample can reasonably be attributed to chance. That is, it answers the question of whether the sample looks like a random sample from the entire population. If not, then further digging is required to determine the reason. The reason could be anything from a flawed sampling process to discrimination to a difference in qualifications or interest between the groups. The chi-square test does not determine a cause—it merely tells us that the differences between the groups can not reasonably be attributed to chance and therefore we should look for another reason.

10.2 The Chi-Square Test of Homogeneity

Objectives

- to recognize when to use a chi-square test of homogeneity
- to perform a chi-square test of homogeneity and to understand that it answers the question "Do these samples from different populations look like samples from populations in which the proportions that fall into the different categories are equal?"
- to see that the chi-square test of homogeneity is an extension of the significance test for the difference of two proportions
- to learn that the degrees of freedom for this test are based on the number of parameters to be tested rather than on the sample size

Important Terms and Concepts

- homogeneous populations
- two-way table
- stacked or segmented bar graph
- chi-square test of homogeneity

Lesson Planning

Class Time

Two to three days

Materials

None. If you do the suggested activity Paper Towel Experiment, on page 204 of this Instructor's Guide, you will need one roll each of three brands of paper towels and a golf ball and ruler for each group of students.

Suggested Assignments

Classwork		
Essential	**Recommended**	**Optional**
D17–D20		
P8–P10		

Homework		
Essential	**Recommended**	**Optional**
E12, E13, E15, E17	E16, E19, E20	E14, E18

Lesson Notes: Categorical Data with Two Variables

Additional References

Note that the chi-square test of this section helps answer only the simple question "Is there evidence to suggest that the population proportions differ?" That leaves several important questions unanswered:

- Suppose, as in the paper towel example, there are more than two populations and the null hypothesis is rejected. Can we decide which of the populations differs from the others?

- If you test the populations against each other two at a time, how do the results compare to a single test?

If your students ask questions such as these, congratulations; they understand what is going on. These questions are answered in more advanced courses in statistics. You can find the answers in books such as these:

Alan Agresti. *Categorical Data Analysis.* New York: Wiley, 1990.

B. S. Everitt. *The Analysis of Contingency Tables.* London: Chapman and Hall, 1977.

Suggested Activity: Paper Towel Experiment

The paper towel example on pages 592–593 of the student text was designed so that you can have students collect their own data to analyze instead of using those given. The data collection goes quickly if you have several groups of students working at once. The tricky part of this experiment is "stretching" the paper towel uniformly each time and dropping the ball into the center of the towel. This is one reason why randomization in the order the towels are tested is necessary. The stretching may be done by laying the paper towel over the top of a bowl and securing it with a rubber band. Depending on the brands you buy, some experimentation may be necessary beforehand to see from what height the golf ball should be dropped so it breaks the towels sometimes but not always.

Be sure to tell students that each paper towel is to be tested only once.

Discussion

D17. No, it appears that Wipe-Ups are more likely to break.

D18. **a.** Because 30 out of 75 paper towels broke, the best estimate of the probability that a paper towel from one of these three brands will break is $\frac{30}{75}$, or .4.

b.

<table>
<tr><td colspan="2" rowspan="2"></td><td colspan="4" align="center">Brand</td></tr>
<tr><td>Wipe-Ups</td><td>Wipe-Its</td><td>Wipe-Outs</td><td>Total</td></tr>
<tr><td rowspan="3">Towel Breaks?</td><td>Yes</td><td>10</td><td>10</td><td>10</td><td>30</td></tr>
<tr><td>No</td><td>15</td><td>15</td><td>15</td><td>45</td></tr>
<tr><td>Total</td><td>25</td><td>25</td><td>25</td><td>75</td></tr>
</table>

c. The three bars in the segmented bar graph would be identical; that is, the lengths of corresponding segments would be equal.

Lesson Notes: Computing Expected Counts

Discussion

D19.

<table>
<tr><td colspan="2" rowspan="2"></td><td colspan="3" align="center">Gender</td></tr>
<tr><td>Male</td><td>Female</td><td>Total</td></tr>
<tr><td rowspan="3">Survived?</td><td>Yes</td><td>559.2</td><td>151.8</td><td>711</td></tr>
<tr><td>No</td><td>1171.8</td><td>318.2</td><td>1490</td></tr>
<tr><td>Total</td><td>1731</td><td>470</td><td>2201</td></tr>
</table>

Practice

P8. **a.** Because the sample sizes are different for the different populations, it is more difficult to compare the proportions in the segmented bar graph than it was in the paper towel example.

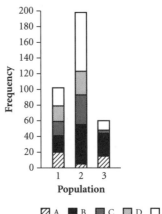

This segmented bar graph shows the percentage in each category, not the frequency, making comparisons easier.

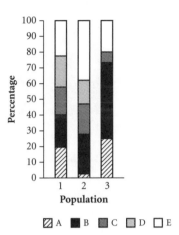

b. Category A: $\frac{40}{360} \approx .111$
Category B: $\frac{100}{360} \approx .278$
Category C: $\frac{60}{360} \approx .167$
Category D: $\frac{50}{360} \approx .139$
Category E: $\frac{110}{360} \approx .306$

c.

Expected Frequencies

		I	II	III	Total
	A	11.33	22.00	6.67	**40**
	B	28.33	55.00	16.67	**100**
Category	**C**	17.00	33.00	10.00	**60**
	D	14.17	27.50	8.33	**50**
	E	31.17	60.50	18.33	**110**
	Total	**102**	**198**	**60**	**360**

d. No. Population III appears to have too many members that fall into Categories A and B and too few in the remaining categories.

Lesson Notes: Computing the Chi-Square Statistic

Practice

P9. $\chi^2 = 6.627 + 13.136 + 10.417 + 1.898 + 0.455 + 9.127 + 0.059 + 0.758 + 3.600 + 2.402 + 0.227 + 8.333 + 2.140 + 3.475 + 2.188 = 64.842$

$df = 8$

χ^2 is significant at the $\alpha = .05$ level because from the table the P-value is less than .001.

Lesson Notes: Procedure for a Chi-Square Test of Homogeneity

Discussion

D20. The expected value in each cell in the first row should be

$$\frac{3080}{5000} \cdot 1000 = 616$$

The expected value in each cell in the second row should be

$$\frac{1770}{5000} \cdot 1000 = 354$$

The expected value in each cell in the third row should be

$$\frac{150}{5000} \cdot 1000 = 30$$

Practice

P10. For 8 degrees of freedom and $\chi^2 = 11.35$, the P-value from the calculator is about .183.

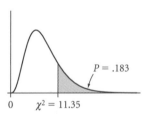

We can not reject the null hypothesis. If the proportion of people in each category is the same in each country, it is reasonably likely to get results as different or even more different than the Gallup Organization did in its five samples.

Multiple z-Tests Versus One Chi-Square Test

Suppose you have the three populations at the bottom of page 601 of the student text. You want to test for homogeneity of proportions and you decide to do this by comparing two populations at a time as in Chapter 8. The first test rejects the null hypothesis that $p_1 = p_2$ with a z-test. This two-sample z-test is equivalent to a two-sample chi-square test of homogeneity (a test with one degree of freedom). As in goodness-of-fit tests, $\chi^2 = z^2$.

But what about the third population? You could test the null hypothesis that $p_2 = p_3$ by using another z-test, which would show that there is no evidence of a difference between these two proportions. That would take another degree of freedom so that two degrees of freedom are used up in determining that the first population has a higher rate of breakage than the others because the other two do not differ. If you had four populations, then it would take three degrees of freedom to test for equality of the proportions, and so on.

Now, suppose you had three outcomes per trial (break, don't break, and can't determine). Then you would need to check equality of proportions across populations for two of the outcomes. (Once plausible values for two of the outcome probabilities are determined, the third one is determined by the fact that the probabilities must sum to one.) For three populations with three outcomes each, you would need a total of $2 \cdot 2 = 4$ tests. In general, for c populations with r outcomes from each, you would need $(r - 1)(c - 1)$ z-tests to determine nonhomogeneity of proportions, and that is the number of degrees of freedom for the problem.

Exercises

E12. **a.** Based on samples of size 1000 from each year, the observed frequencies (top) and expected frequencies (bottom) are shown in each cell of the table.

Most Important Problem

Year	Jobs	Crime	Health Care	Other
1998	110	200	60	630
	175	225	67.5	532.5
1997	180	200	60	560
	175	225	67.5	532.5
1996	200	250	80	470
	175	225	67.5	532.5
1995	210	250	70	470
	175	225	67.5	532.5
Total	**700**	**900**	**270**	**2130**

Because all the sample sizes (row totals) are the same, the expected cell frequencies across all rows are the same.

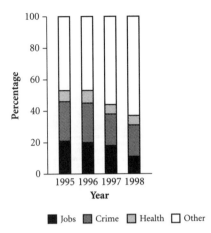

The proportion choosing "other" is increasing over the years, with a corresponding decrease in the other categories.

The biggest relative change is the decrease in the percentage who chose jobs as the most important problem.

b. Although the samples are independently selected from year to year, they are from essentially the same population of residents of the United States. Because the attitudes of the members of this population are changing, it is not too much of a stretch to think of these as different populations.

c. *Check conditions.* The conditions essentially are met in this situation for a chi-square test of homogeneity. We can think of each year's survey as basically four large populations and that a random sample of size 1000 was taken independently from each population. Each response falls into exactly one of four categories. All of the expected counts are at least 5.

State your hypotheses.

H_0: If every year from 1995 through 1998 you had asked all adults in the United States, the distribution of responses would be the same for each year.

H_a: The distribution of responses would not be the same in each of the four years. That is, in at least one year, the proportion of all adults who would give one of the responses is different from the proportion in other years.

Compute the test statistic and draw a sketch.
The test statistic is

$$\chi^2 = 24.143 + 2.778 + 0.833 + 17.852 + 0.143$$
$$+ 2.778 + 0.833 + 1.420 + 3.571 + 2.778$$
$$+2.315 + 7.336 + 7.000 + 2.778 + 0.093$$
$$+ 7.336$$
$$= 83.986$$

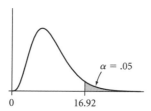

Comparing the test statistic to the χ^2 distribution with $df = 9$, the value of χ^2 from the sample, 83.986, is extremely far out in the tail and certainly greater than 16.92 ($\alpha = .05$). The *P*-value is approximately 0.

Write a conclusion in context. Reject the null hypothesis. You can not attribute the differences to the fact that we have only a sample of adults from each year and not the entire adult population. A value of χ^2 this large is extremely unlikely to occur in four samples of this size if the distribution of responses is the same for each year. We conclude that the proportion of responses in at least one category changed in one of these years.

E13. a. The table of observed values is given here.

	Carbolic Acid Used	Carbolic Acid Not Used	Total
Patient Lived	34	19	53
Patient Died	6	16	22
Total	40	35	75

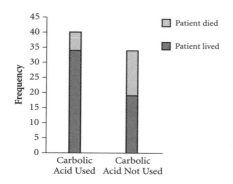

From this plot, it seems clear that there should be a smaller proportion of deaths in operations where carbolic acid is used. This difference looks unlikely to have occurred by chance. However, there is an important caveat here. We do not know how Lister selected the patients who would go into each treatment.

b. The test statistic z is

$$z = \frac{(\hat{p}_1 - \hat{p}_2) - (p_1 - p_2)}{\sqrt{\hat{p}(1 - \hat{p})\left(\dfrac{1}{n_1} + \dfrac{1}{n_2}\right)}}$$

$$= \frac{(.85 - .543) - 0}{\sqrt{.707(1 - .707)\left(\dfrac{1}{40} + \dfrac{1}{35}\right)}}$$

$$\approx 2.914$$

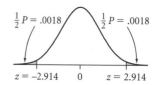

With a test statistic of 2.914, the *P*-value for a two-tailed test is 2(.0018) = .0036.

c. The table of expected values is given here.

	Carbolic Acid Used	Carbolic Acid Not Used	Total
Patient Lived	28.27	24.73	53
Patient Died	11.73	10.27	22
Total	40	35	75

The value of χ^2 is 1.163 + 1.329 + 2.802 + 3.202 = 8.495.

With $df = 1$, the *P*-value is .0036.

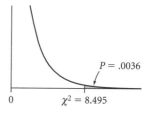

d. The two *P*-values are the same. The values of z^2 and χ^2 are the same as well.

E14. **a.** The expected values are given in the table shown at the bottom of the page.

b.

$$z = \frac{\left(\dfrac{x_1}{n_1} - \dfrac{x_2}{n_2}\right) - 0}{\sqrt{\dfrac{x_1 + x_2}{n_1 + n_2}\left(1 - \dfrac{x_1 + x_2}{n_1 + n_2}\right)\left(\dfrac{1}{n_1} + \dfrac{1}{n_2}\right)}}$$

If you would like your students to have a great deal of practice with elementary algebra, you can ask them to prove that $z^2 = \chi^2$.

E15. The observed and expected values are given in the next two tables.

Observed Values

	No Bandage	Flesh-Colored Bandage	Brightly Colored Bandage	Total
Pain Gone	0	9	15	24
Almost Gone	5	9	2	16
Still There	15	2	3	20
Total	20	20	20	60

Expected Values

	No Bandage	Flesh-Colored Bandage	Brightly Colored Bandage	Total
Pain Gone	8	8	8	24
Almost Gone	5.33	5.33	5.33	16
Still There	6.67	6.67	6.67	20
Total	20	20	20	60

Students might make a segmented bar graph.

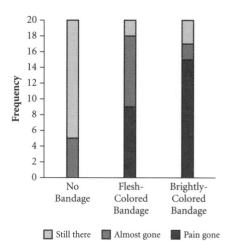

Check conditions. This situation fits the criteria for a chi-square test of homogeneity. The treatments were randomly assigned to the available subjects.

Each answer falls into exactly one of three categories. The expected number of answers in each cell is 5 or more.

State your hypotheses.

H_0: Suppose all 60 children could have been given the no-bandage treatment, all could have been given the flesh-colored bandage, and all could have been given the brightly colored bandage. Then the proportion of answers that would have fallen into each of the three categories would have been the same for all three types of bandage.

H_a: For at least one answer, the proportion of children who give that answer is not the same for all three types of bandage.

Compute the test statistic and draw a sketch. The test statistic is

$$\chi^2 = 8.000 + 0.125 + 6.125 + 0.021 + 2.521 \\ + 2.083 + 10.417 + 3.267 + 2.017 = 34.575$$

Lesson 10.2, E14a

	Population #1	Population #2	Total
Successes	$\dfrac{(x_1 + x_2)}{n_1 + n_2} \cdot n_1$	$\dfrac{(x_1 + x_2)}{n_1 + n_2} \cdot n_2$	$x_1 + x_2$
Failures	$\dfrac{(n_1 - x_1) + (n_2 - x_2)}{n_1 + n_2} \cdot n_1$	$\dfrac{(n_1 - x_1) + (n_2 - x_2)}{n_1 + n_2} \cdot n_2$	$(n_1 - x_1) + (n_2 - x_2)$
Total	n_1	n_2	$n_1 + n_2$

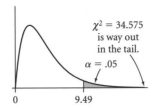

χ² = 34.575 is way out in the tail.

α = .05

0   9.49

Comparing the test statistic to the χ^2 distribution with 4 degrees of freedom, we find that the value of χ^2 from the sample, 34.575, is extremely far out in the tail and certainly greater than 9.49 ($\alpha = .05$). The P-value is close to 0.

Write a conclusion in context. We reject the null hypothesis. We can not reasonably attribute the differences in the answers to the random assignment of treatments to children. A value of χ^2 this large is extremely unlikely to occur if the distribution of answers for all 60 children would have been the same for each type of bandage. We conclude that these children given different bandages tend to give different answers to the questions.

E16. The data in Display 10.21 in the student text are not in the right format for a chi-square test of homogeneity. The numbers in the cells are the percentages by region, not counts. Tables of observed and expected values are shown at the bottom of the page.

Because the table of observed values must contain whole numbers, we rounded to the most reasonable estimate of the actual count in the sample.

Students might make a segmented bar graph.

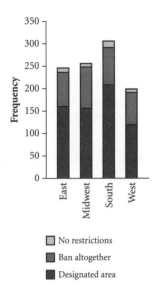

Our visual impression from this graph is that there is little difference in the proportions who give each answer in the various regions in the country. However, again the sample sizes are relatively large, so small differences in percentages may be statistically significant.

Lesson 10.2, E16

Observed Values

Region

		East	Midwest	South	West	Total
	Designated Area	160	156	208	119	**643**
Opinion	**Ban Altogether**	76	92	83	72	**323**
	No Restrictions	10	8	15	8	**41**
	Total	**246**	**256**	**306**	**199**	**1007**

Expected Values

Region

		East	Midwest	South	West	Total
	Designated Area	157.1	163.5	195.4	127.1	**643**
Opinion	**Ban Altogether**	78.9	82.1	98.2	63.8	**323**
	No Restrictions	10.0	10.4	12.5	8.1	**41**
	Total	**246**	**256**	**306**	**199**	**1007**

Check conditions. This situation fits the criteria for a chi-square test of homogeneity. A random sample was taken from each of four large populations. Each answer falls into exactly one of three categories. The expected number of answers in each cell is 5 or more.

State your hypotheses.

H_0: The proportion of answers that fall into each of the three categories is the same for all four regions of the country.

H_a: For at least one answer, the proportion of people who give that answer is not the same for all four regions of the country.

Compute the test statistic and draw a sketch. The test statistic is

$\chi^2 = 0.054 + 0.341 + 0.814 + 0.512 + 0.107 + 1.190 + 2.339 + 1.046 + 0.000 + 0.563 + 0.518 + 0.001 = 7.486$

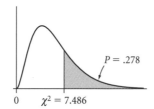

Comparing the test statistic to the χ^2 distribution with 6 degrees of freedom, we find that the value of χ^2 from the sample, 7.486, is close to the center of the distribution. The P-value is .278.

Write a conclusion in context. We do not reject the null hypothesis. We easily can attribute the differences in the answers to the fact that we have only a sample of adults in each region and not the entire population. A value of χ^2 this large is quite likely to occur if the distribution of answers is the same in each part of the country.

E17. The data in Display 10.22 in the student text are not in the right format for a chi-square test of homogeneity. The numbers in the cells are the percentages by year, not counts. Tables of observed and expected values were computed from the percentages and are shown next. Because percentages had been rounded to the nearest whole percent, the computed observed counts may not be exactly those in the sample.

Observed Values

		Year		
		1997	2001	Total
Response	Already Begun	410	540	950
	Within a Few Years	50	40	90
	In My Lifetime	110	130	240
	Future Generations	210	180	390
	Never	140	70	210
	No Opinion	80	40	120
	Total	1000	1000	2000

Expected Values

		Year		
		1997	2001	Total
Response	Already Begun	475	475	950
	Within a Few Years	45	45	90
	In My Lifetime	120	120	240
	Future Generations	195	195	390
	Never	105	105	210
	No Opinion	60	60	120
	Total	1000	1000	2000

Global Warming

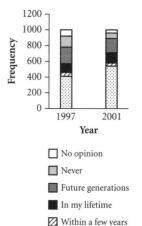

- ☐ No opinion
- ☐ Never
- ☐ Future generations
- ■ In my lifetime
- ☒ Within a few years
- ⬚ Already begun

Check conditions. This situation fits the criteria for a chi-square test of homogeneity. Random samples of size 1000 were taken from the U.S. population in 1997 and in 2001.

Each answer falls into exactly one of six categories. The expected number of responses in each cell is 5 or more.

State your hypotheses.

H_0: The proportion of responses that fall into each category is the same for both years.

H_a: For at least one response, the proportion of the population that gives the response is not the same for both years.

Compute the test statistic and draw a sketch. The test statistic is

$$\chi^2 = 8.895 + 8.895 + 0.556 + 0.556 + 0.833 + 0.833$$
$$+ 1.154 + 1.154 + 11.667 + 11.667 + 6.667$$
$$+ 6.667 = 59.542$$

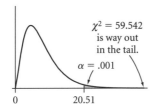

$\chi^2 = 59.542$ is way out in the tail.

$\alpha = .001$

0   20.51

Comparing the test statistic to the χ^2 distribution with 5 degrees of freedom, we find that the value of χ^2 from the sample, 59.542, is extremely far out in the tail, showing large differences between observed and expected values. (For $\alpha = .001$, the critical value is 20.51.) The *P*-value is close to 0.

Write a conclusion in context. We reject the null hypothesis. We can not attribute the differences in the responses to the fact that we have only a sample from both years and not the entire population. A value of χ^2 this large is extremely unlikely to occur if the distribution of responses is the same for each year. We conclude that the proportion of responses in at least one category changed over these five years.

E18. One meaning of "homogeneous" is "essentially alike." Homogeneous populations would be populations that are alike in the characteristics we are observing.

E19. Because chi-square tests are based on counts, it is easy for students to design projects in which they can collect data quickly.

E20. In both cases, the tests require count (or frequency) data. You use a chi-square goodness-of-fit test when there is one sample from one population. You wish to test whether the proportions in that population are the same as those hypothesized. You use a chi-square test of homogeneity when you have a sample from each of two or more populations and you wish to test whether the proportions in those different populations are the same.

10.3 The Chi-Square Test of Independence

Objectives

- to recognize when to use a chi-square test of independence
- to perform a chi-square test of independence and to understand that it answers the question "Does this sample look like it came from a population in which these two categorical variables are independent (not associated)?"
- to see that a chi-square test of independence is not an extension of any significance tests that have come before
- to understand that even if the test tells you there *is* evidence of an association, you must use your knowledge of the situation to know whether the statistical significance has any practical value

Important Terms and Concepts

- independent variables
- chi-square test of independence
- strength of the association

Lesson Planning

Class Time

Three to four days

Materials

None

Suggested Assignments

Classwork		
Essential	**Recommended**	**Optional**
Activity 10.2	D22, D25, D32	D24
D21, D23, D26–D31, D33, D34	P11, P16	
P12–P15		

Homework		
Essential	**Recommended**	**Optional**
E21–E23	E24, E25	

Lesson Notes: Independent or Dependent?

To begin this lesson, you may wish to collect a set of data from your class. For example, have your students fill in a copy of this table by looking around at the students in their classroom. A hat or a cap should not be counted as wearing something *in* the hair. A blackline master of this table appears at the end of this section.

Wearing Something in the Hair?

		Yes	No	Total
Gender	**Male**			
	Female			
	Total			

To review the definition of independence, ask students whether the event of being a girl and the event of wearing something in the hair are independent according to the definition in Chapter 6: $P(A \text{ and } B) = P(A) \cdot P(B)$. That is, is the joint probability equal to the product of the individual probabilities? You can use these data, along with those collected in Activity 10.2, as examples for this section.

Discussion

D21. **a.** Not independent. Darker hair tends to go with darker eyes, and lighter hair tends to go with lighter eyes.
  b. Not independent. Different ethnic groups tend to listen to different types of music. (That's part of what defines an ethnic group.)
  c. The answer will depend on current fashion among students. In the past, women were more likely than men to wear pastel colors, so gender and color of shirt weren't independent. However, the authors of this book aren't willing to make any predictions for your students.
  d. Not independent. Men tend to like and attend action movies more than women do, for example.
  e. Independent. Unless one considers the change in racial make-up of U.S. children, freshmen should be as likely to have a given eye color as are seniors.
  f. Not independent. In high school, typically it is juniors or seniors who take statistics. At

the college level, statistics is usually taken by students in their first or second year.

D22. We need a test of independence for the same reason that we need any other test of significance. We have only a sample from the population and so don't expect it to reflect the proportions in the population exactly. We test to see whether the sample is a reasonably likely result if the two variables are independent in the population.

Activity 10.2: Independent or Not?

For this activity, if your statistics class does not contain at least 30 students, collect or have students collect additional data from other students to bring the total up to 30 or more, with about half males and half females. If you don't have males or if you don't have females in your school, you can substitute another categorical variable that divides the class, such as hair color, whether or not they have a dog or whether or not they're wearing sneakers.

1. These two variables should be independent. There is no reason to suspect that males are more or less likely to have an even number than are females.

2. Two-way tables will vary. A sample two-way table follows.

Phone Number

		Even	Odd	Total
Gender	**Male**	8	10	18
	Female	7	7	14
	Total	15	17	32

3. For each cell in the table, students should determine whether the probability that a randomly selected student in that cell is equal to the probability of being in that row times the probability of being in that column. For example, in the sample two-way table, $P(male \text{ and } even) = \frac{8}{32} = .25$. But $P(male) \cdot P(even) = \frac{18}{32} \cdot \frac{15}{32} \approx .264 \neq P(male \text{ and } even)$.

4. It is unlikely that the variables will be independent by the definition from Chapter 6. However, because this is a relatively small sample, we wouldn't be willing to say that the two variables aren't independent in the population.

5. This is only a sample from the population, so we don't expect things to work out exactly. In fact, sometimes it is not even possible for the numbers to work out exactly. In order to satisfy the definition of independence, the number of males with even phone numbers would have to be 8.4375, which obviously is not possible in a sample.

6. If students didn't save the data, it quickly can be reconstructed.

7. Again, it is unlikely that the variables will be independent by the definition from Chapter 6.

Discussion

D23. You will almost always find they are not independent. The definition of independence of two variables is quite stringent. It has to be the case that

$$P(A \text{ and } B) = P(A) \cdot P(B)$$

for every possible selection A from a row and B from a column. This rarely happens with real data (see answer to step 5 of the activity), even if there is no reason to believe the two variables are associated in any way. Students will learn more about this later in this section.

D24. If two things are "associated," we think of them as going or belonging together. For example, dark hair tends to go with dark eyes, and light hair tends to go with light eyes.

Lesson Notes: Graphical Displays

Discussion

D25. All of these plots give the same information, but some information stands out more clearly in one plot than in the others. The first plot, Frequency by Class of Travel, shows most clearly that there are more third-class passengers than first- and second-class put together. The second plot, Frequency by Survival Status, shows most clearly that more people died than survived. The third plot, the column chart, shows most clearly that a disproportionate number of third-class passengers died. We see this by the fact that the column for those who didn't survive is proportionally much higher for third-class passengers than for passengers in the other classes of travel.

D26. You can see from the segmented bar graph on the right in Display 10.24 that the variables aren't independent by the fact that the bars aren't divided into segments in a proportional manner. For example, the third-class segment of the second bar (didn't survive) is proportionally much larger than it is in the first bar (survived). If the variables were independent, the respective segments of each bar would be proportional in length.

D27. If the variables were independent, the heights of the columns would be proportional both by rows and by columns. In this chart, this isn't the case. For example, the tall column for the third-class passengers who didn't survive is disproportionately tall for its (red) row compared to the height of the column for the third-class passengers who did survive (in the blue row).

D28. Independent variables are shown in column chart A and column chart C. In column chart A, the values double with each step from left to right and triple with each step from front to back. The variables shown in column chart B aren't independent because the light blue columns are decreasing from left to right whereas the red and dark blue columns are increasing. In column chart C, the columns are cut in half at each step from left to right and are multiplied by 9 and then divided by 3 from front to back. In column chart D the light blue columns and dark blue columns are decreasing from left to right whereas the red columns are increasing.

Practice

P11. The height of the columns in any row (either front to back or left to right) are all the same multiple of the heights of the corresponding columns in the previous row. In other words, all rows of columns (either front to back or left to right) have the same "shape," although some rows may be shorter than others.

P12. Graphs will vary according to the data students collect. Here are the graphs using the given sample two-way table in step 2 of Activity 10.2. They show that the variables aren't independent according to the definition from Chapter 6. In the column chart, for example, the two bars in the female row are of equal height whereas the two bars in the male row are not.

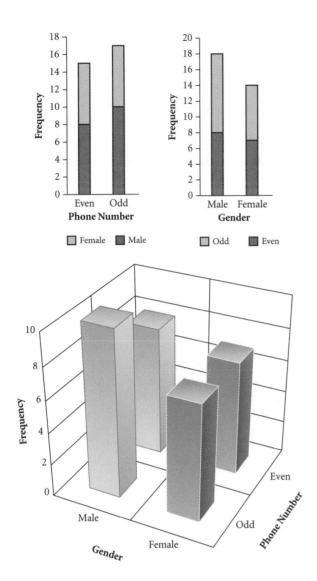

Lesson Notes: Computing Expected Values

Discussion

D29. Tables will vary depending on results from the class. The sample table given in the activity generates this two-way table for the expected values.

Phone Number

		Even	Odd	Total
	Male	8.4375	9.5625	**18**
Gender	**Female**	6.5625	7.4375	**14**
	Total	**15**	**17**	**32**

D30. Tables will vary depending on results from the class.

D31. Probably it will be the table for handedness and eyedness because we do not expect independence there.

D32. Yes, it is exactly the same. The justification was a little different, however.

Practice

P13. a.

	I	II	Total
A	22.5	13.5	**36**
B	11.25	6.75	**18**
C	59.375	35.625	**95**
D	6.875	4.125	**11**
Total	**100**	**60**	**160**

b. These tables are easy to construct. The key is to make one row or column disproportionate to the other rows or columns. Here is one possibility for observed values.

	I	II	Total
A	36	0	**36**
B	18	0	**18**
C	35	60	**95**
D	11	0	**11**
Total	**100**	**60**	**160**

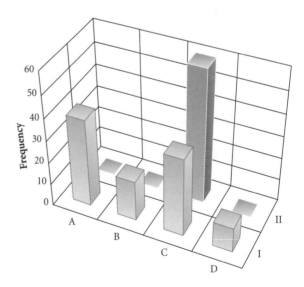

c. The only way to get exact independence is to use the expected counts given in part a. But those aren't whole numbers. If the expected counts are rounded, you get the next table, which looks like the counts reasonably could have come from a population where Variable I and Variable II are independent.

	I	II	Total
A	22	14	**36**
B	11	7	**18**
C	60	35	**95**
D	7	4	**11**
Total	**100**	**60**	**160**

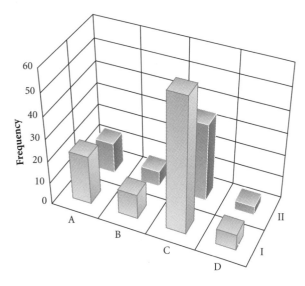

Lesson Notes: Procedure for a Chi-Square Test of Independence

The variables in the Scottish children example, eye color and hair color, can be ordered from lightest to darkest. The chi-square test disregards the order and simply tests for the presence of dependence between the variables. More advanced procedures are available for detecting and modeling trends among ordered categories. However, we reject the null hypothesis of independence (no association) anyway in this case.

Discussion

D33. Results of the test will vary according to the data gathered from your class. It is likely that the null hypothesis can not be rejected. Here is the test for the sample two-way table given in step 2 of Activity 10.2.

Check conditions. This situation fits the criteria for a chi-square test of independence

if we consider the class a simple random sample taken from one large population. Each student in the sample was classified according to *gender* and *phone number*. The expected number in each cell is 5 or more. (See the printout that follows for expected frequencies.)

State your hypotheses.

H_0: *Gender* and *even/odd phone number* are independent.

H_a: *Gender* and *even/odd phone number* are not independent.

Compute the test statistic and draw a sketch. The following Minitab printout shows expected values under the assumption of independence. It also gives the computation of the test statistic χ^2 and the *P*-value.

Chi-Square Test. Expected counts are printed below observed counts.

```
              Even      Odd     Total
Male           8         10      18
             8.4375    9.5625
Female         7         7       14
             6.5625    7.4375
Total         15        17       32
ChiSq = 0.023 + 0.020 + 0.029 + 0.026 = 0.098
df = 1, P = 0.755
```

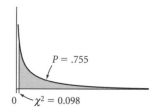

Comparing the test statistic to the χ^2 distribution with 1 degree of freedom, we see from the printout that the value of χ^2 from the sample, 0.098, isn't out in the tail. The *P*-value is about .755.

Write a conclusion in context. We do not reject the null hypothesis. If a random sample this size is taken from a student population where *gender* and *even/odd phone number* are independent, there is a 75.5% chance of getting a χ^2 value of 0.098 or larger. These are typical results in a sample from a population where there is no association between *gender* and *even/odd phone number*.

Practice

P14. Results of the test will vary according to the data gathered from your class. It is likely that the null hypothesis will be rejected.

Lesson Notes: Homogeneity Versus Independence

Discussion

D34. **a.** Design I is the test of homogeneity, and Design II is the test of independence.

b. If you use Design I, you will have exactly the same number of people with curly hair as with straight hair. If you use Design II, you probably won't.

c. If you use Design II, you are likely to end up with a different number of people who have straight hair than who have curly hair. If this difference is too large, you may end up with an expected number in some cells that is less than 5. Also, if the number with straight hair is quite different from the number with curly hair, the chi-square test has less power than if the number with straight hair and the number with curly hair are more nearly equal.

d. Design I

Practice

P15. **a.** Because a single sample was taken (even though men's and women's results were reported separately) these are conditional proportions and you would test for independence.

b. A sample of 1000 divided into 500 men and 500 women produces a χ^2 of 21.09 and a P-value of .0001, with 3 degrees of freedom. There is a highly significant difference between the conditional distribution of men and women on this issue. In other words, gender is associated with effort at eating a healthy diet. The women seem to be making more of an effort than the men. (At least they are saying that they do so.)

c. With the sample size cut in half, the χ^2 value drops to about 11 (about half of its value with a sample of size 1000) and the P-value is about .012. The association is still present, but the evidence for it is much weaker.

Lesson Notes: Strength of Association

Practice

P16. **a.** The χ^2 value for this table is 2733.8, a huge value that would produce a P-value of near 0. This test suggests that you can be very confident that seat belt use and injuries are not independent. Note that the P-value does not measure the strength of the association between seat belt use and injuries (see part b). The point to make with students is that a large χ^2 value (and corresponding small P-value) means that we are very confident that an association exists. Measuring the strength of the association (or the size of the differences between the conditional proportions) is a separate issue.

b. Among passengers wearing seat belts, 6.5% sustained injuries, whereas 22% of passengers not wearing seat belts sustained injuries. There is a strong association between seat belt use and injuries, and the use of seat belts appears to reduce the rate of injuries by about two-thirds. That is an improvement of practical significance as well.

c. One lurking variable might be the safety of the car. People who wear seat belts might also tend to buy safer cars (heavier or with better crash test results). Thus, when they are in an accident, they are less likely to be injured not so much because of the seat belt but because of the safer car. Another possible lurking variable is that stronger or healthier or larger people might tend to be the people who wear seat belts. If they are in an accident, they are less likely to be injured because of their size rather than because of the seat belt.

Degrees of Freedom

Now, back to an important topic that we have mentioned in each of the three sections of this chapter—degrees of freedom. Degrees of freedom may be thought of as the number of individual z-tests that might have to be done in order to reject the null hypothesis.

In the goodness-of-fit test, there is one population from which sample outcomes can fall into one of r cells. The outcomes can be thought of as filling a one-way table for which there must be a probability for each cell, such that the probabilities across all cells add to 1.

Population
p_1
p_2
$\vdots$
p_r

The null hypothesis for the goodness-of-fit test specifies a specific probability for each cell, but actually it need only specify $r - 1$ of them because the last one will be fixed by the fact that the probabilities sum to 1. Thus, there are $(r - 1)$ degrees of freedom associated with this test.

In a test of equality of proportions, suppose, for the moment, that there are two populations with r matching categories of outcomes in each. The possible outcomes can be thought of as filling two one-way tables, but when these are placed side by side, they look like a two-way table, as seen here. Again, each cell must contain a probability, but the column probabilities must add to 1 in each population.

Population 1	Population 2
p_{11}	p_{12}
p_{21}	p_{22}
$\vdots$	$\vdots$
p_{r1}	p_{r2}

Testing the hypothesis that $p_{11} = p_{12}$ takes up one degree of freedom, as you have seen, and this is the same as testing that $p_{11} - p_{12} = 0$. A test like this must be conducted for each of $(r - 1)$ rows because $(r - 1)$ of the p's are free to move about in each population. Thus, the overall test requires $(r - 1)$ degrees of freedom.

If a third population is added to the table, then $(r - 1)$ more tests of the form $p_{12} - p_{13} = 0$ must be added to the scheme. The three-population table looks like this.

Population 1	Population 2	Population 3
p_{11}	p_{12}	p_{13}
p_{21}	p_{22}	p_{23}
$\vdots$	$\vdots$	$\vdots$
p_{r1}	p_{r2}	p_{r3}

The test of homogeneity (equality) of proportions is actually a simultaneous test of the hypotheses shown in Table 1 at the bottom of the page.

There are $3r$ functions of parameters set equal to 0 under the null hypothesis but we only have to test $2(r - 1)$ of them. Therefore, the simultaneous test of all of these statements will have $2(r - 1)$ degrees of freedom.

Because two populations require one set of differences and three populations require two sets of differences, it is easy to see that four populations would require three sets of differences, and so on. For the general case of c populations, there will be $r \cdot c$ differences set equal to 0 by the null hypothesis, but only $(c - 1)(r - 1)$ need to be tested so there are degrees of freedom for the simultaneous test.

We have already argued that the test of independence can be thought of as a test of equality of the conditional distributions in each column of a two-way table. Therefore, degrees of freedom in a test of independence are counted the same way as in a test of homogeneity.

Note that pages 602–604 of the student text give a somewhat easier-to-understand motivation for degrees of freedom. For example, you can give students a table such as the first table at the bottom of the next page and ask whether they can fill in the rest of the cells. They should realize that such a table can be completed if $r - 1$ rows and $c - 1$ columns are filled in, which is $(r - 1)(c - 1)$ entries.

Lesson 10.3, Degrees of Freedom, Table 1

H_0:	Population 1 − Population 2	Population 2 − Population 3	Population 1 − Population 3
	$p_{11} - p_{12} = 0$	$p_{12} - p_{13} = 0$	$p_{11} - p_{13} = 0$
	$p_{21} - p_{22} = 0$	$p_{22} - p_{23} = 0$	$p_{21} - p_{23} = 0$
	$\vdots$	$\vdots$	$\vdots$
	$p_{r1} - p_{r2} = 0$	$p_{r2} - p_{r3} = 0$	$p_{r1} - p_{r3} = 0$

Exercises

E21. **a.** Yes, it seems reasonable to assume that *region of the country* and *grade level* are independent.

b. The percentage of students who fall into each cell under the assumption of independence can be found in the middle table below. (*Note:* The table is accurate to one more decimal place than the brief answers.)

c. The expected number of students who fall into each cell under the assumption of independence is as shown in the bottom table below. (*Note:* This table is a little different from the one given in the brief answers due to rounding in part b).

E22. **a.** *Check conditions.* This situation fits the criteria for a chi-square test of independence because the students are a random sample taken from this large college. Each student in the sample was classified according to class year and favorite team sport. The expected number in each cell is 5 or more. (See the printout on the next page for expected frequencies.)

State your hypotheses.

H_0: Class year and favorite sport are independent among the students in this college.

H_a: Class year and favorite sport are not independent.

Lesson 10.3, Degrees of Freedom, Table 2

		Population 1	Population 2	Population 3	Total
	A	53	35		154
	B	26	18		102
Category	C	18	0		36
	D	4	53		127
	E				106
	Total	174	127	224	525

Lesson 10.3, E21b

<table>
<tr><th></th><th colspan="5">Region</th></tr>
<tr><th></th><th></th><th>NE</th><th>MW</th><th>South</th><th>West</th><th>Total</th></tr>
<tr><th rowspan="3">Grades</th><th>K–8</th><td>.1872</td><td>.1994</td><td>.2319</td><td>.1395</td><td>.7580</td></tr>
<tr><th>9–12</th><td>.0598</td><td>.0636</td><td>.0741</td><td>.0445</td><td>.2420</td></tr>
<tr><th>Total</th><td>.2470</td><td>.2630</td><td>.3060</td><td>.1840</td><td>1.000</td></tr>
</table>

Lesson 10.3, E21c

<table>
<tr><th></th><th colspan="5">Region</th></tr>
<tr><th></th><th></th><th>NE</th><th>MW</th><th>South</th><th>West</th><th>Total</th></tr>
<tr><th rowspan="3">Grades</th><th>K–8</th><td>8,838,274</td><td>9,414,272</td><td>10,948,695</td><td>6,586,213</td><td>35,787,454</td></tr>
<tr><th>9–12</th><td>2,823,337</td><td>3,002,747</td><td>3,498,483</td><td>2,100,979</td><td>11,425,546</td></tr>
<tr><th>Total</th><td>11,661,611</td><td>12,417,019</td><td>14,447,178</td><td>8,687,192</td><td>47,213,000</td></tr>
</table>

Compute the test statistic and draw a sketch.
This Minitab printout shows expected values under the assumption of independence. It also gives the computation of the test statistic χ^2 and the P-value.

Chi-Square Test. Expected counts are printed below observed counts.

	C1	C2	C3	C4	Total
1	12	40	10	1	63
	9.03	36.96	11.55	5.46	
2	12	44	16	8	80
	11.47	46.93	14.67	6.93	
3	9	43	11	11	74
	10.61	43.41	13.57	6.41	
4	10	49	18	6	83
	11.90	48.69	15.22	7.19	
Total	43	176	55	26	300

ChiSq = 0.977 + 0.250 + 0.208 + 3.643 +
0.025 + 0.183 + 0.121 + 0.164 + 0.243 +
0.004 + 0.486 + 3.280 + 0.302 + 0.002 +
0.509 + 0.198 = 10.596

df = 9, P = 0.306

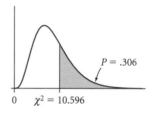

$P = .306$

$0 \quad \chi^2 = 10.596$

Comparing the test statistic to the χ^2 distribution with 9 degrees of freedom, we see from the printout that the value of χ^2 from the sample, 10.596, isn't out in the tail.

The P-value is .306.

Write a conclusion in context. We do not reject the null hypothesis. If a random sample this size is taken from a student population where class year and favorite team sport are independent, there is a 30.6% chance of getting a χ^2 value of 10.596 or larger. These are typical results in a sample from a population where there is no association between class year and favorite team sport.

b. No. It is impossible to make a Type I error if you haven't rejected the null hypothesis.

c. Take a random sample of, say, 80 freshmen and ask them their favorite team sport. Repeat with sophomores, juniors, and seniors.

E23. a. It is easy to see from the following plot that although males and females were saved in about equal numbers, a far lower percentage of males were saved than females. From the plot, gender and survival status appear to be associated. Fewer males survived than would be expected under the assumption of independence.

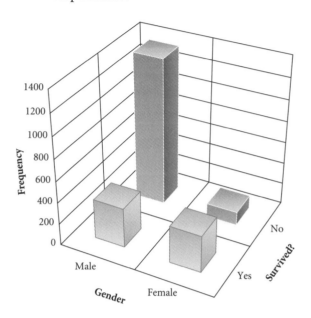

b. ***Check conditions.*** This situation can not reasonably be considered a simple random sample taken from one large population. Thus, we will test whether it is reasonable to attribute the difference in the proportions to chance or whether we should look for some other explanation. Each person on the *Titanic* was classified according to gender and survival status. The expected number in each cell is 5 or more. (See the following printout for expected frequencies.)

State your hypotheses.
H_0: The differences in the proportions of males and females who were saved can reasonably be attributed to chance.
H_a: The differences in the proportions of males and females who were saved can not reasonably be attributed to chance, and we should look for some other explanation.

Compute the test statistic and draw a sketch.
The following Fathom printout shows expected values under the assumption of independence. It also gives the computation of the test statistic χ^2 and the P-value.

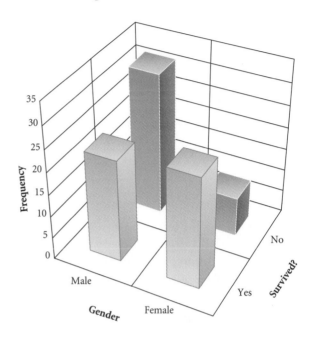

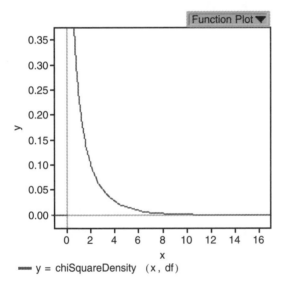

From Summary Statistics		Test for Independence ▼		

First attribute (categorical): <unassigned>
Second attribute (categorical): <unassigned>

		Gender		Row Summary
		Male	**Female**	
Survived	**Yes**	367 (559.2)	344 (151.8)	711
	No	1364 (1171.8)	126 (318.2)	1490
Column Summary		1731	470	2201

First attribute: **Survived**
  Number of categories: **2**
Second attribute: **Gender**
  Number of categories: **2**
Ho: **Survived** is independent of Gender
Chi-square: **456.9**
DF: **1**
P-value: **< 0.0001**

The numbers in parentheses in the table are expected counts.

Function Plot ▼

$y = $ chiSquareDensity (x, df)

Comparing the test statistic to the χ^2 distribution with 1 degree of freedom, we see from the printout that the value of χ^2 from the sample, 456.9, is extremely far out in the tail. The *P*-value is close to 0. The test statistic is quite large and would be difficult to see in a sketch.

Write a conclusion in context. We reject the null hypothesis. These are not the results we would expect if people were placed on lifeboats without regard to gender.

The explanation apparently is that women were indeed the first to be allowed into lifeboats.

E24. a. The following plot shows that although males and females survived in about equal

numbers, a far lower percentage of males survived than females. From the plot, it appears that *gender* and *survival status* are not independent.

b. *Check conditions.* This situation can not reasonably be considered a simple random sample taken from one large population. Thus, we will test whether it is reasonable to attribute the difference in the proportions to chance or whether we should look for some other explanation. Each person in the Donner party was classified according to gender and survival status. The expected number in each cell is 5 or more. (See the following printout for expected frequencies.)

State your hypotheses.

H_0: The difference in the proportions of males and females who lived can reasonably be attributed to chance.

H_a: The difference in the proportions of males and females who lived can not reasonably be attributed to chance, and we should look for some other explanation.

Compute the test statistic and draw a sketch. The following Minitab printout shows expected values under the assumption of independence. It also gives the computation of the test statistic χ^2 and the *P*-value.

Chi-Square Test. Expected counts are printed below observed counts.

	Male	Female	Total
1	23	25	48
	29.66	18.34	
2	32	9	41
	25.34	15.66	
Total	55	34	89

ChiSq = 1.497 + 2.421 + 1.752 + 2.834 = 8.504
df = 1, P = 0.0035

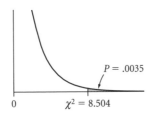

$P = .0035$

$0 \qquad \chi^2 = 8.504$

Comparing the test statistic to the χ^2 distribution with 1 degree of freedom, we see from the printout that the value of χ^2 from the sample, 8.504, is in the tail of the χ^2 distribution. The *P*-value is .0035.

Write a conclusion in context. Whether or not we reject the null hypothesis depends on the significance level, α. Because a value of α wasn't stated in the problem, the usual procedure is to use $\alpha = .05$. Under this criterion, we reject the null hypothesis. These are not the results we would expect if men and women were equally likely to live.

c. Yes, it is possible that we have made a Type I error because we may have concluded that there was some association when there wasn't. However, if there is no association, there is only a .0035 chance of getting a value of χ^2 of 8.504 or larger.

E25. First we need to organize the table in Display 10.37 of the student text according to counts rather than percentages. Because the percentages in the Never row sum to 101, we have to adjust the Never row a little to make the numbers add up to the original 9694.

For example, usually the number of blue-collar workers who never smoked would be .305(9694). But because the percentages in the Never row add up to 101%, finding expected values in this way gives a total of more than 9694 (actually, it gives 1.01 · 9694). Thus, to find the number of blue-collar workers who never smoked, we should multiply 9694 by .305/1.01 to get about 2927. The number of professionals who never smoked should be about 9694(.118/1.01), or about 1133. Finally, the number of others who never smoked should be 9694(.587/1.10), or about 5634. The sum of these numbers is 2927 + 1133 + 5634, or 9694. See the table at the bottom of the page.

Examining the column chart, we find that the rows do appear to have somewhat the same shape. It is not clear whether the differences will turn out to be statistically significant from looking at this chart.

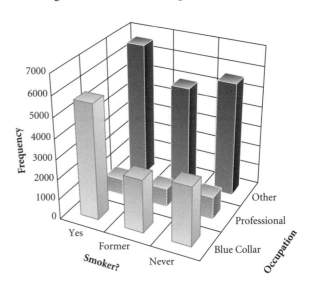

		Occupation			
		Blue-collar	Professional	Other	Total
	Yes	5,664	826	6,622	**13,112**
Smoker?	**Former**	2,629	936	4,944	**8,509**
	Never	2,927	1,133	5,634	**9,694**
	Total	11,220	2,895	17,200	**31,315**

Check conditions. This situation fits the criteria for a chi-square test of independence if the men reasonably can be considered a simple random sample taken from the population. Each man in the sample was classified according to smoking characteristics and type of employment. The expected number in each cell is 5 or more. (See the printout for expected frequencies.)

State your hypotheses.

H_0: Smoking status and type of employment are independent.

H_a: Smoking status and type of employment are not independent.

Compute the test statistic and draw a sketch. The Fathom printout shows expected values under the assumption of independence. It also gives the computation of the test statistic χ^2 and the P-value.

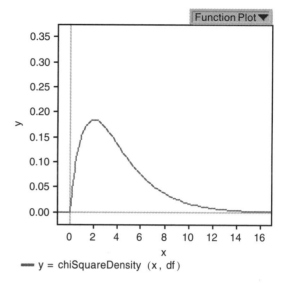

— y = chiSquareDensity (x, df)

Now we compare the test statistic to the χ^2 distribution with 4 degrees of freedom. We see from the printout that the value of χ^2 from the sample, 636.6, is extremely far out in the tail. The P-value is close to 0. The test statistic is quite large and would be difficult to see in a sketch.

Write a conclusion in context. We reject the null hypothesis. These are not the results we would expect for a sample from a population where there is no association between smoking characteristics and profession. A value of χ^2 this large is extremely unlikely to occur in a sample of this size if smoking characteristics and profession are independent. Examining the table and column chart, it appears that professionals are less likely to smoke than are the other two groups.

From Summary Statistics   Test for Independence ▼

First attribute (categorical): <unassigned>
Second attribute (categorical): <unassigned>

		Occupation			Row Summary
		Blue collar	**Professional**	**Other**	
Smoker?	**Yes**	5664 (4698.0)	826 (1212.2)	6622 (7201.9)	13112
	Former	2629 (3048.7)	936 (786.6)	4944 (4673.6)	8509
	Never	2927 (3473.3)	1133 (896.2)	5634 (5324.5)	9694
Column Summary		11220	2895	17200	31315

First attribute: Smoker?
   Number of categories: 3
Second attribute: Occupation
   Number of categories: 3
   Ho: **Smoker?** is independent of **Occupation**
Chi-square: **636.6**
DF: **4**
P-value: **< 0.0001**

The numbers in parentheses in the table are expected counts.

Wearing Something in the Hair?

Gender	Yes	No	Total
Boy			
Girl			
Total			

Statistics in Action Instructor's Guide
© 2004 Key Curriculum Press

Review

Review Exercises

E26. a. Results of the test will vary according to the sample taken. It is likely that the null hypothesis can not be rejected.

b. 01234567890123456789012345678901 23456789 . . . Take a large sample of pairs of random digits. Record each pair in a table like this one (a blackline master of this table appears at the end of this section). Then perform a chi-square test of independence.

First Digit in the Pair

		0	1	2	3	4	5	6	7	8	9
	0										
	1										
	2										
Second	3										
Digit	4										
in the	5										
Pair	6										
	7										
	8										
	9										

E27. a. The infirmary was used most heavily on Monday and Thursday. There were relatively few admissions on Friday. Perhaps students saved their problems until Thursday after classes were over and perhaps the infirmary wasn't open on the weekends, so students who got sick on the weekend had to save their problems until Monday.

b. Yes, you could use a test of independence because there was one large population that was classified according to day and severity of problem. However, some students may consider it a test of homogeneity even though that test requires that independent random samples be drawn from two or more populations. They could argue that the five populations of students were all of the students who came on the five days and they then were classified according to severity of problem. The design of the study involves no random sampling so does not fit the conditions for a chi-square test.

c. A test of independence is the more appropriate test.

First, examining this column chart, we see that there are indeed more visits on Monday and Thursday. However, the pattern of admissions appears roughly to be the same from day to day, which is what a test of independence will test.

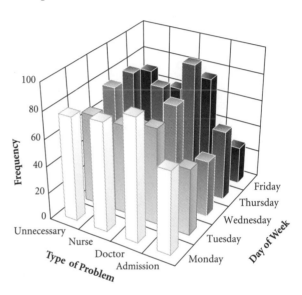

Check conditions. Because the table includes all students who visited the infirmary during a school year, these data can not reasonably be considered a simple random sample taken from one large population. Thus, we will test whether it is reasonable to attribute the difference in the proportions to chance or whether we should look for some other explanation. Each person who visited the infirmary was classified according to day of the week and severity of the problem. The expected number in each cell is 5 or more. (See the printout on the next page for expected frequencies.)

State your hypotheses.

H_0: The differences in the proportions of the various problems from day to day can reasonably be attributed to chance.

H_a: The differences in the proportions can not reasonably be attributed to chance, and we should look for some other explanation.

Compute the test statistic and draw a sketch.
This Minitab printout shows expected values under the assumption of independence. It also gives the computation of the test statistic χ^2 and the P-value.

Chi-Square Test. Expected counts are printed below observed counts.

```
        Mon    Tues    Wed    Thurs    Fri    Total
1        77     67      77     78       70     369
         84.69  69.57   68.19  81.94    64.62
2        80     66      53     73       62     334
         76.66  62.97   61.72  74.17    58.49
3        90     71      76     95       75     407
         93.41  76.73   75.21  90.38    71.27
4        61     49      42     52       28     232
         53.25  43.74   42.87  51.52    40.63
Total   308    253     248    298      235    1342
ChiSq = 0.698 + 0.095 + 1.138 + 0.189 + 0.449 +
0.146 + 0.146 + 1.233 + 0.018 + 0.211 + 0.124 +
0.428 + 0.008 + 0.236 + 0.195 + 1.129 + 0.633 +
0.018 + 0.005 + 3.924 = 11.023
df = 12, P = 0.527
```

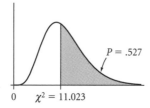

Comparing the test statistic to the χ^2 distribution with 12 degrees of freedom, we see from the printout that the value of χ^2 from the sample, 11.023, is not out in the tail. The P-value is .527.

Write a conclusion in context. We do not reject the null hypothesis. These are typical of the results we would see if there was no association between severity of problem and day of the week. No explanation for these results is needed.

d. We might group Monday, Tuesday, and Wednesday together and Thursday and Friday together as in this table.

		Day of Week	
		MTW	**ThF**
	U	221	148
Problem	N	199	135
	D	237	170
	A	152	80

e. For this test, the differences are not statistically significant either. The type of problem and type of day appear to be independent. Here is the test with all steps.

Check conditions. Again, because this table includes all students who visited the infirmary during a school year, these data can not reasonably be considered a simple random sample taken from one large population. Thus, we will test whether it is reasonable to attribute the difference in the proportions to chance or whether we should look for some other explanation. Each person who visited the infirmary was classified according to type of day and severity of the problem. The expected number in each cell is 5 or more. (See the next printout for expected frequencies.)

State your hypotheses.

H_0: The differences in the proportions of the various problems reported on weekdays when students attend class and on weekdays when students don't attend class can reasonably be attributed to chance.

H_a: The differences in the proportions can not reasonably be attributed to chance, and we should look for some other explanation.

Compute the test statistic and draw a sketch. The Minitab printout shows expected values under the assumption of independence. It also gives the computation of the test statistic χ^2 and the P-value.

Chi-Square Test. Expected counts are printed below observed counts.

```
        MTW      ThF      Total
1       221      148      369
        222.44   146.56
2       199      135      334
        201.35   132.65
3       237      170      407
        245.35   161.65
4       152      80       232
        139.86   92.14
Total   809      533      1342
ChiSq = 0.009 + 0.014 + 0.027 + 0.041 +
0.284 + 0.432 + 1.054 + 1.600 = 3.463
df = 3, P = 0.326
```

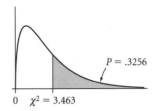

$P = .3256$

$0 \quad \chi^2 = 3.463$

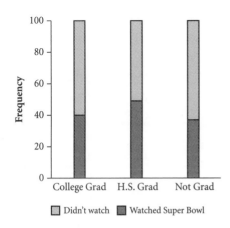

Frequency

College Grad   H.S. Grad   Not Grad

☐ Didn't watch   ■ Watched Super Bowl

Comparing the test statistic to the χ^2 distribution with 3 degrees of freedom, we see from the printout that the value of χ^2 from the sample, 3.463, is not out in the tail. The P-value is .326.

Write a conclusion in context. We do not reject the null hypothesis. These are typical of the results we would see if there was no association between severity of problem and type of day of the week. No explanation for these results is needed.

E28. **a.** Neither.

b. Each person in the poll appears in two different cells of the table. They are counted once under *Your Lifetime* and once under *Your Children's Lifetime.*

E29. **a.** This design suggests a chi-square test of homogeneity because there was a fixed number in each of three samples taken from three different populations. Organizing the data gives this table of observed values.

Type of Graduate

		College	H.S.	None	Total
Watched Super Bowl?	Yes	40	49	37	126
	No	60	51	63	174
	Total	100	100	100	300

b. Examining the segmented bar graph shown here, we see that the respective segments within the bars aren't quite proportional. However, the sample sizes aren't large, so the differences may not be statistically significant.

Check conditions. This situation fits the criteria for a chi-square test of homogeneity. There are three large populations, and a random sample of size 100 is taken from each population. Each answer was classified according to type of graduate and whether or not the graduate watched the Super Bowl. The expected number of outcomes in each cell is 5 or more. (See the printout on the next page for expected frequencies.)

State your hypotheses.

H_0: If we had asked everyone with each level of education whether they had watched the Super Bowl, the proportion who answered "yes" would be the same in each population.

H_a: For at least one level of education, the proportion of all adults who watched the Super Bowl is different from the proportion in the other two levels.

Compute the test statistic and draw a sketch.
The Fathom printout is shown here.

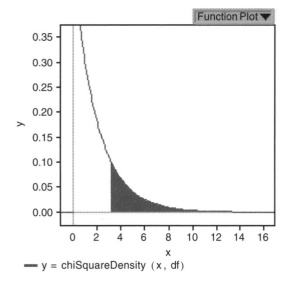

From Summary Statistics		Test for Independence ▼		

First attribute (categorical): <unassigned>
Second attribute (categorical): <unassigned>

		Graduate			Row Summary
		College	H.S.	None	
Watched?	Yes	40 (42.0)	49 (42.0)	37 (42.0)	126
	No	60 (58.0)	51 (58.0)	63 (58.0)	174
Column Summary		100	100	100	300

First attribute: **Watched?**
  Number of categories: **2**
Second attribute: **Graduate**
  Number of categories: **3**
 Ho: **Watched?** is independent of **Graduate**
Chi-square: **3.202**
DF: **2**
P-value: **0.2**

The numbers in parentheses in the table are expected counts.

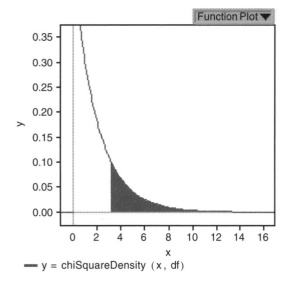

Function Plot ▼

y

0.35
0.30
0.25
0.20
0.15
0.10
0.05
0.00

0   2   4   6   8   10 12 14 16
x

▬▬ y = chiSquareDensity (x , df)

Comparing the test statistic to the χ^2 distribution with 2 degrees of freedom, we find that the value of χ^2 from the sample, 3.202, isn't out in the tail. The *P*-value is close to .20.

Write a conclusion in context. We do not reject the null hypothesis. We can attribute the differences to the fact that we have only a sample of adults from each educational level and not the entire adult population. A value of χ^2 this small is quite likely to occur in three samples of this size if the same proportion of adults in each population watched the Super Bowl.

E30. **a.** The percentages for any given sample (any row) do not sum to 1 because a number of respondents had no opinion or were undecided. These must be taken into account by making a table with five rows and three columns, and 8 degrees of freedom.
b. For a test of homogeneity, the χ^2 statistic has a value of 24.91 and a *P*-value of .0016. We are quite confident that there are differences between the distributions of satisfaction over the months. On the other hand, the sample proportions do not change very much, practically speaking.
c. With the proportions remaining the same but the sample size cut in half, the χ^2 value is also cut in half, to 12.46. The *P*-value jumps all the way to .1319, however, and the hypothesis of homogeneity can no longer be rejected at a reasonable value of α. Emphasize once again that the chi-square test does, indeed, depend on the sample size.

E31. For a test of independence based on these data, the χ^2 statistic is 325.22, with a *P*-value of essentially 0. You can be very confident that there is an association between political ideology and political party. Looking at the conditional proportions for the sample data in the table at the bottom of the page or at a segmented bar graph for each group as shown next, you can see that the degree of conservatism is much higher for Republicans than it is for Democrats; the association is quite strong.

Review 2.3, E31

		Political Ideology			
		Liberal	Moderate	Conservative	Total
Party Affiliation	Democrat	.3581	.4428	.1991	1
	Independent	.2739	.4475	.2786	1
	Republican	.1177	.2757	.6066	1

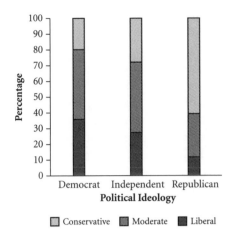

Grade	Observed	Expected
5	30	25.6
4	51	41.6
3	44	54
2	35	40.2
1	40	38.6
Total	**200**	**200**

E32. For this goodness-of-fit test, the probabilities are hypothesized to be .5, .25, and .25 for the respective categories. The χ^2 statistic is 0.88, with 2 degrees of freedom, producing a *P*-value of .644. There is no evidence to reject the percentages claimed.

E33. **a.** If segregation is high, then sampled trees of one species would tend to have neighbors of the same species. Thus, if an adequate sample size is taken, cell counts for A and D would be large relative to B and C. The chi-square value would be large.

b. If integration (mixing) is high, then sampled trees of one species would tend to have neighbors of the other species. Thus, if an adequate sample size is taken, cell counts for B and C would be large relative to A and D. The χ^2 value would again be large. (*Note:* Be careful in the interpretation of large χ^2 values.)

c. Whether or not the trees occur in equal numbers, random mixing would be shown by $\frac{A}{A+C} \approx \frac{B}{B+D}$, which will result in a small value of χ^2.

E34. **a.** Yes, this situation calls for a chi-square test of goodness-of-fit because we are comparing the sample from 2001 to the entire distribution from 1996. (If a student wants to consider the data from 1996 a sample as well and do a test of homogeneity, that is almost as good, as long as the student explains that reason.)

The table for a chi-square goodness-of-fit test appears next.

Check conditions. There were 200 grades, a random sample from the population of all grades in 2001. Each grade is classified into only one of five categories. We computed the expected number that fall into each category based on the distribution of grades in 1996.

The expected frequency in each category is 5 or greater.

State your hypotheses.

H_0: The proportion of all grades in 2001 that fall into the five categories is the same as in 1996.

H_a: The proportion of all grades in 2001 that fall into the five categories is not the same as in 1996.

Compute the test statistic and draw a sketch.
The test statistic is

$$\chi^2 = \Sigma \frac{(O - E)^2}{E}$$
$$\approx 5.456$$

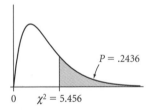

Comparing the test statistic to the χ^2 distribution with $5 - 1 = 4$ degrees of freedom, we find that $\chi^2 = 5.456$ gives a *P*-value of .2436.

Write a conclusion in context. We can not reject the null hypothesis. We have no evidence that once we see the grades for all Calculus AB examinations in 2001 that the distribution will be different from 1996. The sample of 200 grades from 2001 looks as though it could be a random sample from the 1996 grades.

b. Because we know the population standard deviation from 1996, $\sigma = 1.30$, we can use a z-test for a mean. (Once again, if a student believes that the best test is a t-test for the difference of two means because this should be treated as two samples from two different years, that is a reasonable point of view, if not the best in this situation.)

Check conditions. We have a large random sample of size 200 from the population of all grades in 2001. We know the population mean and population standard deviation for 1996.

State your hypotheses.
H_0: The mean grade in 2001 is the same as in 1996.
H_a: The mean grade in 2001 is greater than the mean grade in 1996.

Compute the test statistic and draw a sketch.
The test statistic is

$$z = \frac{2.98 - 2.88}{1.30/\sqrt{200}}$$

$$\approx 1.088$$

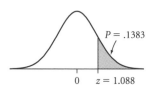

Comparing the test statistic to the normal distribution, we find that $z = 1.088$ gives a P-value for a right-tailed test of .1383.

Write a conclusion in context. We can not reject the null hypothesis. If the mean in 2001 is the same as in 1996 then there is a .1383 chance of getting a difference as large or larger than we did between the sample mean and 2.88. We have no evidence that once we see the grades for all Calculus AB examinations in 2001 that the mean will be different from 1996.

E35. **a.** Description 2 and Design I
b. Description 1 and Design III
c. Description 3 and Design II

Note: Design IV is also a description of a chi-square test of homogeneity, but for a design we don't cover in this textbook that results in a three-way table.

E36. ***Check conditions.*** This sample can not reasonably be considered a simple random sample taken from one large population. Thus, we will test whether it is reasonable to attribute the difference in the proportions to chance or whether we should look for some other explanation. Each person on the *Titanic* was classified according to class of travel and survival status. The expected number in each cell is 5 or more. (See the next printout for expected frequencies.)

State your hypotheses.
H_0: The differences in the proportions of passengers of various classes of travel who were saved can reasonably be attributed to chance.
H_a: The differences in the proportions of passengers of various classes of travel who were saved can not reasonably be attributed to chance, and we should look for some other explanation.

Compute the test statistic. The following printout shows expected values under the assumption of independence. It also gives the computation of the test statistic χ^2 and the P-value.

Chi-Square Test. Expected counts are printed below observed counts.

	First	Second	Third	Total
1	203	118	178	499
	123.23	108.07	267.70	
2	122	167	528	817
	201.77	176.93	438.30	
Total	325	285	706	1316

ChiSq = 51.632 + 0.913 + 30.057 + 31.535 +
0.558 + 18.358 = 133.052

df = 2, P = 0.000

Comparing the test statistic to the χ^2 distribution with 2 degrees of freedom, we see from the printout that the value of χ^2 from the sample, 133.052, is extremely far out in the tail. The P-value is close to 0. The test statistic is quite large and would be difficult to see in a sketch.

Write a conclusion in context. We reject the null hypothesis. These are not the results we would expect if people were placed on lifeboats without regard to class of travel. The explanation apparently is that first-class passengers were indeed the first to be allowed into lifeboats and third-class passengers were last.

E37. These tables give the observed and expected outcomes.

Observed Values

Defendant

		Husband	Wife	Total
Results	Not Prosecuted	35	35	70
	Pleaded Guilty	146	87	233
	Convicted at Trial	130	69	199
	Acquitted at Trial	7	31	38
	Total	318	222	540

Expected Values

Defendant

		Husband	Wife	Total
Results	Not Prosecuted	41.22	28.78	70
	Pleaded Guilty	137.21	95.79	233
	Convicted at Trial	117.19	81.81	199
	Acquitted at Trial	22.38	15.62	38
	Total	318	222	540

a. There are two populations: husbands who are accused of murdering their wives and wives who are accused of murdering their husbands.

b. A segmented bar graph is shown next.

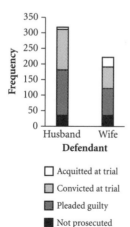

From the chart it appears that the proportions of husbands and the proportions of wives who fall into each category could be about the same in the population. (The proportions in the acquitted and convicted categories look a bit different, though. We can see that there are more husbands accused of murdering their wives than wives accused of murdering their husbands.) However, as we will see when we finish the chi-square test, the relatively large sample sizes result in a statistically significant difference.

c. *Check conditions.* This situation doesn't quite fit the criteria for a chi-square test of homogeneity.

These are not random samples from the populations of husbands accused and wives accused. It is all of the cases from the largest counties in one year. Nevertheless, we can reasonably proceed with a chi-square test either by hoping that this sample is representative of a random sample from the two populations or by acknowledging that these are two distinct populations and asking only whether the difference can reasonably be attributed to chance.

Each case is resolved in exactly one of four ways.

The expected number of cases in each cell is 5 or more.

State your hypotheses.

H_0: The proportion of all accused husbands who fall into each of the four categories is the same as the proportion of all accused wives who fall into that category.

H_a: For at least one category, the proportion of husbands who fall into that category is not the same as the proportion of wives who fall into that category.

Compute the test statistic. The test statistic is

$$\chi^2 = 0.939 + 1.345 + 0.563 + 0.806$$
$$+ 1.401 + 2.006 + 0.567 + 15.137$$
$$= 32.765$$

Comparing the test statistic to the χ^2 distribution with 3 degrees of freedom, we find that the value of χ^2 from the sample, 32.765, is far out in the tail. The P-value is close to 0. The test statistic is quite large and would be difficult to see in a sketch.

Write a conclusion in context. We reject the null hypothesis. We can not attribute the differences in the ways the cases were resolved to chance alone. A value of χ^2 this large is extremely unlikely to occur if cases are resolved in the same proportions for husbands and wives. We conclude that the proportion in at least one category is different for husbands than for wives. However, we must note that this is not a random sample from a larger population, so all we can be sure about is that in these 75 largest counties in 1988, the distributions of outcomes for husbands and wives do not look like they are random samples from identical populations.

Chi-Square Test of Independence

First Digit in the Pair

	0	1	2	3	4	5	6	7	8	9
0										
1										
2										
3										
4										
5										
6										
7										
8										
9										

Second Digit in the Pair

INFERENCE FOR REGRESSION

Overview

The fundamental idea that students will learn in this chapter is that when a regression equation is computed from a random sample, the value of the slope must be considered an estimate of some true underlying relationship.

Goals

The primary goals of this chapter are centered around the slope of the regression line. Your students will learn

- to recognize that the regression line as computed in Chapter 3 sometimes must be considered an estimate of a true, underlying linear model
- to recognize that the slope of a regression line fitted from sample data will vary from sample to sample
- to recognize that the formula for the standard error of this slope reflects the fact that having a wider spread in the values of x and smaller spread in the distances of y from the regression line decreases the variability of the slope
- to construct and interpret a confidence interval for the slope
- to perform a test of significance for the slope
- to check the conditions that are needed before doing inference for a slope
- to transform data to better meet the conditions for inference

Content Overview

After studying the real-world situation and the data to make sure a linear relationship between the mean response and the explanatory variable makes sense, the first question usually asked is whether or not the apparent linear trend is "significant." This question is answered by a significance test on the slope. If the slope is not significantly different from zero, then you can't conclude that a larger value of x tends to be associated with a larger (or a smaller) value of y. If the slope is significantly different from zero, the next question may be, "How much can I expect the response to change as I change values of the explanatory variable?" This question can be answered by a confidence interval estimate of the slope. There are many more questions that could be asked, but we will stop with these two. For beginning students, they are enough to make the essential points about inference in a regression setting.

Now may be the time to show students that there is a pattern to the way the inference sections of this textbook are arranged. For example, suppose your population is all eligible voters in the last presidential election in the United States. You must learn about this population by sampling because there is no list of these people. Not everyone eligible to vote either registers or votes. There are many sorts of questions that may be asked, and they can be organized as in the chart provided as a blackline master at the end of this section.

As is implied in the order of the columns of the chart, one way to think about regression is to think of the values of x as forming many categories, each of which has its own mean value of y. Then regression may be seen as a generalization of inference for sample means. Suppose you have the ages of all of the eligible voters and want to predict distances to their polling places. Think of these ages as forming categories with $x = 18, 19, 20$, and so on. Each value of x will have its mean distance to the polling place. If the scatterplot shows a linear trend, the regression line will go near these means. (In order to apply techniques of inference to this analysis, the data should consist of independent random samples from the different age groups and the standard deviation of the distances must be the same for each age category. See Fixed Versus Random Values of x on the next page.)

Instructional Methods

Toward the AP Statistics Exam

The AP course outline calls for inference for the slope of the least squares line, and the formula for the standard error of the slope is given on the formula sheet. Students should be able to use this standard error formula to construct confidence intervals and compute test statistics with regard to slope. (An example appears in the AP Statistics Teacher's Guide on pages 37–44.)

Students are not expected to derive the formula for the standard error, but they should understand what it measures and that it makes sense. What happens, for example, if the x-values are close together in one case and spread far apart in another? They should also understand that the t-values used in the inference procedures come from an assumption about the normality of the residuals (which should always be plotted).

Inference for the intercept of the regression line and for the correlation coefficient are not on the AP syllabus.

Be sure students who are taking the AP exam can read computer printouts of regression analyses. This chapter is relatively short compared to others because students should already understand the basic principles of statistical inference.

However, if your students will be taking the AP exam, it is worth spending more time than the guidelines below indicate because reading and interpreting a regression printout is likely to occur regularly on that exam. Students don't have to understand everything on the printout, only the parts covered on the AP syllabus and in this chapter.

Reviewing Slope and the Least-Squares Regression Line

Before beginning this chapter, your students may need to review least squares regression. You could use the Mars rock data on page 629 of the student text for this purpose and E1 on page 641 (part a and the first two questions in part c). Since Chapter 3, students haven't had much practice with the ideas of least squares regression. They may need to review the steps for looking for patterns in bivariate data where both variables are measurement data:

Shape. Plot the data in a scatterplot and look for a linear (elliptical) trend in the cloud of points. Look for departures from a linear trend (clusters, curvature, influential points).

Center. If the data are linear, fit a least squares regression line and interpret the slope, which gives the nature of the linear relationship.

Spread. Find the correlation coefficient and interpret it as the strength of the linear association and as the percentage of variation in the values of y that is accounted for by the regression line.

Residual plot. Check the residuals to be sure they don't have a pattern.

Transformation. If the data aren't linear (that is, they don't form an elliptical cloud and so the residuals have a pattern), try to find a transformation that linearizes them. Then fit a least squares regression line to the transformed data. (This is what should be done in practice. However, students sometimes use the somewhat unsatisfactory shortcut fitting exponential and power functions and looking for the one that has residuals from that function with no pattern. Students should know by now that just looking for a function with the largest $|r|$ is not adequate.) Transformations will be reviewed in Section 11.3.

Time Series Data

Stay away from time series data. Contrast the situation about age and distance to the polling place with one that looks at data on the size of a tumor over time. A plot of the data may show a clear linear trend or perhaps an "exponential" trend that can easily be linearized by a transformation. But the response at $time_2$ is highly related to the response at $time_1$ because the $time_2$ response is on the same tumor. The size of the tumor at $time_2$ is just the size at $time_1$ plus the additional growth between $time_1$ and $time_2$. The responses are not independent of one another; even the $time_8$ response would be somewhat dependent upon the $time_1$ response, and all the others in between $time_1$ and $time_8$. Thus, "time series" data do not meet the assumptions needed for inference in regression and so you should stay away from "sequence data" when doing inference for regression. Data of this type require a different methodology for inference.

Fixed Versus Random Values of x

The setting of inference for regression technically calls for a fixed set of x-values, with random y's. (This is different from the usual correlation setting in which x- and y-values can both be random.) In analyzing data for which the x's and y's are both random, the inferences are conditional on the values of x actually observed. That is, it is assumed that similar data would arise if the x's could have been fixed in advance and then a random sample of y's selected at each value of x. For example, when using an eligible voter's age to predict distance to the polling place, the assumption is that the ages of the sample are chosen ahead of time. Then random samples are taken from people with those ages and the distances to their polling places determined. Contrast this with taking a random sample of eligible voters and recording each person's age and distance. The latter method of selecting the sample is often done in practice and it is okay to proceed with inference for regression, as long as it is understood that a different set of x-values could have led to a different conclusion. Note that this latter method is allowed under the first bullet in step 1 in the box on page 645 of the student text. This is a case where the conditions you check before proceeding don't match exactly the mathematical assumptions of the inferential procedure.

Time Required

Traditional Schedule			Block	4 x 4 Block
Section 11.1				
2 days	Day 1	Overview, theoretical linear models, Activity 11.1, conditional distribution of y given x.	1.5 days	1 long, 1 short
	Day 2	Variability in b_1, Activity 11.2, estimating the standard error, summary, exercises		
Section 11.2				
2 days	Day 1	Activity 11.3, test statistic, significance test for a slope	1.5 days	1 long, 1 short
	Day 2	Confidence interval for β_1, summary, exercises		
Section 11.3				
2 days	Day 1	Checking the model, transformations for linearity	1 day	1 long
	Day 2	Summary, exercises		
Review				
1 day			1 day	1 long

Materials

Section 11.1: For Activities 11.1 and 11.2, students will need a calculator that selects a random value from a specified normal distribution. If these aren't available, a box of cards can be used as described in step 3 of Activity 11.1 on page 241.

Section 11.2: None

Section 11.3: None

Suggested Assignments

Classwork

Section	Essential	Recommended	Optional
11.1	Activity 11.1 D1, D3, D4, D6 P1–P5, P7	Activity 11.2 D2, D5	D7 P6, P8
11.2	Activity 11.3 D8, D10, D12 P9–P12	D9, D11 P13	D13
11.3	D14, D15 P14, P15	D16	

Homework

Section	Essential	Recommended	Optional
11.1	E1–E3	E5 (parts a and b)	E4, E5 (parts c, d, and e), E6
11.2	E7–E9, E11	E10, E12–E14	
11.3	E15, E19	E16, E17	E18
Review	E20, E22	E21, E24, E26	E23, E25

11.1 Variation in the Estimated Slope

Objectives

- to learn that the regression line as computed in Chapter 3, $\hat{y} = b_0 + b_1 x$, sometimes must be thought of as an estimate of a true, underlying linear model, $y = \beta_0 + \beta_1 x + \varepsilon$
- to learn that the slope of a regression line fitted from sample data will vary from sample to sample
- to learn that having a wider spread in the values of x and a smaller spread in the values of y (for each x) decreases the variability of the slope
- to learn that it is a condition of inference for regression that the variability in the values of y associated with a given x is equal for all values of x
- to learn that the variability in the values of y from a sample is measured in terms of the difference of y and its predicted value $\hat{y}$ and so is equivalent to the variability in the residuals

Important Terms and Concepts

- true regression line
- line of means
- conditional distribution of y given x
- variability in x
- variability in y at a given x
- standard error of the slope, σ_{b_1}
- estimate of the standard error for the slope, s_{b_1}

Class Time

Two days

Materials

For Activities 11.1 and 11.2, students will need a calculator that selects a random value from a specified normal distribution. If calculators aren't available, a box of cards can be used as described in step 3 of Activity 11.1 on page 241 of this teacher's guide.

Suggested Assignments

Classwork		
Essential	**Recommended**	**Optional**
Activity 11.1	Activity 11.2	D7
D1, D3, D4, D6	D2, D5	P6, P8
P1–P5, P7		

Homework		
Essential	**Recommended**	**Optional**
E1–E3	E5 (parts a and b)	E4, E5 (parts c, d, and e), E6

Lesson Notes: Theoretical Linear Models

Note on *Response = Line + Variation*

For scatterplots, as for all of statistics, *data equals pattern plus deviations from the pattern*. If the trend is linear, you can describe the pattern by giving the equation of a line, and if the deviations are "well-behaved," you can regard them as random draws from a normal distribution with mean 0 and fixed standard deviation. Taken together, these two features give the standard model for simple linear regression:

response = line + random variation

Symbolically, $y = \beta_0 + \beta_1 x + \varepsilon$ or $y = \mu_y + \varepsilon$. Here, ε is the random error and μ_y is the mean of the values of y for the given value of the explanatory variable x. The Greek letters β_0 and β_1 ("beta-sub-naught," or "beta-sub-zero," and "beta-sub-one") refer to the intercept β_0 and slope β_1 for a theoretical line that you don't ordinarily get to see—the line that you would get if you had the whole population for your data instead of just a sample. When you fit a line by least squares to sample data, you get an estimate of the intercept, b_0, and the slope, b_1. The values of y in your sample can be thought of as

observed response = fitted response + residual

which is equivalent to

residual = observed response − fitted response

Symbolically,

$$y = \hat{y} + residual = b_0 + b_1 x + residual$$

Activity 11.1: How Fast Do Kids Grow?

Activity 11.1 is essential for understanding the assumptions of the linear regression model.

1. The completed second column is shown here.

Age, x	Average Height from Model, μ_y
8	51
9	53
10	55
11	57
12	59
13	61

2. $y = 51 + 2(x - 8)$ or $y = 35 + 2x$. The intercept means that the height of a child aged 0 tends to be

51 inches, which is nonsense, so the line does not model heights well outside of a certain age range. The slope means that every year the average child grows 2 inches.

3. If students are using a TI-83, enter randNorm(0,2) on the Home screen to get a random deviation. You find the randNorm(command by pressing MATH PRB 6:randNorm(.

A concrete alternative is to make a box of deviations, ε. Take ten cards and mark one with each of the values -3, -2, 2, and 3, and mark two with each of the values -1, 0, and 1. Make sure the draws from this box of cards are random and with replacement. The box has mean 0 and standard deviation close to 2.

4. Sample results are shown next, using the deviations from the box of cards. (If a calculator is used, deviations aren't likely to be integers.)

Age, x	Average Height from Model, μ_y	Random Deviation, ε	Observed Height, y, of Your Child
8	51	0	51
9	53	2	55
10	55	-1	54
11	57	-2	55
12	59	3	62
13	61	0	61

This scatterplot shows "observed heights" with both the theoretical model and the least squares regression line. (The theoretical model is the one that goes through the point furthest to the right.) The slope of the regression line computed from the sample is 2.06, very close to the theoretical slope of 2.

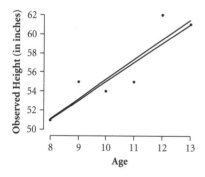

A regression analysis from Minitab is as follows:

```
Observed = 34.7 + 2.06 Age
Predictor    Coef    Stdev    t-ratio      p
Constant    34.733   5.285       6.57   0.003
Age          2.0571  0.4968      4.14   0.014
s = 2.078 R-sq = 81.1%
```

5. The plot should be mound-shaped and centered at 2 (the theoretical value of the slope), with standard deviation about .48 (the theoretical standard error of the slope). The theoretical standard error of the slope is computed as shown at the bottom of the page.

The next plot and summary are for 200 sample slopes generated as in Activity 11.1. Here the mean is 1.9951 and the standard deviation is 0.4979. These are estimates of the slope of the true regression line and the standard error of that slope, respectively.

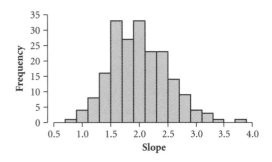

Descriptive Statistics

Variable	N	Mean	Median	TrMean	StDev	SEMean
SampleSlope	200	1.9951	1.9592	1.9820	0.4979	0.0352

Variable	Min	Max	Q1	Q3
SampleSlope	0.7998	3.7229	1.6453	2.3334

6. The average deviation from any mean is 0, so the average deviation of the conditional distribution at each age is 0.

7. It's reasonable because children's heights at each of these ages are known to be approximately normal with the given means. It's not so reasonable because the standard deviations at each age are not constant but increase with age.

Lesson Notes: The Conditional Distribution of *y* Given *x*

Be sure that students understand that when speaking of the mean and the variability in *y* in the context of inference about regression, you typically

are referring to the mean and the variability of the values of *y* "above" a single fixed value of *x*. This is called the conditional distribution of *y* given *x*. Each conditional distribution has a mean, μ_y, and a measure of variability, σ.

The mean of each conditional distribution, μ_y, lies on the theoretical line and so changes with *x* according to the equation $\mu_y = \beta_0 + \beta_1 x$.

It is an assumption of inference for regression that the variability, σ, of the conditional distribution is the same for each value of *x*. Note that this value is not the same as if you simply put all of the values of *y* into a pile and computed their variability. As students saw on pages 144–145 of Chapter 3, that value, computed using the differences $y - \bar{y}$, where $\bar{y}$ is the mean of *all* values of *y*, would generally be much larger than σ, which is computed using $y - \hat{y}$.

Because the language can get confusing, it's always best to refer to a picture when talking about the mean and variability of *y*.

Discussion

D1. For age 10, the mean height is 55 inches with standard deviation 2 inches. For age 12, the mean is 59 inches, and the standard deviation is still 2 inches.

D2. **a.** Use the form $\hat{y} = b_0 + b_1 x$. The slope and intercept were estimated from the data because the "true" values, β_1 and β_0, are unknown.

b. The response is the opening day; the predictor is the number of inches of *swe* at Flattop Mountain; the equation is

$$opening\ day = 150 + \left(\frac{1}{0.57}\right) \cdot (swe - 30)$$

$$= 97.37 + 1.75 \cdot swe$$

c. If *swe* = 51.7, *opening day* = 187.8. So, the prediction is day 188 or July 7. (The actual opening date was June 28, 2002, or day 179.)

d. The random variation, ε, should be relatively large. Numerous and strong conditions other than *swe* affect the opening date and vary widely from year to year. These include temperature, park management concerns, maintenance needs, road crew safety, and how many days of precipitation

---

Lesson 11.1, Activity 11.1, number 5

$$\sigma_{b_1} = \frac{\sigma}{\sqrt{\sum(x_i - \bar{x})^2}} = \frac{2}{\sqrt{(8 - 10.5)^2 + (9 - 10.5)^2 + \cdots + (13 - 10.5)^2}} \approx \frac{2}{\sqrt{17}} \approx 0.47809$$

occur after they begin trying to plow the road. The estimate given on the website for a typical random variation, ε, is about 9 days. Note that if the conditional distributions are approximately normal, the middle 95% of the opening dates for a given level of *swe* has a large range of $swe \pm 1.96(9)$, or about 36 days.

D3. The parameter β_1 is the slope of the theoretical model and generally will not be known; b_1 is an estimate of β_1 that is calculated from observed data. The value of b_1 will vary from sample to sample. Further, the theoretical model takes into account the fact that not every point is expected to lie on the line. An error term is built in. Epsilon, ε, is the deviation of a given point from the true regression line, whereas $y - \hat{y}$ is the residual from the regression line calculated from the sample data.

Practice

P1. **a.** The slope is 9 calories per gram of fat.
b. The number of calories associated with a serving containing no grams of fat.
c. There are calories in pizza from carbohydrates and protein as well as from fat.

P2. **a.** Because Leonardo says that height and arm span should be equal, the theoretical model is $y = x + \varepsilon$, where x is the arm span and y is the height, or *height* = *armspan* + ε.
b. A scatterplot of the data showing both the linear model and the estimated regression line is given next, followed by the regression analysis.

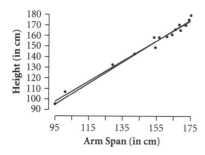

```
The regression equation is
Height = 7.915 + 0.952 Arm Span

Predictor     Coef     Stdev   t-ratio      p
Constant     7.915     5.118      1.55   0.146
Arm Span   0.95166   0.03325     28.62   0.000
```

The interpretation of the sample slope is that height tends to increase by about 0.952 inches for each 1-inch increase in arm span.

Notice that the estimated slope of 0.95166 is very close to Leonardo's theory of 1. The estimated intercept is 7.915, which is quite far from Leonardo's theoretical intercept of 0. But notice also that the estimated intercept has a large standard deviation.

c. This plot shows the random deviations ε from the theoretical line $y = x$ plotted against the x-values. There is a pattern here in that all of the negative deviations are for larger arm spans and the plot shows a downward trend.

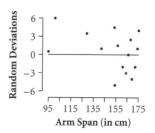

d. The next plot shows the residuals from the regression line, plotted against the x-values. The residuals $y - \hat{y}$ look more random than the values of ε, with one negative residual for small arm spans and no downward trend. Because it has no downward trend, the least squares regression line "fits" the data a little better than the theoretical model.

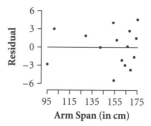

Lesson Notes: Variability in b_1

Variability of Residuals

For each conditional distribution of y given x, the variability σ is defined as the variability in y about μ_y. Because it is an assumption of inference for regression that the variability, σ, is equal for each conditional distribution of y given x and because μ_y lies on the regression line, then σ may be estimated by the variability of *all* values of y *about the regression line.* That is, σ may be estimated from the data by looking at the differences from the regression line, $y - \hat{y}$:

$$\sigma \approx s = \sqrt{\frac{\sum(y_i - \hat{y}_i)^2}{n-2}} = \sqrt{\frac{SSE}{n-2}}$$

Activity 11.2: What Affects the Variation in b_1?

This activity is recommended.

1. To generate the deviations, use the following instructions. Sample results may be found in the student text on pages 636–637.

Generating Values from a Normal Distribution with a TI-83. Use the randNorm(command, which is found by pressing MATH PRB 6:randNorm(. Enter the command on the Home screen in the form randNorm(*mean, standard deviation, number of trials*) and store the results in a list. For example, randNorm(10,3,4)→L1 generates four values from the normal distribution with mean 10 and standard deviation 3 and stores them in list L1.

Generating Values from a Normal Distribution with Minitab. Choose **Normal** from the Calc|Random Data menu.

In the dialog box, enter the number of rows of values desired (use **4** for this activity), the column in which the values are to be stored, the mean, and the standard deviation.

2. Stemplots of 50 slopes (values of b_1) generated for each of the four cases of the Activity are shown next, followed by a statistical summary for each distribution. The columns at the left represent the cumulative number of values from the closest end.

```
Stem-and-leaf of Slopes      Stem-and-leaf of Slopes
Case 1                       Case 2

Leaf Unit = 0.10             Leaf Unit = 0.10
  2  -3  88                    1  0  6
  2  -2                        1  0
  3  -1  5                     4  1  011
  7  -0  5531                  7  1  233
 17   0  0011144579           12  1  44455
 25   1  33445668             17  1  66666
 25   2  03447778             23  1  888999
 17   3  1233345889          (10)  2  0000011111
  7   4  03                   17  2  22223333
  5   5  4                     9  2  555
  4   6  12                    6  2  7
  2   7  12                    5  2  8888
                              1  3  0
```

```
Stem-and-leaf of Slopes      Stem-and-leaf of Slopes
Case 3                       Case 4

Leaf Unit = 0.10             Leaf Unit = 0.10
  2  -6  98                    1  -1  0
  3  -5  2                     1  -0
  3  -4                        1  -0
  3  -3                        1   0
  5  -2  64                    5   0  5799
  7  -1  95                   18   1  0001222333444
 14  -0  8775320             25   1  5666777
 19   0  03338               25   2  001111222224
 25   1  024689              13   2  5556799
 25   2  0579                 6   3  0113
 21   3  013569               2   3  66
 15   4  01234688
  7   5  8
  6   6  0134
  2   7  03
```

Summary Statistics for Simulated Sampling Distributions of the Slope

	N	MEAN	MEDIAN	STDEV	THEORY SE
Slope Case 1	50	2.024	1.939	2.350	2.12
Slope Case 2	50	1.979	2.069	0.531	0.53
Slope Case 3	50	1.833	1.963	3.331	3.53
Slope Case 4	50	1.912	1.930	0.879	0.88

The theoretical slope, β_1, is 2 in each case, and all four simulated sampling distributions have mean close to 2. That is, although the slopes vary from sample to sample, their mean is equal to the slope of the true regression line. Observe also that all of the distributions of slopes are somewhat bell-shaped.

3. The theoretical standard errors for the slopes can be calculated using

$$\sigma_{b_1} = \frac{\sigma}{\sqrt{\sum(x_i - \bar{x})^2}}$$

because σ is known for each case; these are shown in the column "THEORY SE." Again, observe that the standard deviations calculated from the four simulated sampling distributions of the values of b_1 are very close to the theoretical standard errors.

As the variation in the conditional responses (the given standard deviation) increases, so will the variation in the slopes. (Compare cases 1 and 3, then cases 2 and 4.) As the explanatory variable x spreads out more, the variation in the possible slopes of the regression line will decrease, assuming the conditional variation in the y's does not change. (Compare cases 1 and 2, then cases 3 and 4.)

Note: Now is another opportunity to point out the difference between the conditional distributions of the responses for a given x and the unconditional (marginal) distribution of the responses ignoring x.

Consider case 1, in which there are only two values of x. The (unconditional) variability in the y's can be made larger simply by, say, adding 10 to each value of y over $x = 1$. Now half the y's have values around 10 and half around 22. This does not increase the conditional variability of the y's, which continues to be $\sigma = 3$ for $x = 0$ and for $x = 1$. Further, this will increase the values of the slope but will not increase the variability in the slopes of the regression lines computed from random samples.

Teacher Demonstration

To fix an impression in your students' minds that larger spread in the values of x results in less variation in the value of b_1, place a meterstick over your wrists when your arms are stretched out. Note that the stick is more stable when your arms are farther apart than when they are close together.

Discussion

D4. Plot II will produce regression lines with the smallest variation in slopes because the conditional distributions of responses have smaller variation than in I and the x-values have greater spread than in III. Plot I has about twice the variability in x as III but also twice the variability in y. Consequently, the two have roughly the same variation in slopes of the regression line.

D5. There are two potential problems here. First, the data appear to have curvature. The centers of the conditional distributions of y do not lie on a straight line, which is one of the conditions for a linear fit. Second, the conditional distribution of responses at $x = 2$ has far greater variation than either of the other two conditional distributions. The assumption of equal variances of responses across all values of x is violated.

Practice

P3. $\sqrt{\sum(x_i - \bar{x})^2} \approx \sqrt{5.3814} = 2.3197845;$

$$s = \sqrt{\frac{\sum(y_i - \hat{y}_i)^2}{n - 2}} \approx \sqrt{\frac{0.349593}{5 - 2}} \approx 0.341366$$

P4. **a.** 5, because you saw in Activity 1.2 that a greater variability in the conditional distributions of y results in greater variability in the slope.

b. 3, because you saw in Activity 1.2 that a smaller spread in the values of x results in greater variability in the slope.

c. 10, because, all else being equal, a larger (random) sample size tends to result in a closer approximation to the parameter and less variability.

Each of these two histograms show 100 sample slopes from regression lines computed from repeated random samples taken from a population of (x, y) pairs with regression slope 0.8. The top plot is for samples of size 10, and the bottom plot is for samples of size 20. Note that both distributions center at about 0.8, but there is much more variability in the distribution of the sample slopes for the samples of size 10.

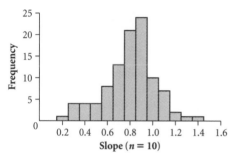

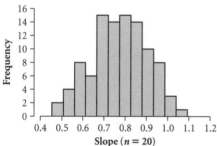

d. The theoretical slope does not matter, everything else being equal. (There is more on this in D7.)

e. The theoretical intercept does not matter because, all else being equal, all it does is indicate whether one cloud of points is higher or lower than another.

Lesson Notes: Estimating the Standard Error

Discussion

D6. For this study, the response is the actual temperature of your oven, which you could measure by a very accurate thermometer placed inside. The explanatory variable x is the temperature given on the oven's thermostat. You should set the oven to a specific temperature x, let it heat up fully, and then check the temperature y inside. If you want to design a study with small variation in the slope of the regression line, you should spread out the x-values across the allowable range for temperatures for the oven. Be sure to use both relatively high temperatures and relatively low temperatures. You should also use ones in the middle to check for curvature. To minimize the variation in the values of y, be sure the oven is fully heated up before checking the thermometer inside and be sure that the thermometer itself gives readings with little variation for the same temperature. If there is considerable variation in the responses for the same x, the sample size should be fairly large.

D7. Because, all else being equal, a larger spread in the values of x results in smaller variation in the estimated slope.

Practice

P5. **a.** Using the values from P3,

$$s_{b_1} = \frac{\sqrt{\Sigma(y_i - \hat{y}_i)^2/(n-2)}}{\sqrt{\Sigma(x_i - \bar{x})^2}} \approx \frac{0.341366}{2.3197845} \approx 0.1472$$

b. The standard error for the slope appears in the row "Sulfate" and column "s.e. of Coeff." (On some printouts, "Sulfate" will be replaced with x. This means the standard error of the coefficient of x—the standard error of the slope.) The estimate s of the variability in y about the line is found in the fourth row of Display 11.9 as $s = 0.3414$. The equation of the regression line is

$$\hat{y} = 1.71525 + 0.524901x$$

c. The first value is the slope of the regression line, b_1. The second value is the estimated standard error of that estimated slope, as explained in part b. The third value is the first divided by the second,

$$t = \frac{b_1}{s_{b_1}} = \frac{0.524901}{0.1472} \approx 3.57$$

The final value, .0376, is a two-sided P-value for $t = 3.57$, computed with $df = 3$.

P6. **a.** *Note:* If your students have had enough practice computing the standard error, you can give them this next printout to use for P6.

The "true" line should pass through the points (0, 10) and (4, 18), so its equation is $y = \beta_0 + \beta_1 x = 10 + 2x$. From the regression analysis in the display, $\hat{y} = b_0 + b_1 x = 9.91 + 2.03x$. The estimated slope is very close to 2, and the estimated intercept is close to 10.

Regression Analysis

```
The regression equation is
y = 9.91 + 2.03 x

Predictor    Coef    Stdev   t-ratio       p
Constant   9.9100   0.9889     10.02   0.000
x          2.0300   0.3496      5.81   0.000

s = 3.127  R-sq = 65.2%  R-sq(adj) = 63.3%

Analysis of Variance
SOURCE        DF        SS       MS       F       p
Regression     1    329.67   329.67   33.71   0.000
Error         18    176.01     9.78
Total         19    505.68

Unusual Observations
                                 Stdev.
Obs.    x      y     Fit    Fit    Residual  StResid
8    0.00  2.600   9.910  0.989    -7.310    -2.46R

R denotes an obs. with a large st. resid.
```

b. The standard deviation, s, of the residuals is 3.127, very close to the theoretical value of 3.

c. The standard deviation of b_1 is 0.3496. In theory, the slope should have standard deviation

$$\frac{\sigma}{\sqrt{\Sigma(x_i - \bar{x})^2}} = \frac{3}{\sqrt{80}} = 0.335$$

d. The mean of the responses at $x = 0$ is 9.91, and the mean at $x = 4$ is 18.03. The regression line with intercept 9.91 and slope 2.03 passes through these means at $x = 0$ and $x = 4$, respectively.

P7. V, II, I, IV, III

P8. The standard errors are I: $\frac{2}{2.8284} = 0.7071$; II: $\frac{1}{2.8284} = 0.3536$; III: $\frac{3}{5.9161} = 0.5071$; IV: $\frac{1}{5.9161} = 0.1690$. So the order from largest to smallest is I, III, II, IV.

Exercises

E1. **a.** The plot of (*hp, price*) has a fairly strong positive linear trend, although there is a tendency for the spread in y to increase as x increases.

The plot of (*hp, mpg*) has a fairly strong negative trend, although there is a hint of curvature. Perhaps a transformation is in order.

The plot of (*l, mpg*) has a fairly strong negative trend, but there are two potentially influential points on the left side. You might want to fit regression lines with and without these points to see their influence.

The plot of (*rpm, mpg*) shows that this is not a good data set for supporting a linear regression model. Although there is a slight positive trend in the data, the variation in responses is too great at the larger values of *x* (*rpm*) for inferential techniques to be correct or useful.

b. The largest estimated standard error should be for (*rpm, mpg*) because the values of *y* have such a large spread around a line compared to the spread in *x*. The smallest is (*hp, price*) because the values of *y* have the smallest spread around a line compared to the spread in *x*.

c. The estimated slope is $b_1 = -0.0693953$. This means that for every increase of 1 unit in horsepower, the gas mileage tends to drop by 0.0693953 miles per gallon. The standard error of the slope is about 0.023288.

d. The estimated slope appears under "Linear Fit." It also can be found under "Parameter Estimates" in row "HP" and column "Estimate." The standard error is found in column "Std Error" and row "HP." The value of *s* is the Root Mean Square Error = 4.778485 (found under "Summary of Fit").

E2. a. π or about 3.1416. This means that for every 1 cm increase in the distance across, the circumference will increase by 3.1416 cm.

b. In this case, there is a linear model that is known to fit the situation perfectly: $C = \pi d$. However, it is difficult to measure *C* and *d* with much accuracy. Further, because π is irrational, it is impossible to measure both the diameter and the circumference with complete accuracy.

E3. a. The soil samples should have the larger variability in the slope because the distance of *y* from the regression line tends to be larger compared to the spread in *x*.

b. The standard error for the soil samples is 0.36165. (Again, you may decide to have

students do this by reading a computer printout.) From P5, the standard error for the rocks samples was 0.1472. As predicted, the standard error for the soil samples is much larger.

E4. First, you need an estimate of both the mean and the variability of the conditional distribution of redness for a sulfur content like Half Dome's of 2.72%. The regression line gives you the estimate of the mean. That line, from P5, is $\hat{y} = 1.71525 + 0.524901x$, so when $x = 2.72$, $\hat{y} = 1.71525 + 0.524901(2.72) = 3.14298$. An estimate of the variability may also be found in the printout of P5, $s = 0.3414$. Thus, your instructions should read:

Pick a value at random from a normal distribution with mean 0 and standard deviation 0.3414.

Add that value to 3.14298. This is your estimate of the redness for a rock with sulfate percentage 2.72.

Note that this is the same thing as picking a value at random from $N(3.14298, 0.3414)$.

This model is reasonable given the limited information we have, but it may not be reasonable given that this is a sample of only a few rocks and we can't be sure that (1) the relationship is linear, (2) the variation in *y* is constant for all values of *x*, or (3) the distribution of the errors is normal.

E5. a. The plot shows a linear trend with large but homogeneous variation in heights across values of age.

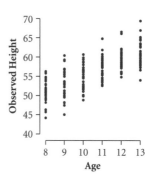

b. The plot shows a linear trend with homogeneous variation that is smaller than the variation in part a.

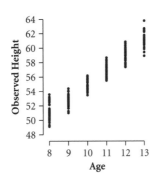

c. The plot shows a linear trend with pronounced heterogeneity of variation.

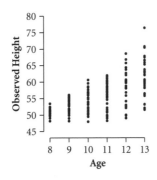

d. The plot shows a curved trend in the means with homogeneous variation.

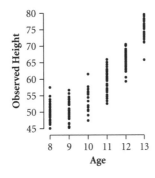

e. The plot shows a curved trend in the means with heterogeneity of variation.

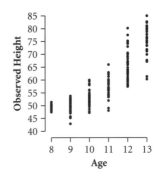

Overall, the conditions for the inference methods of this chapter are met for the plots in parts a and b but not for the plots in parts c, d, and e.

E6. From largest to smallest: V, I, II, III, IV

Some Possible Hypotheses

Explanatory Variable

Response Variable	One category (eligible voters)	Two categories (male eligible voters, female eligible voters)	More than two categories (registered Republicans, registered Democrats, registered others, those eligible but not registered)	One measurement (age)	Several measurements (age, income)
Two categories (voted, didn't vote)	What percentage of eligible voters voted? Inference for a single proportion (8.1, 8.2)	Is the percentage of eligible males who voted equal to the percentage of eligible females who voted? Inference for the difference of two proportions (8.3, 8.4)	Are each of the groups above equally likely to vote? Chi-square test of homogeneity or independence (10.2, 10.3)	Is whether the person voted related to age? Logistic regression (not covered in this text)	Is whether the person voted related to age and income? Logistic regression (not covered in this text)
More than two categories (would have voted Republican, Democrat, or other)	Is the proportion who would have voted Republican, Democrat, or other equal to the percentage in the actual election? Chi-square test of goodness of fit (10.1)	Are males and females equally likely to have voted Republican, Democrat, or other? Chi-square test of homogeneity or independence (10.2, 10.3)	Are each of the groups above equally likely to have voted Republican, Democrat, or other? Chi-square test of homogeneity or independence (10.2, 10.3)	Is there a relationship between age and how the person would have voted? Logistic regression (not covered in this text)	Is there a relationship between age and income and whether the person would have voted Republican, Democrat, or other? Logistic regression (not covered in this text)
One measurement (how far to polling place)	What is the average distance to the polling place for eligible voters? Inference for a mean (9.1, 9.2, 9.3)	Is the mean distance to the polling place equal for eligible male voters and eligible female voters? Inference for the difference of two means (9.5)	Is the mean distance to the polling place equal for all of the groups above? Analysis of variance (ANOVA) (not covered in this text)	Can you predict distance to the polling place from age? Inference for regression (11.2)	Can you predict distance to the polling place from age and income? Multiple regression (not covered in this text)

11.2 Making Inferences About Slopes

Objectives

- to perform a test of significance for the slope
- to construct and interpret a confidence interval for the slope
- to understand why the degrees of freedom for inference for the slope are $n - 2$ (optional)

Important Terms and Concepts

- test statistic for a slope
- significance test for a slope
- confidence interval for a slope
- degrees of freedom for inference for a slope

Lesson Planning

Class Time

Two days

Materials

None

Suggested Assignments

Classwork		
Essential	**Recommended**	**Optional**
Activity 11.3	D9, D11	D13
D8, D10, D12	P13	
P9–P12		

Homework		
Essential	**Recommended**	**Optional**
E7–E9, E11	E10, E12–E14	

Lesson Notes: The Test Statistic

The following regression analysis is for the Mars rock data on page 629 of the student text. The printout is annotated so you will know how each number is computed—just in case your students ask.

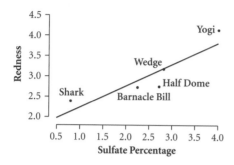

Name of Rock	Sulfate %	Redness
Shark	0.80	2.39
Barnacle Bill	2.25	2.73
Half Dome	2.72	2.75
Wedge	2.82	3.18
Yogi	4.01	4.14

Regression Analysis

See the bottom of the page.

(A) Sometimes named "Variable," the "Predictor" column lists the variables in the regression: the y-intercept (Constant) and the slope (Sulfate%). (In multiple regression, more than two predictors will be listed.)

(B) The "Coef" column lists the estimated value of the y-intercept, b_0, and of the slope, b_1. These are the coefficients in the regression equation.

(C) Sometimes named "s.e. of coeff," the "Stdev" column gives an estimate of the standard deviation of the sampling distribution of the y-intercept and of the sampling distribution of the slope. That is, it estimates how much the y-intercept and slope vary from sample to sample.

(D) The "t-ratio" column is equal to $\frac{\text{Coef}}{\text{Stdev}}$ and is used in a significance test of the hypothesis that a coefficient (slope or intercept) is zero.

(E) Sometimes called "prob," the "p" column is the P-value for the significance test, using the t-ratio with $n - 2$ degrees of freedom.

(F) The estimated value of the y-intercept, b_0, computed using b_1 and $b_0 = \bar{y} - b_1\bar{x}$.

(G) The estimated standard deviation of the sampling distribution of the y-intercept:

$$SE(b_0) \approx s_{b_0} = s\sqrt{\frac{1}{n} + \frac{\bar{x}^2}{\sum(x - \bar{x})^2}}$$

(H) (F) divided by (G):

$$t = \frac{b_0}{s_{b_0}}$$

(I) The P-value of the significance test of the y-intercept, using $n - 2$ degrees of freedom.

(J) The estimated value of the slope, b_1, computed using the formula on page 124 of the student text:

$$b_1 = \frac{\sum(x - \bar{x})(y - \bar{y})}{\sum(x - \bar{x})^2}$$

(K) The estimated standard deviation of the sampling distribution of the slope:

$$SE(b_1) \approx s_{b_1} = \frac{s}{\sqrt{\sum(x_i - \bar{x})^2}}$$
$$= \frac{\sqrt{\sum(y_i - \hat{y}_i)^2/(n-2)}}{\sqrt{\sum(x_i - \bar{x})^2}}$$

(L) (J) divided by (K):

$$t = \frac{b_1}{s_{b_1}}$$

Lesson 11.2, Notes

```
The regression equation is
Redness = 1.72 + 0.525 Sulfate%

Predictor (A)    Coef (B)    Stdev (C)    t-ratio (D)        p (E)
Constant         1.7153 (F)  0.4010 (G)      4.28 (H)    0.023 (I)
Sulfate%         0.5249 (J)  0.1472 (K)      3.57 (L)     .038 (M)

s = 0.3414 (N)  R-sq = 80.9% (O)  R-sq(adj) = 74.6% (P)

Analysis of Variance (Q)
SOURCE (R)    DF (S)        SS (T)        MS (U)       F (V)        p (W)
Regression    1 (X)      1.4827 (Y)    1.4827 (Z)   12.72 (AA)   0.038 (BB)
Error         3 (CC)     0.3496 (DD)   0.1165 (EE)
Total         4 (FF)     1.8323 (GG)
```

(M) The P-value of the significance test of the slope, using $n - 2$ degrees of freedom.

(N) The estimate of σ, the variability in the residuals. Alternatively, s is the estimate of the standard deviation of the values of y for any fixed value of x:

$$\sigma \approx s = \sqrt{\frac{\sum(y_i - \hat{y}_i)^2}{n - 2}}$$

$$= \sqrt{\frac{\text{SS Regression (or SSE)}}{n - 2}}$$

(O) The square of the correlation coefficient, r. Called the coefficient of determination:

$$\text{R-sq} = 1 - \frac{\text{SS Error}}{\text{SS Total}}$$

(P) An adjustment of R-sq to account for the fact that when you add a predictor to the model, R-Sq will get larger, even if the predictor is of no real value. It is an unbiased estimate of the population R-sq:

$$\text{R-sq(adj)} = 1 - \frac{\text{SS Error}/(n - p)}{\text{SS Total}/(n - 1)}$$

where p is the number of predictors ($p = 2$ in this case). Note that R-sq(adj) can be negative.

(Q) The F-test used in this analysis of variance is equivalent to the t-test for the significance of a slope. For example, if there are only two values of x and they are coded so as to be one unit apart, then the slope is equal to the difference between the means of the two sets of values of y. So in an experiment with two treatments coded 1 and 2 with sets of responses y_1 and y_2, the slope of the regression line is equal to $\bar{y}_2 - \bar{y}_1$.

(R) This column gives the source of the "error."

(S) The degrees of freedom for the source of error

(T) The sum of the squared errors

(U) The mean square error: $\frac{\text{SS}}{\text{DF}}$

(V) The F-ratio

(W) The P-value for the F-ratio

(X) Degrees of freedom for the regression equation, always equal to 1 for simple linear regression

(Y) SS Regression is equal to $\sum(\hat{y}_i - \bar{y})^2$ and gives the sum of the squared errors of the predicted values of y from the mean value of all y's. It is sometimes called SS Model. (See pages 144–145 of the student text.)

(Z) MS Regression $= \frac{\text{SS Regression}}{\text{DF}}$

(AA) The F-ratio, computed by dividing MS Regression by MS Error:

$$F = \frac{\text{MS Regression}}{\text{MS Error}} = \frac{\sum(\hat{y}_i - \bar{y})^2/1}{\sum(y_i - \hat{y}_i)^2/(n - 2)}$$

(BB) The P-value for the F-ratio. Note that it is the same as the P-value for the significance of the slope, 0.038 (M). This can be found on a calculator using 1 and $n - 2$ degrees of freedom: Fcdf(12.72,99999999, 1, 3) $\approx$ .0376.

(CC) Degrees of freedom for Error, $n - 2$

(DD) SS Error is the same thing as the SSE: $\sum(y_i - \hat{y}_i)^2$. It is sometimes called SS Residual.

(EE) MS Error $= \frac{\text{SS Error}}{\text{DF}}$. It is sometimes called MSE.

(FF) Sum of the degrees of freedom for Regression and for Error, $n - 1$

(GG) Total sum of squares, SS Regression + SS Error, or

$$\sum(y - \bar{y})^2$$

It is sometimes called SST (see pages 144–145 of the student text). Note the amazing fact that SST = SS Regression + SS Error:

$$\sum(y - \bar{y})^2 = \sum(\hat{y}_i - \bar{y})^2 + \sum(y_i - \hat{y}_i)^2$$

Activity 11.3: Phone Numbers and Names

If your class is unable to do Activity 11.3, here are some data from another class of 25 students. This class counted the letters in their first and last names only.

Sum of Last Four Digits of Phone Number	Number of Letters in First and Last Name
30	15
13	12
25	12
17	11
27	15
15	11
22	15
14	10
15	16
23	19
14	12
24	10
10	11
26	9
12	13
14	14
11	12

(continued)

(continued)

Sum of Last Four Digits of Phone Number	Number of Letters in First and Last Name
22	14
9	18
18	11
17	12
20	11
20	13
23	13
22	13

The scatterplot follows. The equation of the regression line is $\hat{y} = 12.425 + 0.02457x$, and the correlation is .058.

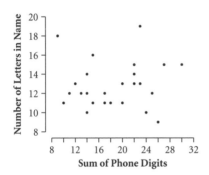

Discussion

D8. The test statistic is

$$t = \frac{b_1 - \beta_1}{s_{b_1}} \approx \frac{0.524901 - 0}{0.1472} \approx 3.57$$

with $df = 5 - 2 = 3$. Using the t-table, the P-value is between 2(.01) and 2(.02), which is consistent with the .0376 given in the printout.

D9. The t-statistic will be larger than that for either the rocks sample or the soil sample. That's because the value of s_{b_1} is going to be much smaller for the combined values, mainly because the spread of the values of x is larger. Notice how in the next plot the points cluster more closely to the regression line than they did in the individual samples

in Display 11.1 on page 629 or in Display 11.13 on page 642.

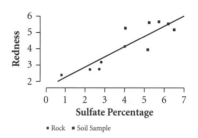

(From P5 of Section 11.1, $t = 3.57$ for the rocks. As students will see in P9 of this section, $t = 0.3617$ for the soil. And they will see in P10 of this section that $t = 5.6982$ for the two samples together.)

Practice

P9. The test statistic is

$$t = \frac{b_1 - 0}{s_{b_1}} = \frac{0.133399 - 0}{0.3617} = 0.3688$$

From the TI-83, with $df = 4$, the P-value is .731. From Table B, you can say only that the P-value is larger than 2(.25). You can not reject the null hypothesis that the slope is 0. There is no evidence here of a linear relationship between the percentage of sulfate and the redness for soil samples from Mars.

Lesson Notes: Significance Test for a Slope

Inference for Regression on the TI-83

All parts of a regression analysis can be done on the TI-83. First enter the x- and y-values into two lists, say L1 and L2. Press STAT CALC 8:LinReg(a+bx). Follow the LinReg(a+bx) command with the list names and a function name separated by commas, for example, LinReg(a+bx) L1,L2,Y1. The residuals are automatically stored in a list called RESID.

Use Stat Plot 1 to make a scatterplot of the data using L1 and L2. Function Y1 will graph the regression line on the plot.

Use Stat Plot 2 to make a residual plot using L1 and RESID.

You can perform a *t*-test for the significance of the slope by pressing $\boxed{\text{STAT}}$ TESTS E:LinRegTT. Specify the lists and regression equation, arrow down to Calculate, and press $\boxed{\text{ENTER}}$. This gives the value of *t*, the *P*-value (denoted "p"), *df*, and *s*, as well as the coefficients of the regression equation and the correlation *r*.

Nonlinear Association

The only association we are testing is a linear one; that is all simple linear regression models. A curved relationship can give a nonsignificant slope, so failure to reject a zero slope does not imply "no relationship." Further, rejecting a zero slope doesn't mean the relationship is linear. That's why you must always check residual plots.

Testing the Significance of a Correlation

In the simple linear case, the test for zero slope is exactly the same as the test for zero correlation. Suppose you have a linear regression of *y* on *x*. Under the hypothesis that the true slope is 0, the test statistic is

$$t = \frac{b_1}{s_{b_1}} = \frac{b_1}{\dfrac{\sqrt{\dfrac{\sum(y_i - \hat{y}_i)^2}{n - 2}}}{\sqrt{\sum(x_i - \bar{x})^2}}}$$

where b_1 is the estimate of the slope. With a little algebra—well, a lot of algebra—you can show that this is algebraically equivalent to the test statistic for testing that the correlation is 0:

$$t = \frac{r}{\sqrt{\dfrac{1 - r^2}{n - 2}}}$$

The conditions for the two tests are a bit different, however. Further, the *t*-statistic above works only for testing zero correlation ($\rho = 0$, where ρ is the correlation in the population). If you want to test other hypothesized values, produce confidence intervals for correlations, or compare correlations, then you need some additional theory. All of this is beyond the introductory course, so we suggest that you stick to testing the significance of a slope with introductory students.

The Random Sample Condition: Checking Data Production

Shark: Remind yourself of why you need inference: You have reasons to think there's a hidden "true relationship" and that the data set you

see is *just one of many possible data sets* you might have gotten. IF—and this is the biggest "if" in all of statistics—IF the connection between the hidden true relationship and what you get to see is a connection for which a probability model is appropriate, THEN you can use the data to reach conclusions about the true relationship. To the degree that a probability model is *not* appropriate, you're not doing statistics, you're just doing wishful thinking dressed up in numbers.

Yogi: Nice speech. Bravo. Wake me up if you figure out what it means in actual practice.

To help students understand the randomness assumption, tell them to think about repetitions. If you could redo the process of selecting your cases and determining the values of the variables for those cases, what would change and what would remain the same? There are basically three different scenarios in which regression is used: fixed *x*'s, fixed *y*'s; random *x*'s, random *y*'s; and fixed *x*'s, random *y*'s.

Fixed x's, fixed y's. Both variables are measured on all of the (*x*, *y*) pairs in the population. Generally, inference is not used because what you see is all there is; regression is simply a data exploration tool. (You could use inferential techniques only to help decide whether any pattern reasonably could be attributed to chance alone.)

You find *height* versus *number of stories* for the 100 tallest buildings in the world. If you repeat this, nothing should change.

Random x's, random y's. You take a random sample from cases that make up a bivariate population. This produces a set of ordered pairs (*explanatory, response*).

You study the possible association between *amount of exercise* and *heart rate* by randomly sampling students from your school. If you took another random sample, you probably would have entirely different cases and so different values for both variables. Inference about the slope of the regression line for your school is valid but it is conditional upon the observed *x*'s.

Fixed x's, random y's. The values of the explanatory variable, *x*, are predetermined. For each of these fixed values of *x*, a random sample is taken independently of the samples for the other *x*'s.

You want to analyze the trend in the average selling price of a certain model of the Ford Explorer over the past three years. You do this by getting a random sample of 100 purchases from this year, a random sample of 100 purchases from last year, and a random sample of 100 purchases from the year before. If you repeated this, you would most likely get different purchases but you would still have 100 prices from each year. Inference about the slope of the regression line for these three years is valid.

In an experiment, treatments consist of different levels of the amount of active ingredient in a sunscreen (your explanatory variable). You compare the responses (say, how much burning takes place) after randomly assigning the treatments to a group of subjects agreeing to participate in the experiment. With a different randomization of treatments to subjects, the levels of ingredient (values of x) would still stay the same, but the amounts of burning would be different. Inference about the slope of the regression line to this group of subjects is valid.

Discussion

D10. If your class was unable to do Activity 11.3, you can use the results in the table at the beginning of the Lesson Notes for Activity 11.3. The following sample solution is for those data.

> *Check conditions.* First, this is not a random sample, but the problem says we may assume it is. (Textbooks are so much more accommodating than real life!) A scatterplot, the residual plot, and a plot of the residuals are shown next.

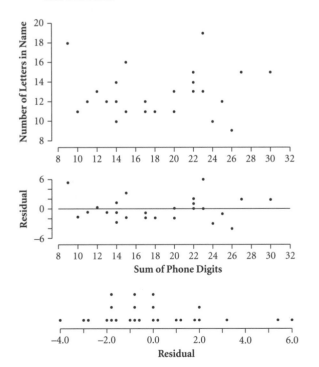

Second, the residual plot shows scattered points about the line, so the relationship looks linear. Third, the residuals stay about the same size over all values of x. Fourth, the plot of the residuals is skewed a bit right. The distribution is not as symmetric as we would like, but not too bad for inference.

State your hypotheses.
H_0: $\beta_1 = 0$
H_a: $\beta_1 \neq 0$
where β_1 is the slope of the theoretical regression line relating the number of letters in the last name to the sum of the last four digits in the student's phone number.

Compute the test statistic and draw a sketch. The test statistic is $t = 0.2788$. There are 23 degrees of freedom (two less than the sample size). The P-value from the calculator is .7829.

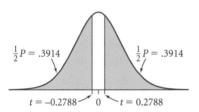

Write a conclusion in context. We can not reject the null hypothesis because the P-value is large. If it were true that the slope of the regression line were equal to 0 (the null hypothesis) and you performed the sampling process repeatedly, it is very probable that you would get a value of t as large as or larger in absolute value than the one from the sample. There is no evidence that there is a linear relationship between the sum of the last four digits in his or her phone number and the number of letters in a student's last name.

D11. The t-statistic for the coefficient of x is testing the null hypothesis that the true regression slope is zero against the alternative that it is not zero. The P-value measures the chance of seeing a t-statistic as extreme as or more extreme (farther from zero) than the one observed under the assumption that the true regression slope is zero. If the P-value is small, the chance of seeing a t-statistic this far out in the tail of the t-distribution is small when the null hypothesis is true. This gives cause to doubt the null hypothesis and suggests that the true slope is not zero.

Practice

P10. The *t*-statistic is

$$t = \frac{0.6268 - 0}{0.11} \approx 5.6982$$

With $11 - 2 = 9$ degrees of freedom, the *P*-value from the calculator is .00029. With a *P*-value this small, you reject the hypothesis that there is no linear relationship between percentage of sulfur and redness.

P11. The scatterplot with regression line is shown next. It looks like a straight line will serve as a good model of the relationship between average temperature and number of chirps per second.

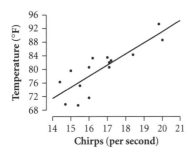

a. The equation is $\hat{y} = 25.232 + 3.291x$. You can expect the temperature to tend to rise about 3.291 degrees if the number of chirps per second increases by 1.

b. The plots appear here.

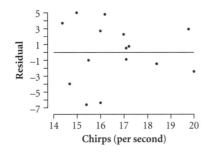

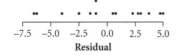

The residual plot shows no obvious pattern, so a linear model fits the data well. There is no evidence that the residuals tend to change in size as *x* increases. The dot plot of the residuals shows no outliers or obvious skewness or any other indications of non-normality. Of course, these plots can't check the condition that you have a random sample of cricket chirping.

c. From the printout, the *P*-value is close to 0. You reject the hypothesis that there is no linear relationship between rate of chirping and temperature.

Lesson Notes: Confidence Interval for β_1

Discussion

D12. **I.** From the regression analysis for the rocks in P5 of Section 11.1, $b_1 = 0.524901$, $s_{b_1} = 0.1472$, and $df = 3$. From Table B, $t^* = 3.182$. Thus, the 95% confidence interval is

$$0.524901 \pm 3.182(0.1472)$$

or 0.5249 ± 0.4684. You are 95% confident that the slope of the true regression line for predicting redness from percentage of sulfur in Mars rocks is in the interval 0.0565 to 0.9933.

II. From the regression output for the rocks in P9, $b_1 = 0.133399$, $s_{b_1} = 0.3617$, and $df = 4$. From Table B, $t^* = 2.776$. Thus, the 95% confidence interval is

$$0.133399 \pm 2.776(0.3617)$$

or 0.133399 ± 1.0041. You are 95% confident that the slope of the true regression line for predicting redness from percentage of sulfur in Mars soil samples is in the interval -0.8707 to 1.1375.

III. For both groups together, from the calculator, $b_1 = 0.6268$, $df = 9$, $t = 5.6990$, and $s = 0.6331$. However, the calculator does not give you s_{b_1}. You can get s_{b_1} from P10 or, better, from the fact

$$t = \frac{b_1}{s_{b_1}} \quad \text{so} \quad s_{b_1} = \frac{b_1}{t} = \frac{0.6268}{5.6990} = 0.10998$$

The 95% confidence interval is

$$0.6268 \pm 2.262(0.10998)$$

or 0.6268 ± 0.2488. You are 95% confident that the slope of the true regression line for predicting redness from percentage of sulfur is in the interval 0.3780 to 0.8756.

The widest interval is for soil samples, and the smallest is for both together. The interval for the soil samples is the widest because the points tend to be relatively far from the regression line, so it has the largest standard error. As discussed in D9, the points in the combined sample cluster relatively close to the regression line. So the combined sample has the smallest standard error. Plus, the larger sample size also contributes to a narrower confidence interval.

D13. Because the P-value for the two-sided test of a slope is less than .05, a 95% confidence interval estimate of the slope does not include 0.

Practice

P12. **a.** The 90% confidence interval is

$$b_1 \pm t^* \cdot s_{b_1} = -0.033718 \pm 2.353(0.0039)$$

You are 90% confident that the slope of the true regression line for predicting titanium dioxide content from silicon dioxide content for Mars rocks is in the interval -0.0337 ± 0.0092, or -0.0429 to -0.0245.

b. The value $s = 0.0257$ is an estimate of σ, the standard deviation of the residuals from the true regression line. In other words, it is an estimate of a typical distance of the points from that line. It can also be interpreted as an estimate of the variability in y at each fixed x.

P13. The 90% confidence interval is

$$b_1 \pm t^* \cdot s_{b_1} = 0.026856 \pm 2.132(0.0461)$$

You are 90% confident that the slope of the true regression line for predicting titanium dioxide content from silicon dioxide content for Mars soil is in the interval 0.02686 ± 0.09829, or -0.0714 to 0.1251.

Because the confidence interval for the soil samples entirely overlaps the one for the rocks, you can't conclude that the slopes are different.

Dialogue on Degrees of Freedom

This topic typically is not covered in an introductory statistics course and is not on the AP syllabus, so the dialogue on pages 654–655 of the student text is optional.

Exercises

E7. **a.** A straight line with a negative slope seems to fit the data well, although there is an influential point (Suzuki) with high gas mileage and low horsepower that does not quite fit the pattern.

b. The equation of the regression line is $\hat{y} = 38.9805 - 0.0694x$.

c. The standard deviation of the residuals is $s = 4.778$.

d. The estimated standard error of b_1 is 0.0233.

e. Yes. For testing that the true slope is 0, the t-statistic is -2.98, which has an associated P-value of .0106.

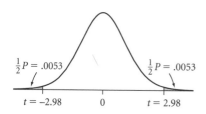

The slope is significantly different from zero. There is a negative association between horsepower and miles per gallon that can not simply be attributed to chance variation in b_1.

f. For a 90% confidence interval estimate based on 13 degrees of freedom, use $t^* = 1.771$. The confidence interval is

$$b_1 \pm t^* \cdot s_{b_1} = -0.069395 \pm 1.771(0.0233), \text{ or}$$

$$-0.69395 \pm 0.04126, \text{ or } (-0.1107, -0.0281).$$

This interval gives the plausible values of the expected decrease in miles per gallon per 1 unit increase in horsepower. In other words, an increase of 100 horsepower is expected to decrease gas mileage by somewhere between 2.8 and 11 miles per gallon.

E8. Here are the scatterplot and regression analyses for *mpg* as a function of maximum *rpm*, the residual plot, and a plot of the residuals.

Regression Analysis

```
The regression equation is
MPG = 10.8 + 0.00320 RPM

Predictor        Coef       Stdev    t-ratio       p
Constant        10.84       12.62       0.86   0.406
RPM          0.003201    0.002285       1.40   0.185

s = 5.778  R-sq = 13.1%  R-sq(adj) = 6.4%

Analysis of Variance
SOURCE       DF         SS        MS       F       p
Regression    1      65.56     65.56    1.96   0.185
Error        13     434.04     33.39
Total        14     499.60

Unusual Observations
Obs.   RPM     MPG    Fit  Stdev.Fit  Residual  St.Resid
  3   4000   20.00  23.64       3.71     -3.64     -0.82X
 13   6000   43.00  30.04       1.90     12.96      2.37R

R denotes an obs. with a large st. resid.
X denotes an obs. whose X value gives it large influence.
```

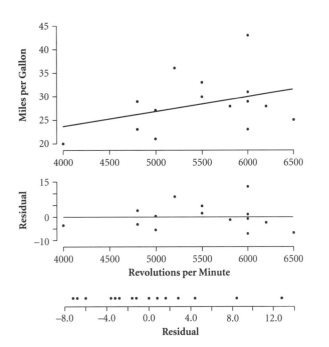

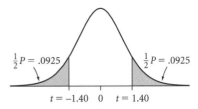

Check conditions. The models of cars were selected at random. The trend appears linear; however, the residuals show a slight tendency to increase with *x*. (In the next section, students will learn how to transform data like these.) So you must proceed with caution.

State your hypotheses.

$H_0: \beta_1 = 0$

$H_a: \beta_1 \neq 0$

where β_1 is the slope of the regression line for predicting the *mpg* from the *rpm* computed from the population of all models of cars.

Compute the test statistic and draw a sketch. The test statistic is $t = 1.40$. There are 13 degrees of freedom (2 less than the sample size). The *P*-value from the printout is .185.

![Normal curve with shaded tails labeled ½P = .0925 on left and ½P = .0925 on right; horizontal axis marked t = −1.40, 0, t = 1.40]

Write a conclusion in context. Do not reject the null hypothesis. The slope is very near zero, and the *t*-statistic for the test of signifi-

cance of the slope is small, producing a *P*-value of .185. There is no evidence of a linear association between expected gas mileage and the maximum speed of the engine in rpm's. In other words, if it were true that the slope of the regression line were equal to 0 (the null hypothesis) and you performed the sampling process repeatedly, it is very probable that you would get a value of *t* as extreme as or more extreme than the one from the sample.

E9. a. i. You checked the conditions in P11. Using the information in the printout in P11 with 13 degrees of freedom,

$$b_1 \pm t^* \cdot s_{b_1} = 3.2911 \pm 2.160(0.6012)$$
$$= 3.2911 \pm 1.2986$$

A 95% confidence interval is 1.9925 to 4.5897. You are 95% confident that the true slope of the regression line for predicting the temperature from the chirp rate is in this interval.

ii. First, note that the assumptions were not checked in P11, given that the residuals will be different when you reverse the roles of *chirp rate* and *temperature*. The residual plot and a dot plot of the residuals appear next with the regression printout. The conditions of linear trend, same spread across *x*, and normal residuals look like they are met. Using the information in the printout with 13 degrees of freedom,

$$b_1 \pm t^* \cdot s_{b_1} = 0.21192 \pm 2.160(0.03871)$$
$$= 0.21192 \pm 0.08361$$

A 95% confidence interval is 0.12831 to 0.29553. You are 95% confident that the true slope of the regression line for predicting chirp rate from temperature is in this interval.

```
The regression equation is
Chirps = -0.31 + 0.212 Temp

Predictor      Coef    Stdev   t-ratio       p
Constant     -0.309    3.109     -0.10   0.922
Temp        0.21192  0.03871      5.47   0.000

s = 0.9715  R-sq = 69.7%  R-sq(adj) = 67.4%
```

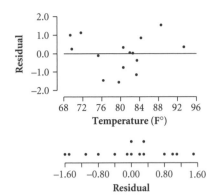

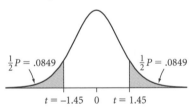

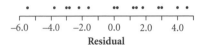

The residual plot appears in the solution to P2, part d, in Section 11.1. It shows that a linear trend is reasonable because the residuals show no pattern and stay roughly the same size across all values of *x*. This plot of the residuals shows that they could reasonably have come from a normal distribution.

b. When you reverse the roles of *chirp rate* and *temperature,* the entire regression line changes. The unit of the slope changes from degrees per chirp to chirps per degree. The sizes of the residuals change too because they are measured from a different line and from a different direction. Further, they are measured in different units (difference in temperature versus difference in chirp rate). *Note:* The two slopes are not reciprocals of one another either.

E10. First, note that it is not appropriate to do a test of significance that the slope of the regression line for predicting height from arm span is 0. You are interested in whether 1 is a plausible value for the slope, not 0. You have two choices. You can do a test that $\beta_1 = 1$ using the *t*-statistic:

$$t = \frac{b_1 - 1}{s_{b_1}} = \frac{0.95166 - 1}{0.03325} \approx -1.45383$$

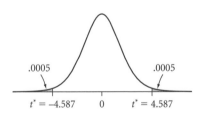

With 13 degrees of freedom, you can not reject the hypothesis that the slope is 1. It is plausible that if one person has an arm span 1 cm longer than another, they tend to be 1 cm taller.

Or you can get a 95% confidence interval for the slope:

$$b_1 \pm t^* \cdot s_{b_1} = 0.95166 \pm 2.160(0.03325)$$
$$= 0.95166 \pm 0.07182$$

This interval (0.8798, 1.0235) includes 1 as a plausible value for β_1. So these data are consistent with Leonardo's model.

E11. A regression analysis and needed graphs appear next. The regression equation is *size* = 31.83 − 0.712 *acid*. The slope of −0.712 means that for every increase of 1 *μg*/ml in acid concentration, the radius of the fungus colony tends to decrease by 0.712 mm. The test of the significance of the slope follows.

Check conditions. The text does not say whether the petri dishes were randomly selected to receive the different concentrations. But that's a safe bet, given that the experiment was published in *Science*. The residual plot shows that a linear trend is reasonable and the residuals stay roughly constant across all values of *x*. The plot of the residuals shows no reason to suspect that the population of residuals isn't normal.

State your hypotheses.
H₀: $\beta_1 = 0$
Hₐ: $\beta_1 \neq 0$
where β_1 is the slope of the true regression line for predicting colony radius from acid concentration.

Compute the test statistic and draw a sketch. The printout gives $t = -19.84$, $df = 10$, and a *P*-value of 0. From Table B, the *P*-value is < .001.

Write a conclusion in context. Because the *P*-value is so small, reject the null hypothesis. There is a negative linear relationship between colony radius and acid concentration. The more acid applied, the smaller the radius, at least over the range of acid concentrations applied.

```
The regression equation is
Size = 31.8 - 0.712 Acid

Predictor      Coef     Stdev   t-ratio      p
Constant    31.8298    0.5569     57.15  0.000
Acid       -0.71201   0.03589    -19.84  0.000

s = 1.295 R-sq = 97.5% R-sq(adj) = 97.3%

Analysis of Variance

SOURCE      DF       SS      MS       F      p
Regression   1   660.57  660.57  393.64  0.000
Error       10    16.78    1.68
Total       11   677.35
```

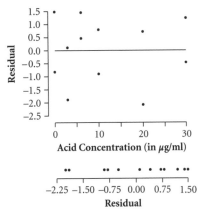

E12. The linear regression analysis for predicting *price* from *area* follows. The data fit a linear model well. There is a strong positive trend with a highly significant slope. The value of the slope, $b_1 = 68.3855$, estimates the expected increase in price (in thousands of dollars) per 1000–square foot increase in area. Note that this is equivalent to about $68.39 per square foot. (The cost of housing in Gainesville, Florida, is lower than in many other parts of the country.)

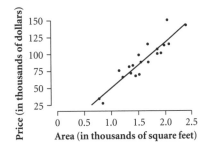

```
Dependent variable is:   Price
No Selector
R squared = 85.1%    R squared (adjusted) = 84.3%
s = 12.12 with 20 - 2 = 18 degrees of freedom

Source       Sum of Squares  df  Mean Square  F-ratio
Regression   15129.9          1     15129.9    103
Residual     2643.77         18     146.876

Variable  Coefficient  s.e. of Coeff  t-ratio     prob
Constant   -17.9615        10.98        -1.64    0.1191
Area        68.3855         6.738       10.1   ≤ 0.0001
```

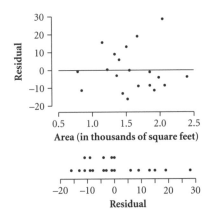

E13. The plot of the price as a function of the number of bedrooms, including the regression line, and a regression output is shown next. The regression equation is *price* = −32.3263 + 39.4553 *bedrooms*.

There is a positive trend with a statistically significant slope. The value of the slope, $b_1 = 39.4553$, indicates that the expected increase in price is about $39,455 per bedroom. However, the residual plot does not show randomly scattered points.

The main problem with this analysis is that there is only one two-bedroom house and there are three four-bedroom houses. The two-bedroom house is influential. Most of the houses have three bedrooms, and this group shows a much greater variability in prices than is seen among the four-bedroom houses. To get a fairer picture of the true relationship between *average selling price* and *number of bedrooms,* more two- and four-bedroom houses should be brought into the picture. If two-bedroom houses are simply quite rare, that category should be dropped from the analysis.

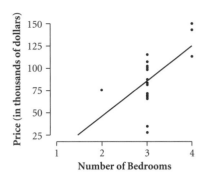

Dependent variable is: Price
No Selector
R squared = 33.3% R squared (adjusted) = 29.6%
s = 25.67 with 20 - 2 = 18 degrees of freedom

Source	Sum of Squares	df	Mean Square	F-ratio
Regression	5915.53	1	5915.53	8.98
Residual	11858.2	18	658.787	

Variable	Coefficient	s.e. of Coeff	t-ratio	prob
Constant	-32.3263	41.22	-0.784	0.4431
Bedrooms	39.4553	13.17	3.00	0.0077

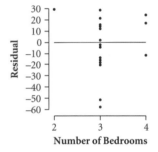

E14. A plot of price as a function of the number of bathrooms shows that there are only two groups (one-bathroom and two-bathroom houses) in this sample of houses for sale. Fitting the regression line and testing for significance of the slope is equivalent to the two-sample *t*-test for the difference of two means, as introduced in Chapter 9. Both the regression analysis and two-sample analysis are shown next.

The first analysis, using regression, lets you reject the hypothesis that the slope is 0. As the number of bathrooms increases from 1 to 2, the price tends to go up by $53,002. The 95% confidence interval for this slope is

$$b_1 \pm t^* \cdot s_{b_1} = 53.002 \pm 2.101(15.2039)$$
$$= 53.002 \pm 31.943$$

or about (21, 85). The best estimate of the true difference in mean prices for one- and two-bathroom houses is somewhere between $21,000 and $85,000, a pretty big interval due to the small sample for one bathroom and large variability in prices.

The second analysis, the two-sample *t*-test also lets you reject the hypothesis that the mean price for one-bathroom houses is equal to the mean price for two-bathroom houses. However, the 95% confidence interval for the difference in mean prices is estimated to be $(-102.343, -3.661)$, or $3,661 to $102,343.

And why the discrepancy in the *P*-values in the two tests? The procedure for inference for a slope assumes that the residuals have the same standard deviation across all values of *x*. That would be equivalent to a two-sample *t*-test with pooled variances. Checking that box on the software gives the third analysis below. Now, this test is equivalent to the regression analysis, with the same *P*-value, and generating the same confidence interval for the difference in prices.

Regression Analysis

Dependent variable is: Price
No Selector
R squared = 40.3%   R squared (adjusted) = 37.0%
s = 24.28 with 20 - 2 = 18 degrees of freedom

Source	Sum of Squares	df	Mean Square	F-ratio
Regression	7163.48	1	7163.48	12.2
Residual	10610.2	18	589.456	

Variable	Coefficient	s.e. of Coeff	t-ratio	prob
Constant	-8.06863	28.65	-0.282	0.7814
Bedrooms	53.0020	15.20	3.49	0.0026

Two-sample *t*-test

```
2-Sample t-Test of μ1 - μ2
No Selector
Individual Alpha Level 0.05
H₀: μ1 - μ2 = 0    Hₐ: μ1 - μ2 ≠ 0

1:Price - 2:Price
Test   H₀: μ(1:Price) - μ(2:Price) = 0  vs
       Hₐ: μ(1:Price) - μ(2:Price) ≠ 0
Difference Between Means = -53.001961
    t-Statistic = -3.558 w/2 df
Reject H₀ at Alpha = 0.05
p = 0.0422

2-Sample t-Interval for μ1 - μ2
No Selector
Individual Confidence 95.00%
Bounds: Lower Bound < μ1 - μ2 < Upper Bound

With 95.00% Confidence, -102.34324 <
    μ(1:Price) - μ(2:Price) < -3.6606862
```

Two-sample *t*-test assuming
equal (pooled) variances

```
Pooled t-Test of μ1 - μ2
No Selector
Individual Alpha Level 0.05
H₀: μ1 - μ2 = 0    Hₐ: μ1 - μ2 ≠ 0
```

1:Price - 2:Price
```
Test   H₀: μ(1:Price) - μ(2:Price) = 0  vs
    Hₐ: μ(1:Price) - μ(2:Price) ≠ 0
Difference Between Means = -53.001961
    t-Statistic = -3.486 w/18 df
Reject H₀ at Alpha = 0.05
p = 0.0026
```

```
Pooled t-Interval for μ1 - μ2
No Selector
Individual Confidence 95.00%
Bounds: Lower Bound < μ1 - μ2 < Upper Bound
```

```
With 95.00% Confidence, -84.944210 <
    μ(1:Price) - μ(2:Price) < -21.059712
```

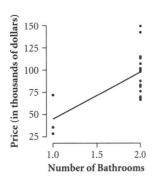

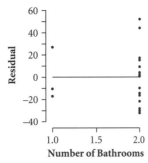

11.3 Transforming for a Better Fit

Objectives

- to practice checking the conditions for inference for the slope
- to practice constructing confidence intervals and performing tests of significance for a slope
- to review log and log-log transformations and their use in straightening exponential and power functions
- to learn how these transformations also can reduce heteroscedasticity
- to learn how influential points can influence a confidence interval and a test of significance for the slope

Important Terms and Concepts

- log transformation and exponential functions
- log-log transformation and power functions

Lesson Planning

Class Time

Two days

Materials

None

Suggested Assignments

Classwork		
Essential	**Recommended**	**Optional**
D14, D15	D16	
P14, P15		

Homework		
Essential	**Recommended**	**Optional**
E15, E19	E16, E17	E18

Lesson Notes: Checking the Model

Linearity Versus Association

Students sometimes need to be reminded how to interpret the significance test for a slope from Section 11.2 and the importance of checking the residual plot.

If the test rejects the null hypothesis, students shouldn't conclude that the relationship is linear unless they have checked that the residual plot shows a patternless, elliptical cloud of points. The slope of the linear regression line may be nonzero, for example, when the underlying relationship is exponential. A residual plot would have shown the nonlinear relationship and that this test shouldn't have been used before doing a transformation.

If the test fails to reject the null hypothesis, students shouldn't interpret this as meaning that there is no association or no relationship. The interpretation is simply that there is no evidence of a linear relationship. The points may follow a parabolic path, for example, and have a quadratic relationship.

Illustrating Heteroscedasticity

For a nice example of heteroscedasticity, give your students a copy of the U.S. National Center for Health Statistics growth charts available at http://www.cdc.gov/growthcharts.

These show how the standard deviation of children's heights increases with age.

Discussion

D14. **a.** Plot III. The residual plot shows a negative-positive-negative pattern indicating curvature.

b. The variation in the residuals tends to increase or decrease as x increases: Plots I and II.

c. The dot plot of the residuals looks skewed or has outliers: Plots II and IV.

d. Plot IV and maybe Plots II and III. If the two influential points in Plot IV are removed, the line becomes almost horizontal. If the point at the far right of Plot II is removed, the line becomes less horizontal, but not by much. If the point at the far left of Plot III is removed, the line becomes a little less steep. See the plots shown next.

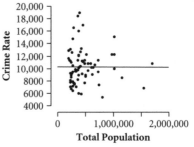

$Cr = -0.0000494 \cdot pop + 10303; r^2 = .0000257$

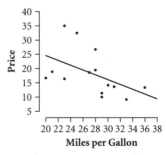

$price = -0.858 \cdot mpg + 41.71; r^2 = .239$

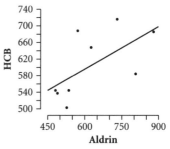

$HCB = 0.341 \cdot aldrin + 391.63; r^2 = .389$

Lesson Notes: Transformations to Improve Linearity

NOTE: Fathom users should note that nonverbose-style printouts found in the student edition starting on page 668 may be different from your display in Fathom, depending upon your version of the software. Specifically, the independent and dependent attributes may be switched in the "versus" statement. ■

Discussion

D15. **a.** Removing the outliers results in a much more randomly scattered residual plot and only one outlier and so improve the conditions for inference. However, the residuals are still skewed right.

The five cities were very influential. In the t-test for the significance of the slope, the

P-value went from .0054 to .97. The appearance of a positive linear relationship was due entirely to these five cities. Note that in both cases, the slope is very small. Even when the outliers are present and the slope is significant, it means that the increase in the percentage of renters is less than .3 per 100,000-people-increase in the population.

b. The residuals are more symmetric, so there is a slight improvement in satisfying the conditions for linearity. The P-value for the significance of the slope remains very high, and the slope is still not significantly different from 0. With the five very large cities removed, there appears to be no linear relationship between size of a city and the percentage of renters whether or not a log transformation is done.

c. The regression line is meaningful whether you have a sample or the entire population. It was useful to do a significance test for the slope here, but the conclusion must be stated something like this: The slope of the relationship between the percentage of renters and population of the city is no different from what you would expect if the percentage of renters had been assigned at random to the cities.

D16. Testing that the true power is 3 in the exponential model is approximately the same as testing that the true slope is 3 in the corresponding linear model after the log-log transformation.

Check conditions. These were checked in the example in the text.

State your hypotheses.

H_0: If you had the entire population of large-mouth bass, the slope, β_1, of the regression line for the relationship of ln(*weight*) versus ln(*length*) would be equal to 3.

H_a: $\beta_1 \neq 3$.

Compute the test statistic. Display 11.30 shows the printout for a test that the slope is 0. However, you can compute t for testing that the slope is 3 by using the value of the estimated slope and its standard error given there:

$$t = \frac{3.38051 - 3}{0.0353} \approx 10.7793$$

With 9 degrees of freedom, the P-value is very close to 0.

The test statistic is quite large and would be difficult to see in a sketch.

Write a conclusion in context. Reject the null hypothesis that the slope is 3. If the slope of the true regression line were 3, it would be extremely unlikely to get results such as those in this sample. This is consistent with the conclusion from the confidence interval of (3.301, 3.460) in the example on page 663 of the student text.

Note that it is the fact that the standard error is so small that enables you to reject the null hypothesis. The points cluster very closely to the regression line, allowing you little leeway in estimating the slope of the true regression line.

Practice

P14. **a.** The untransformed data clearly have curvature. Both the log transformation and the log-log transformation straighten the pattern considerably. There are so few points that it is difficult to choose between them on the basis of the residual plots or dot plots of the residuals. However, because there tends to be a close-to-cubic relationship between length and weight, we should use the log-log transformation, as our experience with largemouth bass suggests.

b. The regression equation is ln(*weight*) = $-6.17 + 2.51$ ln(*length*). The estimated slope is 2.51.

Check conditions. The conditions were checked in part a. We will assume this is a random sample of black crappies.

State your hypotheses.

H_0: If you had the entire population of black crappies, the slope, β_1, of the regression line for the relationship of ln(*weight*) versus ln(*length*) would be equal to 3.

H_a: $\beta_1 \neq 3$.

Compute the test statistic and draw a sketch. From the value of the estimated standard error of the slope, 0.1130, given in the printout, it is easy to compute the value of t for the hypothesis that $\beta_1 = 3$:

$$t = \frac{2.5115 - 3}{0.1130} \approx -4.3230$$

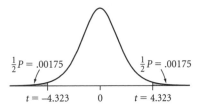

$\frac{1}{2}P = .00175$ $\frac{1}{2}P = .00175$

$t = -4.323$ 0 $t = 4.323$

From Table B, the P-value associated with this value of t with 7 degrees of freedom and a two-tailed test is between 2(.001) and 2(.0025). From the calculator, the P-value is .0035.

Write a conclusion in context. Reject the null hypothesis that the slope of the true regression line for $\ln(weight)$ versus $\ln(length)$ is equal to 3. If the slope were 3, there would be only a .0035 chance of getting a slope farther from 3 than 2.5115 from a random sample of nine black crappies.

c. The estimated standard error is 0.1130 (see printout in part b).

For the black crappies, a 95% confidence interval for the slope of the relationship $(\ln(length), \ln(weight))$ is

$$b_1 \pm t^* \cdot s_{b_1} = 2.5115 \pm 2.365(0.1130)$$

or about (2.244, 2.779). You are 95% confident that if you could measure all black crappies, the slope of the regression line for $(\ln(length), \ln(weight))$ would be in this interval. The 95% confidence interval for widemouth bass was (3.301, 3.460). Because there is no overlap in these confidence intervals, you can conclude that the relationships are different. The power function that relates length to weight of a black crappie has a smaller exponent than that for widemouth bass.

P15. a. $\log(img) = 0.679 + 0.195(5) = 1.654$. The distribution of $\log(img)$ should be approximately normal with mean around 1.654 and standard deviation around $s = 0.2588$. We'd predict the img for a country with $fr = 5$ to be $10^{1.654} \approx 45.082$.

b. You are 95% confident that in the population of all countries, the slope of the regression line for $(fg, \log(img))$ is 0.19502 ±

2.052(0.02569), or 0.19502 ± 0.0527. This indicates that the power function that best fits the relationship between fr and img has an exponent of about 0.19502 ± 0.0527, or (0.1423, 0.2477).

Exercises

E15. a. Yes. The residuals are more evenly scattered rather than being lumped up to the left. The scatterplot shows that five new influential points may have been created, however, and there are new outliers in the boxplot of the residuals. The slope of the regression line has gone from negative to positive, which seems like a change, but in both cases it is close to 0 and, in fact, is not significantly different from 0. Removing outliers can change the analysis quite a bit. However, it didn't in this case.

A log-log transformation definitely improved the conditions for inference. The residual plot shows random scatter about the 0 line, and the boxplot of the residuals is nicely symmetric. Nevertheless, the slope is not significantly different from 0. Nor does there appear to be a power relationship between *crime rate* and *total population* of the city.

b. The regression line is meaningful whether you have a sample or the entire population. It allows you to explore the relationship between crime rate and population. It was also useful to do a significance test for the slope here, but the conclusion must be stated something like this: The slope of the relationship between the *crime rate* and *total population* of the city is no different from what you would expect if the crime rate had been assigned at random to the cities.

E16. a. The plot of *number of police* versus *violent crime rate* shows a bit of upward curvature reminiscent of exponential growth and shows that variation in *y* is increasing with increasing *x*. The scatterplot of $\ln(police)$ versus *violent crime rate* shows a more linear trend and a regression line that fits the transformed data quite well. The plots are shown on the following page.

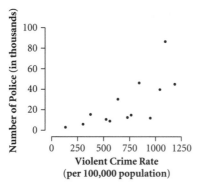

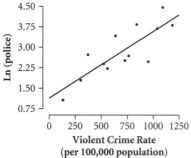

```
Dependent variable is:   Ln Police
No Selector
R squared = 68.5%   R squared (adjusted) = 65.6%
s = 0.5537  with 13 - 2 = 11 degrees of freedom

Source      Sum of Squares  df   Mean Square   F-ratio
Regression  7.33671          1    7.33671       23.9
Residual    3.37258         11    0.306598

Variable  Coefficient  s.e. of Coeff  t-ratio   prob
Constant  1.13738      0.3822         2.98      0.0126
Violent   2.44121e-3   0.0005         4.89      0.0005
```

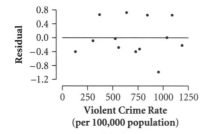

b. Here, the slope for the relationship of ln(*police*) versus *violent crime rate* is estimated as 0.00244, with a standard error of 0.005. A 95% confidence interval for the slope of this relationship is approximately

$$b_1 \pm t^* \cdot s_{b_1} = 0.00244 \pm 2.201(0.0005)$$
$$= 0.00244 \pm 0.00110$$

or (0.00134, 0.00354). Exponentiating both endpoints of this interval gives an interval estimate of (1.0013, 1.0035). Thus, the growth rate is between 0.0013 and 0.0035 thousand police officers (1.3 to 3.5 police officers) per 1-unit increase in the violent crime rate.

E17. Plotting the flow-through values versus the static values yields a plot with some curvature and with increasing variation in *y* for increasing *x*. A log-log transformation produces a situation much more conducive to regression analysis in terms of homogeneity, although there is still some curvature in the pattern of residuals. There is a very strong positive association between ln(*flow*) and ln(*static*). To change static readings to flow readings, first predict on the natural log scale using ln(*flow*) = −1.01 + 1.12 · (ln(*static*)) and then exponentiate the result back to the original scale, if that is necessary.

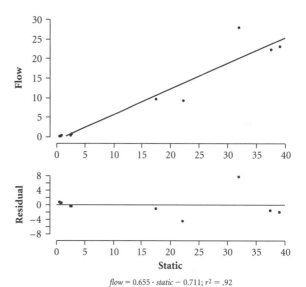

flow = 0.655 · *static* − 0.711; r^2 = .92

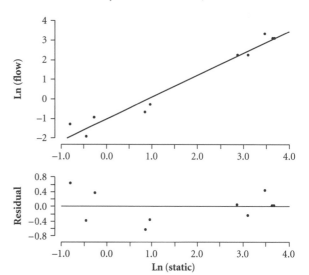

ln(*flow*) = 1.12 · ln(*static*) − 1.01; r^2 = .96

```
Dependent variable is:   Ln Flow
No Selector
R squared = 96.3%  R squared (adjusted) = 95.8%
s = 0.4284 with 10 - 2 = 8 degrees of freedom

Source       Sum of Squares  df  Mean Square  F-ratio
Regression   37.8087          1   37.8087      206
Residual      1.46800         8    0.183501

Variable  Coefficient  s.e. of Coeff  t-ratio  prob
Constant  -1.01287     0.1901         -5.33    0.0007
Ln Static  1.12386     0.0783         14.4     ≤0.0001
```

E18. *Weight of wax* has a strong negative linear association with *sintering time* because more heating causes the voids between the particles to grow smaller. As seen from these plots, no transformation is necessary.

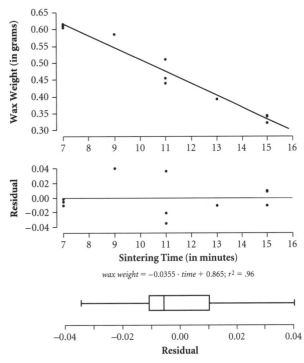

wax weight = −0.0355 · time + 0.865; r² = .96

```
Dependent variable is:   WaxWeight
No Selector
R squared = 96.2%    R squared (adjusted) = 95.8%
s = 0.0239 with 11 - 2 = 9 degrees of freedom

Source       Sum of Squares  df  Mean Square  F-ratio
Regression   0.130924         1   0.130924     230
Residual     0.005128         9   0.000570

Variable  Coefficient  s.e. of Coeff  t-ratio  prob
Constant  0.865016     0.0267         32.4     ≤0.0001
Time     -0.035481     0.0023        -15.2     ≤0.0001
```

A 95% confidence interval for the slope is

$-0.0355 \pm (2.262)(0.0023) = -0.0355 \pm 0.0052$

or $(-0.0407, -0.0303)$. The weight of the wax is expected to decrease from about 0.03 to 0.04 grams for each minute increase in the sintering time.

E19. *Check conditions.* We were told on page 663 of the student text that this is a random sample of countries. The residual plot and scatterplot look like these data could have been drawn from a population that is linear, with constant standard deviation in the response variable across values of *x*. The dot plot of the residuals appears next. It is reasonable to assume that the residuals are taken from a normal distribution.

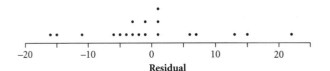

State your hypotheses.

H_0: $\beta_1 = 0$, where β_1 is the slope of the regression line predicting percentage of the parliamentary seats occupied by women from the girls' share of secondary school enrollment if you had all countries rather than just a random sample.

H_a: $\beta_1 \neq 0$.

Compute the test statistic and draw a sketch. From the printout in Display 11.43, $t = 1.65$ with 17 degrees of freedom. The P-value is .12.

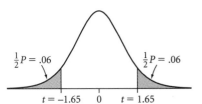

Write a conclusion in context. Do not reject the null hypothesis. It is quite plausible that these data came from a population where the slope of the true regression line for predicting percentage of parliamentary seats occupied by women from girls' share of secondary school enrollment is 0. You can not conclude that there is a linear relationship with nonzero slope between the two variables.

The three points on the left of the scatterplot may be influential (Equatorial Guinea, Mali, and the Solomon Islands), so the analysis should be redone without them to check their influence. The scatterplot and regression line are shown next. The line becomes less steep and farther from being statistically significant.

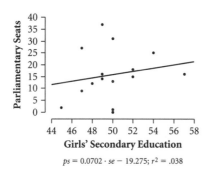

Girls' Secondary Education

$ps = 0.0702 \cdot se - 19.275; r^2 = .038$

Test of World's Women Minus 3 with Small	Test Slope ▼

Independent attribute (continuous): se

Dependent attribute (continuous): ps

Least-squares linear regression of **ps** versus **se**

Count: **16**
Equation: **ps = 0.702117 se − 19.275**

Ho: Slope = 0
Ha: Slope is **not equal to** 0

Student's t: **0.7472**
DF: **14**
P-value: **0.47**

Review

Homework	
Essential	E20, E22
Recommended	E21, E24, E26
Optional	E23, E25

Review Exercises

E20 **a.** Plot I looks excellent. Plot III is also a possibility at least for all points but those at the ends. Plot II is curved, IV shows no linear trend, and V has a very influential data point on the upper right.

b. Plot IV should produce a regression line with slope close to zero.

c. Plot V has correlation closest to 1. Note that the different scales can make correlation difficult to judge.

d. For Plot II, perhaps a transformation, such as squaring the y's or taking the square root of the x's, could make the points appear

more linear. Plot V would be a good bet for a linear model if there is justification to remove the one point that does not fit the pattern. There is no hope for any linearity out of Plot IV.

E21. The narrowest confidence interval should be for all depths together (the last plot) because the points cluster relatively close to the regression line compared to the other plots *and* the sample size is larger. The widest confidence interval should be for the mid-depth measurements (second plot) because the outlier will result in a large estimated standard error for the response.

Note that the outlier in the plot for all depths together is neither an outlier among the values of x nor an outlier among the values of y. However, it stands out on the residual plot.

The margins of error for a 95% confidence interval for the slope are

Surface 0.378826

Mid-depth 0.7069

Bottom 0.353189

All 0.195114

E22. **a.** The association between calories and fat is a strong positive linear one, as seen in the plot, and the regression line fits the data well.

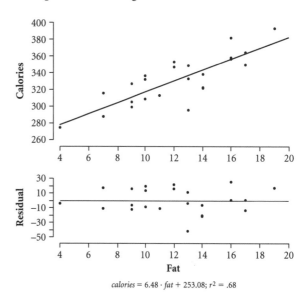

Fat

$calories = 6.48 \cdot fat + 253.08; r^2 = .68$

A 95% confidence interval for the slope is $6.47992 \pm (2.074)(0.9527)$ or 6.47992 ± 1.9758998 or $(4.50, 8.46)$. This is the number of calories you can expect to lose in a 1-gram decrease in the fat content per serving of pizza.

b. The reduction in calories per 5-gram reduction in fat content is simply five times the interval found in part a, or (22.5, 42.3).

c. Although cost looks like it might have a slightly negative association with fat content, in the next analysis the slope is not significantly different from zero. You can not conclude that reducing the fat content will reduce the cost.

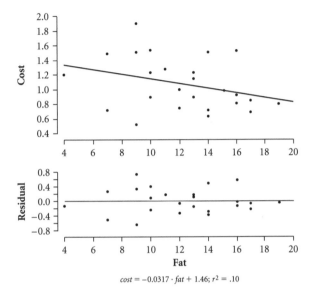

$cost = -0.0317 \cdot fat + 1.46;\ r^2 = .10$

```
Dependent variable is:    Cost
No Selector
R squared = 10.4%    R squared (adjusted) = 6.3%
s = 0.3529 with 24 - 2 = 22 degrees of freedom

Source      Sum of Squares   df   Mean Square   F-ratio
Regression  0.317019          1   0.317019      2.55
Residual    2.73938          22   0.124517

Variable   Coefficient  s.e. of Coeff  t-ratio    prob
Constant   1.46035      0.2523          5.79      ≤0.0001
Fat        -0.031707    0.0199         -1.60       0.1248
```

E23. **NOTE:** You may want either to give your students the printouts here or to have them do this problem on the computer. ■

All conditions are met for inference in this problem because treatments were assigned at random to the laboratory rats and all relationships appear linear, with reasonably constant values of the residuals across values of *x*.

a. There are no significant linear trends for *amplitude* versus *blood pressure* for any of the three anesthetics individually. See the next plots and output.

Treatment C

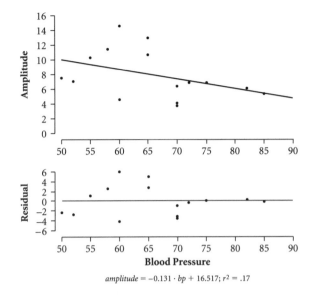

$amplitude = -0.131 \cdot bp + 16.517;\ r^2 = .17$

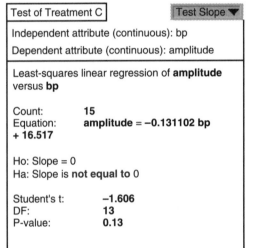

Test of Treatment C	Test Slope ▼
Independent attribute (continuous): bp	
Dependent attribute (continuous): amplitude	

Least-squares linear regression of **amplitude** versus **bp**

Count: **15**
Equation: **amplitude = −0.131102 bp + 16.517**

Ho: Slope = 0
Ha: Slope is **not equal to** 0

Student's t: **−1.606**
DF: **13**
P-value: **0.13**

Treatment H

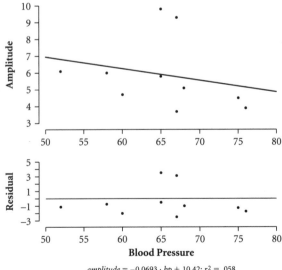

$amplitude = -0.0693 \cdot bp + 10.42;\ r^2 = .058$

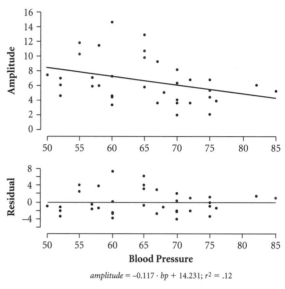

Test of Treatment H ▼ Test Slope

Independent attribute (continuous): bp

Dependent attribute (continuous): amplitude

Least-squares linear regression of **amplitude** versus **bp**

Count: **10**
Equation: **amplitude = −0.0692981 bp + 10.415**

Ho: Slope = 0
Ha: Slope is **not equal to** 0

Student's t: **−0.7022**
DF: **8**
P-value: **0.5**

Treatment P

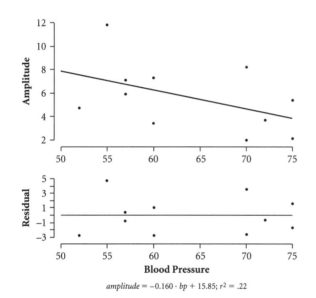

$amplitude = -0.160 \cdot bp + 15.85; \ r^2 = .22$

Test of Treatment P ▼ Test Slope

Independent attribute (continuous): bp

Dependent attribute (continuous): amplitude

Least-squares linear regression of **amplitude** versus **bp**

Count: **11**
Equation: **amplitude = −0.16032 bp + 15.846**

Ho: Slope = 0
Ha: Slope is **not equal to** 0

Student's t: **−1.601**
DF: **9**
P-value: **0.14**

However, note that all three have a negative slope even though none is significantly different from zero. When the data for all three treatments are combined, the slope is significant, as shown here:

All Treatments

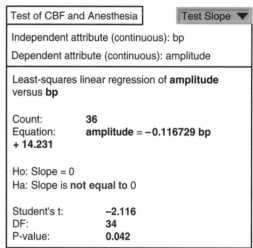

$amplitude = -0.117 \cdot bp + 14.231; \ r^2 = .12$

Test of CBF and Anesthesia ▼ Test Slope

Independent attribute (continuous): bp

Dependent attribute (continuous): amplitude

Least-squares linear regression of **amplitude** versus **bp**

Count: **36**
Equation: **amplitude = −0.116729 bp + 14.231**

Ho: Slope = 0
Ha: Slope is **not equal to** 0

Student's t: **−2.116**
DF: **34**
P-value: **0.042**

b. For *frequency* versus *blood pressure*, pentobarbital shows a significant increase in frequency with increasing blood pressure, whereas the others show no significant trend. Pentobarbital could cause problems for a patient with high blood pressure, at least for a patient that is a laboratory rat.

Treatment P

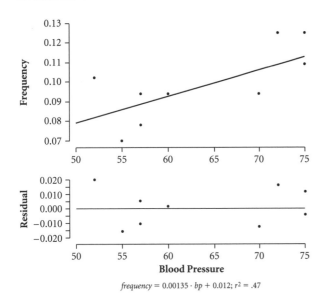

frequency = 0.00135 · bp + 0.012; r^2 = .47

```
Dependent variable is:   Freq
cases selected according to    Selected CASE16.TXT
36 total cases of which 25 are missing
R squared = 46.8%    R squared (adjusted) = 40.9%
s = 0.0130 with 11 - 2 = 9 degrees of freedom

Source      Sum of Squares  df  Mean Square  F-ratio
Regression  0.001338         1  0.001338     7.91
Residual    0.001521         9  0.000169

Variable  Coefficient  s.e. of Coeff  t-ratio  prob
Constant  0.011756     0.0309         0.380    0.7128
Blood     1.35091e-3   0.0005         2.81     0.0203
```

Treatment C

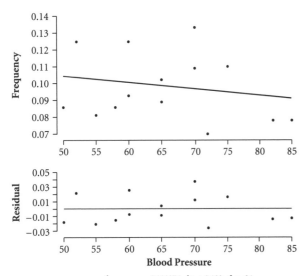

frequency = −0.000376 · bp + 0.123; r^2 = .04

```
Dependent variable is:   Freq
cases selected according to    Selected CASE16.TXT
36 total cases of which 21 are missing
R squared = 3.9%    R squared (adjusted) = -3.4%
s = 0.0199 with 15 - 2 = 13 degrees of freedom

Source      Sum of Squares  df  Mean Square  F-ratio
Regression  0.000211         1  0.000211     0.535
Residual    0.005140        13  0.000395

Variable  Coefficient  s.e. of Coeff  t-ratio  prob
Constant  0.123075     0.0343         3.59     0.0033
Blood     -3.76261e-4  0.0005         -0.731   0.4776
```

Treatment H

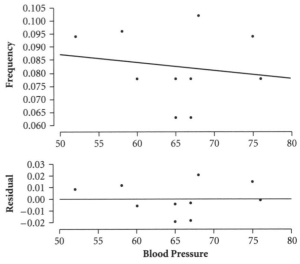

frequency = −0.000302 · bp + 0.102; r^2 = .026

```
Dependent variable is:   Freq
cases selected according to    Selected CASE16.TXT
36 total cases of which 26 are missing
R squared = 2.6%    R squared (adjusted) = -9.5%
s = 0.0142 with 10 - 2 = 8 degrees of freedom

Source      Sum of Squares  df  Mean Square  F-ratio
Regression  0.000044         1  0.000044     0.216
Residual    0.001624         8  0.000203

Variable  Coefficient  s.e. of Coeff  t-ratio  prob
Constant  0.102149     0.0427         2.39     0.0437
Blood     -3.02437e-4  0.0007         -0.465   0.6543
```

E24. NOTE: You may want either to give your students the printouts on the next page or to have them do this problem on the computer.

a. The scatterplot with regression line and statistical analysis is provided on the following page. ∎

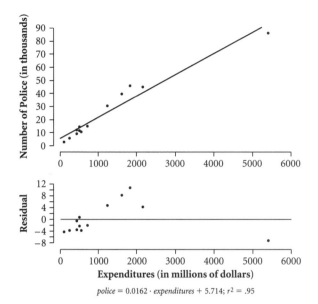

police = 0.0162 · expenditures + 5.714; $r^2 = .95$

```
Dependent variable is:   Police
No Selector
R squared = 94.9 %    R squared (adjusted) = 94.4%
s = 5.581 with 13 - 2 = 11 degrees of freedom

Source       Sum of Squares  df  Mean Square  F-ratio
Regression   6339.67         1   6339.67      204
Residual     342.565         11  31.1422

Variable  Coefficient  s.e. of Coeff  t-ratio   prob
Constant  5.71384      2.075          2.75      0.0188
Expend    0.016249     0.0011         14.3      ≤0.0001
```

The first state is expected to have 0.016249 thousand, or 16.249, more police officers.

You may want to ask your students to construct a confidence interval around this estimate:

All conditions are met for inference in this problem because this is a random sample of states and all relationships appear linear, with reasonably constant values of the residuals across values of x.

Using the values for the estimated slope and its standard error on the printout, a 95% confidence interval for the expected increase in the number of police (in thousands) for a $1 million increase in expenditure is

0.016249 ± (2.201)(0.0011)

or (0.0138, 0.0187). Because the increase in police is measured in thousands, this is equivalent to a predicted increase of between 13.8 and 18.7 police officers per $1 million increase in expenditures. (The final digit may be different if you use a calculator.) However, you should be leery of this result because of the influential point, California.

b. The right end of the regression line is pulled down a bit by the influential point (California) and will spring upward if it is removed. That effect is seen in the next analysis, which shows much better behaved residuals.

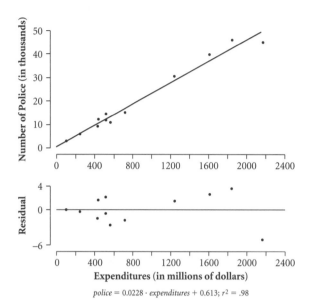

police = 0.0228 · expenditures + 0.613; $r^2 = .98$

```
Dependent variable is:   Police
No Selector
R squared = 97.5%    R squared (adjusted) = 97.3%
s = 2.583 with 12 - 2 = 10 degrees of freedom

Source       Sum of Squares  df  Mean Square  F-ratio
Regression   2615.88         1   2615.88      392
Residual     66.7245         10  6.67245

Variable  Coefficient  s.e. of Coeff  t-ratio   prob
Constant  0.612506     1.246          0.492     0.6336
Expend    0.022849     0.0012         19.8      ≤0.0001
```

The expected increase in the number of police officers is now 0.022849 thousand, or 22.849.

The 95% confidence interval for this slope is 0.022849 ± (2.228)(0.0012), or (0.0201, 0.0255), which translates into 20.1 to 25.5 police officers per $1 million. The governments will get fewer police for their dollars if they attempt to keep up with California!

c. The analysis of the relationship between number of police and the population of the states yields:

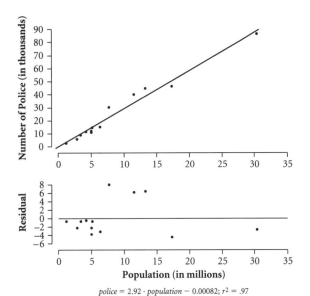

police = 2.92 · population − 0.00082; r² = .97

```
Dependent variable is:    Police
No Selector
R squared = 96.9%    R squared (adjusted) = 96.6%
s = 4.333 with 13 - 2 = 11 degrees of freedom

Source      Sum of Squares  df  Mean Square  F-ratio
Regression  6475.75          1  6475.75       345
Residual    206.478         11  18.7707

Variable  Coefficient  s.e. of Coeff  t-ratio   prob
Constant  -8.17156e-4  1.822          -0.000    0.9997
PopIn     2.92147      0.1573         18.6      ≤0.0001
```

You expect the first state to have 2.92147 thousand, or 2921.47, more police officers.

Again, you may want to ask your students to construct a confidence interval for this estimate:

A 95% confidence interval on the expected increase in the number of police officers per million increase in the population is 2.9215 ± (2.201)(0.1573), or (2.575, 3.268). A state with a million more people than another is predicted to have between 2575 and 3268 more police officers.

d. With California removed, the results are:

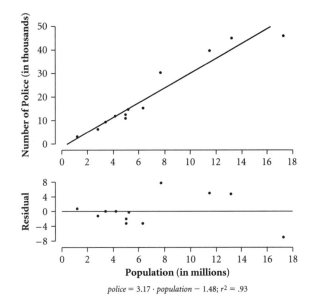

police = 3.17 · population − 1.48; r² = .93

```
Dependent variable is:    Police
No Selector
R squared = 93.1%    R squared (adjusted) = 92.5%
s = 4.289 with 12 - 2 = 10 degrees of freedom

Source      Sum of Squares  df  Mean Square  F-ratio
Regression  2498.65          1  2498.65       136
Residual    183.954         10  18.3954

Variable  Coefficient  s.e. of Coeff  t-ratio   prob
Constant  -1.48433     2.247          -0.660    0.5239
PopIn     3.16802      0.2718         11.7      ≤0.0001
```

The predicted increase in the number of police officers is now 3.16802 thousand, or 3168.02.

The resulting 95% confidence interval on the slope is 3.1680 ± (2.228)(0.2718), or (2.562, 3.774). The increase in the number of police officers per million increase in population is predicted to be between 2562 and 3774, which is not much different from the interval found in part c. Note that the influence of California on the estimated slope is greater in the case of expenditures, where California is farther away from the linear pattern generated by the rest of the data, than in the case of population, where California lies closer to the linear pattern.

E25. If "standard deviation of the responses" is interpreted as meaning "for each fixed x," then this is a description of σ and so both values are equal. To see this, note that each error can be written as $y - \mu_y$. For a fixed x, μ_y is a constant, so the standard deviation of the errors, $y - \mu_y$, is equal to the standard deviation of the values of *y*, or σ. Because this is true for each value of *x*, it is true for the entire population of errors.

If "standard deviation of the responses" is interpreted as meaning "for all values of *y*, regardless of *x*," then this value will be larger than the standard deviation of the errors, σ. In the unusual case where the regression line has 0 slope, the two values will be equal.

E26. **a.** To give the exponential model a chance of fitting, you first have to subtract from each *y* an estimate of the value of the horizontal asymptote toward which the points seem to be approaching. This value is about 10. The resulting graph looks like the one shown here and appears to have a horizontal asymptote at *y* = 0.

Note: Some students might want to subtract from *y* the smallest value of *y*, which is a good thought. However, that will lead to a problem in the next step when taking logs because log 0 is undefined.

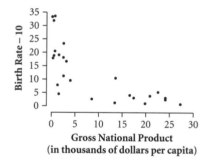

b. If you continue and take the log of the values of *birth rate minus 10*, you get this scatterplot and regression line. These transformed data fit quite well to a linear function.

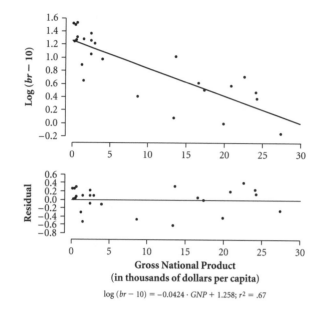

$\log (br - 10) = -0.0424 \cdot GNP + 1.258; r^2 = .67$

c. For a country with *GNP* equal to 15,

$$\log (br - 10) \approx -0.0424(15) + 1.258 \approx 0.622$$
$$br - 10 \approx 4.188$$
$$br \approx 14.188$$

d. No. It's quite reasonable that the *x*-axis is a horizontal asymptote in this case. As the infant mortality rate for boys increases toward 1000 out of 1000, the average life expectancy of males should drop to 0.

STATISTICS IN ACTION: CASE STUDIES

Overview

In this chapter, students will examine data from more extensive case studies and select the most appropriate statistical techniques to use. They will get a chance to practice most of the techniques they learned in this textbook. The first case study is taken from an experiment conducted at the University of Florida to determine which growth inhibitors were most effective in reducing the stem length of chrysanthemums. The second case study asks students to determine relationships between variables such as average salary, batting average, and percentage of wins for the teams in major league baseball. The final case study returns to the Westvaco case of Chapter 1. Students will be able to use the exploratory and inferential statistical techniques they have learned in order to evaluate whether Westvaco has some explaining to do or whether the fact that older employees appear to be laid off in disproportionate numbers can reasonably be attributed to chance alone.

The three sections are independent, so you can have your class do any selection of the three case studies.

A few topics are included that are not usually covered in an introductory statistics class. These topics are identified at the beginning of each section of this instructor's guide.

Goals

The three sections of this chapter will allow students

- to review the statistical techniques they have learned
- to examine situations that are somewhat more complicated than those found in most of the examples and problems in the textbook
- to be introduced to some slightly more advanced ideas in statistical inference
- to find out what finally happened with Robert Martin and Westvaco

Time Required

Traditional Schedule			Block	4 x 4 Block
Section 12.1				
1 day	Day 1	Introduction, analyzing the experiment	1 day	1 short
Section 12.2				
2 days	Day 1	Is inference appropriate?, winning from league to league	1.5 days	1 long, 1 short
	Day 2	Simulating a P-value, ecological correlations		
Section 12.3				
2 days	Day 1	Comparing termination rates for two age groups	1.5 days	1 long, 1 short
	Day 2	Looking for a better approach		

Materials

Section 12.1: None

Section 12.2: For the analyses in D5, D11–D13, P7–P10, students will need a computer or copies of the analyses in this section.

Section 12.3: For D20, several sets of 50 blank cards or slips of paper

Suggested Assignments

The discussion questions in Chapter 12 most likely will require a bit more guidance from the instructor than those in previous chapters. Practice questions may be assigned as individual classwork or as homework.

Classwork			
Section	**Essential**	**Recommended**	**Optional**
12.1	D1–D3 P1, P4	P2, P3	
12.2	D4–D9 P7, P10a, P12a		D10–D13
12.3	D14, D16, D17, D19–D23 P13, P18–P20	D18 P14–P17	D15

Homework			
Section	**Essential**	**Recommended**	**Optional**
12.1	P5, P6		
12.2	P8, P10b, P11, P12b		P9
12.3	Any of the practice problems can be assigned as homework.		

12.1 Mum's the Word!

This case study is based on a real experiment with plant growth inhibitors conducted at the University of Florida.

Objectives

Students will review the following topics:

- experimental design
- summary statistics
- construction and interpretation of boxplots
- construction and interpretation of scatterplots
- interpreting the slope of a linear regression line
- two-sample t-tests and confidence intervals for the difference of two means

Important Terms and Concepts

- experimental design
- boxplot
- slope of the regression line

- significance test for the difference of two means
- confidence interval for the difference of two means

Lesson Planning

Class Time

One day

Materials

None

Suggested Assignments

Classwork		
Essential	**Recommended**	**Optional**
D1–D3	P2, P3	
P1, P4		

Homework		
Essential	**Recommended**	**Optional**
P5, P6		

Lesson Notes: Analyzing the Experiment

This experiment involves seven treatments, so a full analysis would require analysis of variance (ANOVA), which is used to compare the means of more than two groups. ANOVA is a generalization of the two-sample t-test. To compare seven treatments means that two at a time, $\binom{7}{2} = 21$ two-sample t-tests would be necessary. Such an analysis would suffer from the problem of *multiple comparisons* on the same data. That is, if you do 21 two-sample t-tests using $\alpha = .05$ and the null hypothesis is true for each of them, then the chance of making at least one Type I error is very high. A technique for dealing with multiple comparisons is described at the end of this section. This technique decreases α in each individual test in order to keep the overall probability of making at least one Type I error at most .05.

If students choose to do multiple t-tests or confidence intervals, tell them that the individual confidence intervals should have very high confidence levels, or individual tests should have very low P-values, in order for the composite error rate across all comparisons to be reasonably small.

Discussion

D1. Block on location of the plants in the greenhouse or on initial health of the plants.

The part of the design discussed so far emphasizes the random assignment of treatments to plants that are to be grown under nearly identical conditions. Because we are talking about 70 plants, it may not be possible to grow them under "identical conditions" in a greenhouse. If the greenhouse has variation in light or temperature, it may be appropriate to block on sections of the greenhouse in such a way that each treatment is used on some plants in each section. (In the real experiment, involving 18 treatments, the treatments were randomized to plants within blocks of the greenhouse; here, we ignore the possible effect of blocking for the seven treatments we have chosen to analyze.)

Another issue is the initial condition of the plants, as they were probably not identical before dividing them among the treatments. Initial height of the plant was taken into account by using the amount of growth

rather than the final height as the response variable, but other features of the health of a plant were not. Hopefully, randomization will take care of balancing these features across the treatments, but blocking on one or more of these factors could improve the design.

D2. The plants have differing initial heights (Ht_i), which can be taken into account by measuring stem growth using the difference $Ht_f - Ht_i$.

D3. A two-sample t-procedure—a significance test or confidence interval estimate of the difference in mean growth—could be used here. For these procedures, you must check that the treatments were randomly assigned to the plants and that plots of the two sets of differences are fairly symmetric with no outliers. (See the student text, pages 532–533 for a confidence interval, pages 537–538 for a two-sample t-test, and page 523 for the 15/40 rule.)

Practice

P1. Treatments 1 and 5 appear to be best because they are centered at the lowest values (least growth), but their large variability makes this conclusion uncertain. It looks more certain that Treatment 4 is the least effective, and Treatment 3 is next on the least effective list. They are centered at the highest values, have small variability, and there is almost no overlap between their distributions and the others.

P2. The centers vary widely, as do the spreads. As you can see from the following scatterplot, the spreads for the smaller means are larger than the spreads for the larger means. That is, as the means increase, the spreads tend to decrease. (It is more typical in a data set for the spreads to increase as the means increase.)

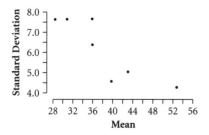

A possible explanation comes from the fact that the treatments are growth inhibitors. If a treatment is not effective, the plants are growing normally and, because they come from similar stock, all grow to about the same height. If a treatment is effective, it may not affect all plants the same way; some will absorb more of the treatment and some less, depending upon how evenly the treatment was applied, the amount of moisture and other ingredients in the soil, and a host of other factors. It is quite common for experimental units to show more variation than usual when they are subjected to an effective treatment.

P3. The regression analysis of *standard deviation* versus *mean* for the growth data is shown below. The scatterplot in P2 looks a little curved, but using the slope of the regression line as an exploratory tool still allows you to conclude that, roughly, if one treatment has a mean growth of 1 cm more than another treatment, you expect its standard deviation to be 0.16 cm smaller.

```
Dependent variable is:    StdDev
No Selector
R squared 74.9%    R squared (adjusted) = 69.9%
s = 0.8388 with 7 - 2 = 5 degrees of freedom

Source        Sum of Squares   df   Mean Square   F-ratio
Regression    10.4886          1    10.4886       14.9
Residual      3.51771          5    0.703543

Variable   Coefficient   s.e. of Coeff   t-ratio   prob
Constant   12.3660        1.635          7.56      0.0006
Mean       -0.162543      0.0421         -3.86     0.0119
```

P4. The difference in mean growth between Treatment 1 and Treatment 5 is not statistically significant, as shown by the two-sample *t*-test that follows.

Check conditions. Treatments were randomly assigned to the plants. The boxplots for these two treatments on page 681 of the student text show no reason to suspect departure from normality.

State your hypotheses. The null hypothesis is that the mean growth in height that would have resulted from giving all 20 plants Treatment 1 would be the same as the mean growth in height that would have resulted from giving all 20 plants Treatment 5; the mean growth in height for Treatment 1 would equal that for Treatment 5. The alternative is that the mean growth for these two treatments would have been different.

In symbols: $H_0: \mu_1 - \mu_5 = 0$ versus $H_a: \mu_1 - \mu_5 \neq 0$, where μ_1 would be the mean growth if all of the plants had been given Treatment 1 and μ_5 would be the mean growth if all of the plants had been given Treatment 5.

Compute the test statistic and draw a sketch. Difference between sample means: 2.4000
t-statistic: 0.702 with 17 *df*
P-value: .4914

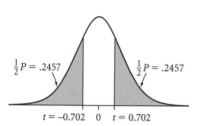

Write a conclusion in context. Do not reject the null hypothesis; the *P*-value is so large that there is no evidence to suggest that the treatment means differ.

Note: Treatments 1 and 5 have about the same spread, so either the pooled or the unpooled *t*-test should work well (and they should give similar answers). Pooling the variances yields a *t*-statistic of 0.702 with 18 *df* and a *P*-value of .4914, which is the same *P*-value as resulted from the unpooled test.

P5. Treatments 4 and 5 appear to have widely differing means, given that the boxplots of the data do not even overlap. (They also have quite different spreads, as the standard deviation for Treatment 4 is only a little over half that for Treatment 5.)

Checking this conclusion with a confidence interval, we find that we are 95% confident that if all plants could have been given both Treatment 4 and Treatment 5, the difference in the mean growth that would have resulted from giving all the plants Treatment 4 and the mean growth that would have resulted from giving all the plants Treatment 5 would be in the interval $18.4 < \mu_4 - \mu_5 < 30.2$. This interval lies completely above 0, so you can reject the hypothesis that the mean growth in height that would have resulted from giving all 20 plants Treatment 1 would be the same as the mean growth in height that would have resulted from giving all 20 plants Treatment 5.

P6. The boxplots and summary statistics are shown here.

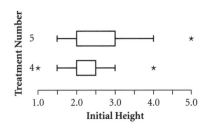

	Treatment 4	Treatment 5
Min	1.0	1.5
Q_1	2.0	2.0
Median	2.5	2.0
Q_3	2.5	3.0
Max	4.0	5.0
IQR	0.5	1.0

Any outliers for Treatment 4 lie above $2.5 + 1.5(2.5 - 2) = 3.25$ or below $2 - 1.5(2.5 - 2) = 1.25$. Thus, both the minimum initial stem height of 1 cm and the maximum of 4 cm are outliers. Any outliers for Treatment 5 lie above $3 + 1.5(3 - 2) = 4.5$ or below $2 - 1.5(3 - 2) = 0.5$. Thus, only the initial stem height of 5 cm is an outlier. (The outlier for Treatment 5 contributes to its skewness, but the outliers for Treatment 4 are part of the symmetry of the distribution.)

From these boxplots, we see that the plants given Treatment 5 were slightly taller and more variable in height to begin with, but these differences do not appear large, especially compared to the total growth in each group. The median is slightly higher for Treatment 4 (2.5 versus 2.0), and the mean is slightly higher for Treatment 5 (2.65 versus 2.35), as reflected in its more skewed shape. Overall, the initial height distributions do not differ enough to call into question the decision reached in the growth analysis of P5.

Further Analyses of the Mums Data: Transformations

The unpooled two-sample *t*-test is more powerful if the standard deviations of the two samples are nearly equal (that is, the variances are nearly homogeneous). As mentioned earlier, the mums data shown in Display 12.3 should be analyzed

using analysis of variance, which allows the comparison of the means of more than two independent random samples. One assumption used in the theory of ANOVA is that the populations from which the samples were drawn are normal with equal standard deviations. The condition actually checked for the latter is that the ratio of the largest sample standard deviation to the smallest is less than 2 or so. As you can see from Display 12.1 in the student text, the ratio fits in that range for the mums. However, most of these distributions are skewed toward the smaller numbers.

So you might ask students to look for a transformation that will make the variances more nearly equal across the treatment groups and, if possible, make the distributions somewhat more symmetric. (This is a lot to ask from one simple transformation!) Students will want to try the transformations that have worked for them in the past, the log being one of the possibilities. Alas, that simple transformation will make the situation worse! The following display shows the parallel boxplots for the growth transformed by natural logs—$\ln(Ht_f - Ht_i)$. The distributions are more skewed, and the spreads change even more radically as the means increase.

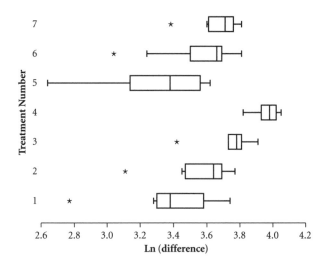

You need a transformation that expands the scale more for the larger measurements than the smaller. (The log transformation does the opposite: shrinks the scale more for the larger measurements than the smaller.) Squaring each difference—$(Ht_f - Ht_i)^2$—might work well; the transformed data yield the summaries given on the following page. The plot of standard deviations versus means for the transformed data (shown next) does not show the decreasing trend observed in the earlier plot.

```
Summary of          DiffSquare
For categories in   treat
No Selector
Group  Count    Mean    Median   Variance   StdDev
0 1      10   1004.33   870.250   218601   467.548
0 2      10   1329.03   1444      185418   430.602
0 3      10   1876.17   1936      160114   400.143
0 4      10   2799.03   2889.62   191207   437.272
0 5      10    861.875  870.500   167648   409.448
0 6      10   1341.65   1503.12   257365   507.311
0 7      10   1598.88   1662.12   117658   343.013
```

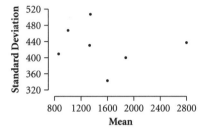

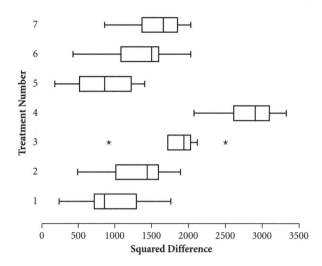

The next two displays compare the boxplots for the original growth measurements with those for the growth measurements transformed by squaring. For the transformed data, the spreads are more even and the distributions more symmetric. Even in the case of Treatment 3, which had an outlier on the low side in the original data, more desirable symmetry is achieved: less severe outliers show up, and they are now balanced between one on the low side and one on the high side. For the transformed data, the mean and standard deviation appear to be appropriate summary statistics and comparisons between means can be made by use of the *t*-procedures that assume nearly equal variances.

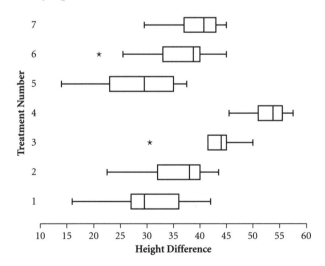

More on Multiple Comparisons

As mentioned in the Lesson Notes at the beginning of this section, multiple comparisons within the same analysis pose a problem. To see how this issue can be partially resolved, consider the following argument. Suppose confidence interval A is constructed to estimate the difference between the means of Treatments 1 and 2 and confidence interval B is constructed to estimate the difference between the means of Treatments 1 and 3. Let *A* denote the event *confidence interval A covers the true difference between the means of 1 and 2,* and *B* the event that *confidence interval B covers the true difference between the means of 1 and 3.* Let $1 - \alpha$ denote the confidence level of each interval. Thus,

$$P(A) = P(B) = 1 - \alpha$$

and

$$P(not\ A) = P(not\ B) = \alpha$$

Now, the probability that both confidence intervals cover their respective parameters is shown at the bottom of the page.

For example, the simultaneous coverage probability for two 95% confidence intervals could drop as low as $1 - 2(.05) = .90$. A conservative method of keeping an overall coverage probability of at least 95% is to construct each interval at the 97.5% level.

Lesson 12.1, Lesson Notes

$$P(A \text{ and } B) = 1 - P(not\ A \text{ or } not\ B) \geq 1 - [P(not\ A) + P(not\ B)] = 1 - 2\alpha$$

Corresponding two-sided tests of significance should be done at the .025 significance level. (This is called the Bonferroni method.)

Back to the Mums

Suppose you want to make all six possible comparisons among the four lowest observed means, those for Treatments 1, 2, 5, and 6. Then, each two-sample test should be done at the $\frac{.05}{6} = .0083$ level in order to ensure an overall Type I error rate of at most .05. The P-values for the six tests on the untransformed data are shown here. (These are for the pooled analysis because that method is generally used in ANOVA problems. The P-values for the unpooled analysis are almost the same.) Note that none of the P-values fall below the .0083 level. Thus, this conservative rule would not allow us to declare any significant differences among the means of these four treatments, although it does suggest that perhaps the relationships between 5 and 2 and between 5 and 6 deserve further study.

Treatment Comparison	P-Value
1 versus 2	.1227
1 versus 5	.4914
1 versus 6	.1574
2 versus 5	.0284
2 versus 6	.9875
5 versus 6	.0430

12.2 Baseball: Does Money Buy Success?

In this case study, students will determine relationships between variables such as average salary, mean batting average, and percentage of wins for major league teams in the 2001 season.

Objectives

Students will review the following topics:

- exploratory analysis
- conditions for inference
- correlation and regression, including interpreting the slope
- inference for regression
- t-test for the difference of two means
- z-test for the difference of two proportions
- chi-square test of homogeneity
- simulation

They also will learn about the following topics, which are not usually taught in the introductory statistics class:

- ecological correlation
- ecological fallacy

Important Terms and Concepts

- exploratory analysis
- conditions for doing inference
- correlation and regression, including interpreting the slope
- inference for regression
- t-test for the difference of two means
- z-test for the difference of two proportions
- chi-square test of homogeneity
- simulation
- ecological correlation
- ecological fallacy

Lesson Planning

Class Time

Two days

Materials

For the analyses in D5, D11–D13, P7–P10, students will need a computer or copies of the analyses in this section.

Suggested Assignments

Students should use a computer to do this case study completely. If they do not have access to a computer, you can either provide students the analyses and plots from the solutions that follow or assign only the following:

Discussion: D4, D6–D10
Practice: P11, P12

The material in the last two sections, "Simulating a *P*-Value" and "Ecological Correlations," is optional.

Lesson Notes: Exploring the Table of Data

Discussion

D4. The teams are listed in decreasing order of payroll, so it is easy to spot the huge variation in payrolls, the lowest being less than 25% of the highest. The higher payrolls tend to be in large cities, the lower in small cities. The larger attendance numbers tend to be toward the top of the list, the smaller toward the bottom, indicating some positive association between the two variables. Batting averages do not vary a lot, so it is hard to see any pattern there. Percentages of wins bounces around a lot, with one of the larger values close to the bottom of the list, so a strong pattern is not readily apparent.

Look, for example, at New York, Boston, and Los Angeles as compared to Cincinnati, Milwaukee, and Oakland. Payrolls and attendance are much lower in the smaller cities, but batting averages are similar. Oakland has one of the top two winning percentages. So payroll and attendance do not necessarily correlate strongly with winning.

D5. The following histograms and the scatterplot matrix at the bottom of the next page show all quantitative variables. A blackline master may be found at the end of this section.

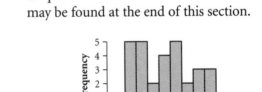

Payroll (in millions of dollars)

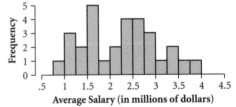

Average Salary (in millions of dollars)

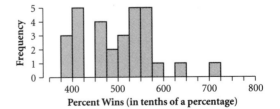

Percent Wins (in tenths of a percentage)

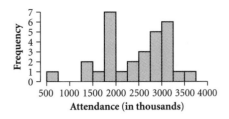

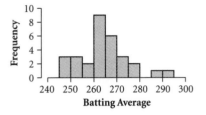

An example of what students may discover appears in the boxplot on the following page showing batting average by league. The outlier

is Colorado. In the scatterplot of *batting average* versus *percent wins* for all teams, Colorado is the point in the upper left. Thus, such a high team batting average is surprising given Colorado's relatively low percentage of wins. The explanation, apparently, is the "Coors Field effect," which also generates an astonishing number of home runs. Coors Field has an unusually large outfield, allowing base hits to drop in, and the thinner air at the mile-high altitude allows a hit ball to travel farther. According to the Denver Rockies' Web site: "But the ball still travels 9 percent farther at 5,280 feet than at sea level. It is estimated that a home run hit 400 feet in sea-level Yankee Stadium would travel about 408 feet in Atlanta and as far as 440 feet in the Mile

Lesson 12.2, D5

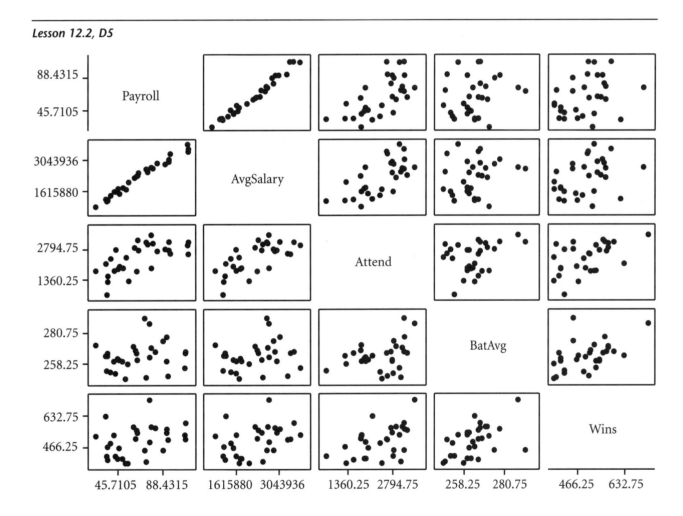

High City." (Source: http://colorado.rockies. mlb.com/NASApp/mlb/col/ballpark/col_ ballpark_history.jsp, July 2002) But, then, the team with the second highest batting average, Seattle (at the upper right of the scatterplot), plays at sea level.

In general, the relationship between *percent wins* and *batting average* may not be as strong as students would have expected.

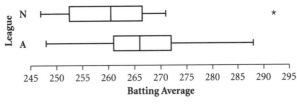

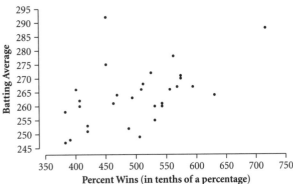

D6. Average salary is most strongly associated with payroll. Because most teams have approximately equal numbers of players on the payroll, it should not matter which variable, payroll or average salary, is used in deciding whether money buys success. The following scatterplot shows the strong association between the two.

Avg Salary = 0.0318 *Payroll* + 0.20 r^2 = .97

D7. This is an observational study—no random sampling or random assignment of treatments to subjects—so inference using traditional hypotheses and conclusions should not be done. On the other hand, it does make sense to ask questions such as "Could the observed pattern be due to chance alone?" So, guarded inferential statements can be made if they are carefully phrased in terms of finding relationships that can't reasonably be explained by random behavior. However, statements can not be made in terms of cause and effect or in reference to a larger population. See the discussion on pages 684–685 of the student text.

Lesson Notes: Differences Between the Leagues

Discussion

D8. The American League has much greater variability in the percentage of wins, even when considering the conditional distributions at various levels of payroll. That is, the residuals for the American League tend to be much larger in absolute value than those for the National League.

D9. Conditions are listed on page 645 of the student text. In regression analysis you must check that the residual plot indicates a linear relationship and that the variation in the responses is the same for each value of the explanatory variable. The plots in Display 12.6 of the student text show some decrease in variation of percentage of wins as the payroll increases, especially for the National League. (This pattern is counter to the usual picture of increasing variation in *y* with increasing values of *x*.)

You should also check that the residuals look like they reasonably could have come from a normal distribution; nothing in the boxplots of Display 12.6 suggests extreme non-normality in the residuals, although the distributions are slightly skewed.

All in all, it is reasonable to assume that these other conditions are met.

Practice

You may wish to break the class into three groups to work on P7, P8, and P9 and have each group report their work to the rest of the class. Alternatively, you could do P7 as classwork and assign P8 and possibly P9 as homework.

For P7–P9, the conditions listed on page 645 of the student text must be checked.

P7. **a.** The scatterplot for *attendance* versus *payroll* for all teams is shown next. The relationship is linear with fairly homogeneous variation in responses, and the residual plot shows no obvious pattern. The boxplot of the residuals is approximately symmetric with no outliers. Thus, it is fair to conclude that there is a statistically significant ($t = 4.56$, $df = 28$, P-value $\leq .0001$) positive trend. On the average, there is an 18.7 thousand increase in attendance for each million-dollar increase in payroll. Remember, this is descriptive of the observed pattern, not cause and effect.

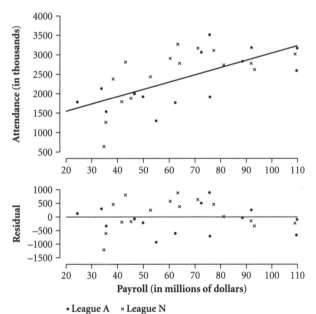

• League A   × League N

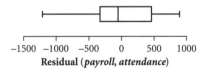

Residual (*payroll, attendance*)

```
Dependent variable is:    Attend
No Selector
R squared 42.6% ,    R squared (adjusted) = 40.5%
s = 548.5 with 30 - 2 = 28 degrees of freedom

Source        Sum of Squares   df   Mean Square   F-ratio
Regression    6244413           1   6244413       20.8
Residual      8422584          28    300807

Variable   Coefficient   s.e. of Coeff   t-ratio   prob
Constant   1198.60       284.0           4.22      0.0002
Pay        18.7832       4.123           4.56      ≤0.0001
```

b. The American League mirrors essentially the same pattern as both leagues together, with a statistically significant ($t = 3.313$, $df = 12$, P-value $= .0062$) increasing trend of about 17.9 thousand in increased attendance for each million-dollar increase in payroll, on the average.

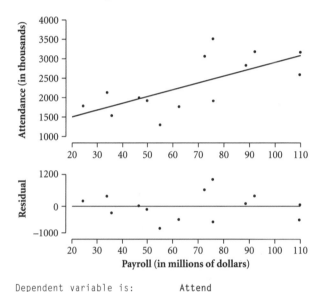

```
Dependent variable is:          Attend
cases selected according to    Selected MLB payroll-tab
30 total cases of which 16 are missing
R squared 47.8%    R squared (adjusted) = 43.4%
s = 531.2 with 14 - 2 = 12 degrees of freedom

Source        Sum of Squares   df   Mean Square   F-ratio
Regression    3097140           1   3097140       11.0
Residual      3385727          12    282144

Variable   Coefficient   s.e. of Coeff   t-ratio   prob
Constant   1146.38       386.0           2.97      0.0117
Pay        17.8783       5.396           3.31      0.0062
```

c. For the National League there is a serious problem with curvature! And no simple transformation (such as logs or square roots) will straighten it out. These data show a quadratic effect, and the better way to handle the problem would be to fit a quadratic model, but that is beyond the scope of this course. For now, you should not try to interpret the slope of 20.7 as an average rate of increase across the levels of payroll seen here. The rate of increase is much greater than that at the low end of the payrolls and much less (perhaps even negative) at the high end.

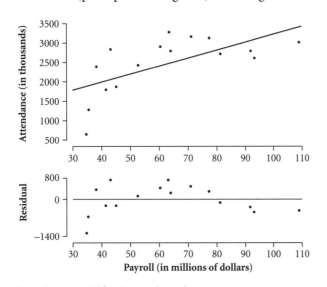

```
Dependent variable is:      Attend
cases selected according to    Selected MLB payroll-tab
30 total cases of which 14 are missing
R squared 41.9%   R squared (adjusted) = 37.8%
s = 577.5 with 16 - 2 = 14 degrees of freedom

Source       Sum of Squares   df   Mean Square   F-ratio
Regression   3371846          1    3371846       10.1
Residual     4669333          14   333524

Variable   Coefficient   s.e. of Coeff   t-ratio   prob
Constant   1179.26       432.0           2.73      0.0163
Pay        20.6616       6.498           3.18      0.0067
```

P8. None of the three slopes is statistically significant.

a. The scatterplot for all teams appears to be fairly linear, with nearly homogeneous variation in *y* across values of *x*, and the residual plot shows no serious pattern, although there are two teams with unusually

high batting averages (Colorado in the National League and Seattle in the American League). The boxplot of the residuals shows little skewness, but has two outliers. The regression analysis shows no significant linear trend. In other words, there appears to be little association between payroll and batting average. Even if Colorado and Seattle are removed, a similar result is obtained.

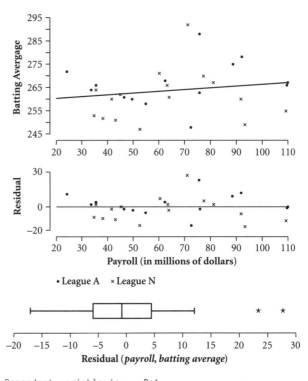

• League A   × League N

```
Dependent variable is:      Bat
No Selector
R squared = 3.3%   R squared (adjusted) = -0.2%
s = 10.62 with 30 - 2 = 28 degrees of freedom

Source       Sum of Squares   df   Mean Square   F-ratio
Regression   107.168          1    107.168       0.951
Residual     3155.63          28   112.701

Variable   Coefficient   s.e. of Coeff   t-ratio   prob
Constant   258.784       5.497           47.1      ≤0.0001
Pay        0.077814      0.0798          0.975     0.3378
```

b. Similarly for the American League, the slope isn't statistically significant (*P*-value = .4760).

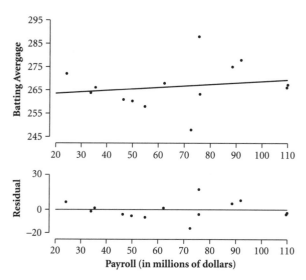

Dependent variable is: Bat
cases selected according to   Selected MLB payroll-tab
R squared = 4.3%   R squared (adjusted) = -3.7%
s = 9.802 with 14 - 2 = 12 degrees of freedom

Source	Sum of Squares	df	Mean Square	F-ratio
Regression	52.0114	1	52.0114	0.541
Residual	1152.85	12	96.0705	

Variable	Coefficient	s.e. of Coeff	t-ratio	prob
Constant	261.841	7.122	36.8	≤0.0001
Pay	0.073265	0.0996	0.736	0.4760

c. Similarly for the National League, the slope isn't statistically significant (*P*-value = .6208).

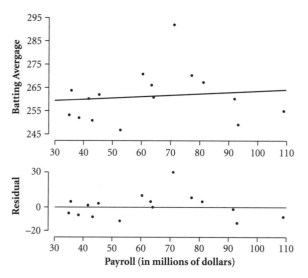

Dependent variable is: Bat
cases selected according to   Selected MLB payroll-tab
30 total cases of which 14 are missing
R squared = 1.8%   R squared (adjusted) = -5.2%
s = 11.35 with 16 - 2 = 14 degrees of freedom

Source	Sum of Squares	df	Mean Square	F-ratio
Regression	32.9358	1	32.9358	0.256
Residual	1802.06	14	128.719	

Variable	Coefficient	s.e. of Coeff	t-ratio	prob
Constant	257.204	8.487	30.3	≤0.0001
Pay	0.064575	0.1277	0.506	0.6208

P9. a. The analysis for all teams of the relationship between *batting average* and *percent wins* is shown next. The plot shows two teams, one in each league (Colorado and Seattle again), that may have undue influence on the analysis. With these teams in the picture, the linear trend is significant and shows a 3.72 percentage point increase in wins for each one-point increase in team batting average. (If the two potentially influential points are removed, the resulting increase of 4.5 percentage points per one-point increase in batting average is still highly significant with about the same *P*-value.)

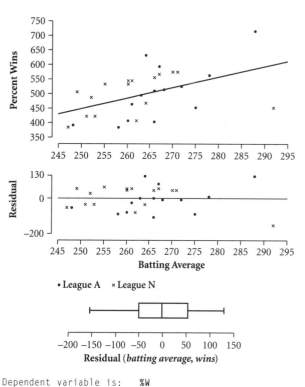

• League A   × League N

Dependent variable is: %W
No Selector
R squared   = 24.1%   R squared (adjusted) = 21.4%
s = 71.39 with 30 - 2 = 28 degrees of freedom

Source	Sum of Squares	df	Mean Square	F-ratio
Regression	45239.6	1	45239.6	8.88
Residual	142684	28	5095.86	

Variable	Coefficient	s.e. of Coeff	t-ratio	prob
Constant	-482.222	329.9	-1.46	0.1550
Bat	3.72361	1.250	2.98	0.0059

b. For the American League, the average increase in *percent wins* jumps way up to 7.2 per one-point increase in *batting average*! But Seattle is having tremendous influence here, and if this team is omitted, the average increase drops to 5.3 with a *P*-value of .071 (only marginally significant at best).

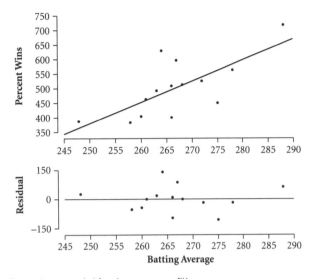

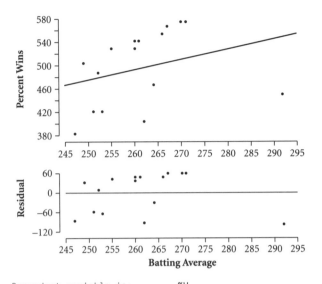

Dependent variable is: %W
cases selected according to   Selected MLB payroll-tab
30 total cases of which 16 are missing
R squared = 50.3%   R squared (adjusted) = 46.1%
s = 71.92 with 14 - 2 = 12 degrees of freedom

Source	Sum of Squares	df	Mean Square	F-ratio
Regression	62746.5	1	62746.5	12.1
Residual	62062.4	12	5171.87	

Variable	Coefficient	s.e. of Coeff	t-ratio	prob
Constant	-1422.03	552.9	-2.57	0.0245
Bat	7.21650	2.072	3.48	0.0045

c. The analysis for the National League is shown next. Colorado has tremendous influence in the opposite direction from the general trend. With Colorado, the data show no significant trend. Without Colorado, the slope jumps to an estimated 5.8 increase in *percent wins* for each one-point increase in *batting average*. The *P*-value drops to .006. So, without the influential points the two leagues exhibit about the same trends, but the one for the American League is not as highly significant because of its greater variability in winning percentages.

Dependent variable is: %W
cases selected according to   Selected MLB payroll-tab
30 total cases of which 14 are missing
R squared = 9.2%   R squared (adjusted) = 2.7%
s = 63.90 with 16 - 2 = 14 degrees of freedom

Source	Sum of Squares	df	Mean Square	F-ratio
Regression	5763.22	1	5763.22	1.41
Residual	57167.8	14	4083.41	

Variable	Coefficient	s.e. of Coeff	t-ratio	prob
Constant	34.7609	390.0	0.089	0.9302
Bat	1.77221	1.492	1.19	0.2546

Here is the regression analysis for the National League when Colorado is deleted.

The regression equation is
Wins = -1000 + 5.79 BatAvg

Predictor	Coef	Stdev	t-ratio	p
Constant	-1000.1	453.7	-2.20	0.046
BatAvg	5.791	1.750	3.31	0.006

s = 50.30   R-sq = 45.7%   R-sq(adj) = 41.6%

Analysis of Variance

SOURCE	DF	SS	MS	F	p
Regression	1	27711	27711	10.95	0.006
Error	13	32889	2530		
Total	14	60600			

The following two plots show the slopes of the regression lines for all teams in the two leagues with and then without the influential points of Colorado and Seattle.

All Teams

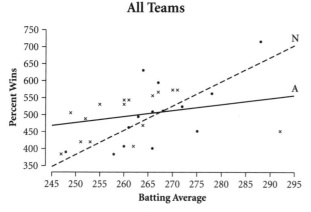

• League A   × League N

All Teams Except Colorado and Seattle

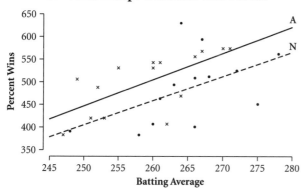

• League A   × League N

P10. For both parts of P10, the conditions listed on pages 537–538 of the student text must be checked, except for random samples. The 15/40 rule may be found on page 523.

a. The following boxplot shows skewness, including one outlier, for the National League attendance. The sample size is 16 and so we should proceed with caution according to the 15/40 rule on page 523 of the student text. A transformation isn't feasible because the attendance for the American League teams is not skewed in the same direction.

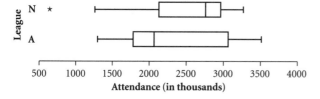

The null hypothesis is: The attendance figures are consistent with a model that randomly assigned them to the two leagues.

As you can see in the following printout, the *P*-value is .6, and so the difference in

mean attendance for the two leagues is not statistically significant.

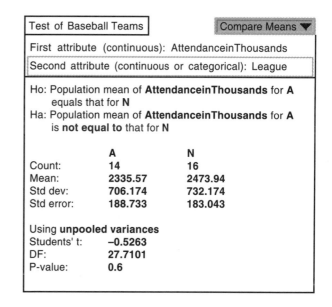

Note: Here's another example of how a randomization test works. Write the 30 attendance figures on cards. Shuffle thoroughly. Count out 14 to be the attendance figures for the American League. The remaining 16 will be the attendance figures for the National League. Compute the difference in mean attendance: *American League – National League.* Repeat this many times. The following stemplot shows the results from 100 repetitions of such a simulation—attendance figures were assigned to the 30 teams completely at random. The observed difference in mean attendance of $2473.94 - 2335.57 = 138.37$ was exceeded (in absolute value) 29 times on the positive side and 25 times on the negative side. This gives an estimated *P*-value of $\frac{54}{100} = .54$, which is quite close to the *P*-value of .60 for the two-sample *t*-test in the preceding printout.

Simulation of Difference in Mean Attendance for Two Leagues

```
Stem-and-leaf of C5      N = 100
Leaf Unit = 10

   1   -5 | 8
   4   -4 | 970
   8   -3 | 9300
  15   -2 | 9988400
  29   -1 | 88776555443321
  44   -0 | 777775554432221
 (20)   0 | 11233345555666888889
  36    1 | 12223334556778999
  19    2 | 034445567
  10    3 | 0336
   6    4 | 02
   4    5 | 1457
```

b. The boxplot of the batting averages for the National League teams has an outlier, so, again, we will proceed with caution.

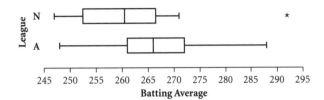

The null hypothesis is: The batting averages are consistent with a model that randomly assigned them to the two leagues.

As you can see from the following printout, the difference in mean batting averages for the two leagues is not statistically significant. The two-sample *t*-test of equal means gives a *P*-value of .16.

Test of Baseball Teams	Compare Means ▼

First attribute (continuous): BattingAverage

Second attribute (continuous or categorical): League

Ho: Population mean of **BattingAverage** for **A** equals that for **N**
Ha: Population mean of **BattingAverage** for **A** is **not equal to** that for **N**

	A	**N**
Count:	**14**	**16**
Mean:	**266.714**	**261.25**
Std dev:	**9.62711**	**11.0604**
Std error:	**2.57295**	**2.76511**

Using **unpooled variances**
Students' t:	**1.447**
DF:	**28**
P-value:	**0.16**

P11. The null hypothesis can be stated as, "A difference in percentages this large can reasonably be attributed to chance alone." A two-sample *z*-test on the difference between proportions can be used to answer the question. The conditions listed on page 468 of the student text must be checked. Sample sizes meet the *np* and $n(1 - p) \geq 5$ criteria. The winning proportions of .594 for New York and .568 for Arizona can be considered independent because the teams are in different leagues. The calculations show

$$z = \frac{.594 - .568}{\sqrt{(.581)(.419)\left(\frac{1}{162} + \frac{1}{162}\right)}} = 0.4743$$

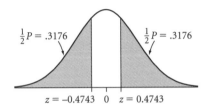

which has a *P*-value of .6353 and is not close to being significant. (If you use the TI-83's 2-PropZTest, you get $z = .4503$ and a *P*-value of .6525.) There is no evidence of a real difference between the winning percentages of these two teams; a difference this small can reasonably be attributed to chance.

P12. *Check conditions.* You are asked to compare the winning percentages for three teams. This is a test of homogeneity (equality) of proportions and requires a chi-square statistic. The conditions on page 598 of the student text must be checked. Expected counts are large enough, but the three teams are division winners in the same league and play each other during the season, so the outcomes are not independent. Further, when one of these teams plays another, that same game is counted in two different cells (as a win for one of the teams and a loss for the other). On the other hand, of the 162 games played by each team, only a small number are played against the other two teams, so the dependence is not too serious. You can still use the chi-square statistic as a measure of how far apart the three observed percentages actually are, but you should not put too much weight on the actual *P*-value that arises. To use the chi-square test, the percentages of wins must be turned into the number of wins and losses.

State your hypotheses. In both parts a and b, the null hypothesis is: The differences in the proportions of games won by the division leaders is consistent with a model that randomly assigned the wins and losses to the three teams. The alternate hypothesis is that the differences are too large to attribute reasonably to chance.

a. The following table shows the observed values for the National League.

	Atlanta	St. Louis	Arizona
Wins	88	93	92
Losses	74	69	70

This table shows the expected values.

	Atlanta	St. Louis	Arizona
Wins	91	91	91
Losses	71	71	71

The chi-square value is only 0.351 with two degrees of freedom and *P*-value of .84, which is not close to being significant. These percentages differ only by amounts that could well be produced by chance.

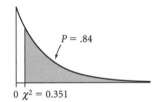

P = .84

0 χ^2 = 0.351

b. The table of observed values for the American League follows. The table of expected values is the same as in part a for the National League.

	New York	Cleveland	Seattle
Wins	96	91	116
Losses	66	71	46

The chi-square value is 9.203 with 2 degrees of freedom, which results in a *P*-value of approximately .01. There is strong evidence to support the conclusion that these differences in percentages of wins were not produced by chance alone. (The superior performance of Seattle is more than is reasonable to attribute to chance alone.)

Lesson Notes: Simulating a *P*-Value

Discussion

D10. a. A simulated *P*-value for the relationship of *percent wins* versus *payroll* was found by randomly reassigning the values of *percent wins* to different teams while keeping the payroll for each team the same. Then the slope

was computed. This process was repeated until there were 100 trials and 100 slopes.

b. Students might write the *percent wins* for the 16 National League teams on slips of paper, shuffle them, and then assign them at random to teams. They then compute the slope using the ordered pairs (*original payroll for each team, randomly assigned percent wins*). A sample set of ordered pairs is shown next. The slope of −0.843 would be added as an 8 to the fourth line down on the stemplot in Display 12.8 in the student text.

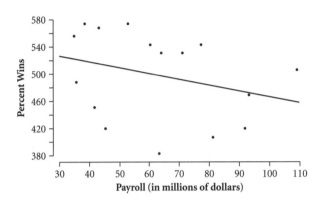

c. For the National League, the observed slope of 1.49 was equaled or exceeded only twice, giving a simulated one-sided *P*-value of .02. The *t*-test in Display 12.6 of the student text gives a two-sided *P*-value of .035. Once again the simulation (a randomization test) gives approximately the same *P*-value as a *t*-test. So the question of whether or not the observed pattern could have been generated by mere chance is answered in the affirmative for the American League but in the negative for the National League.

Lesson Notes: Ecological Correlations

Discussion

D11. As can be seen in the regression analyses shown next, the points for teams have a positive slope that is significantly different from zero. The points for divisions have a positive slope (and a higher correlation), but the slope is not significantly different from zero. In using the means of divisions rather than team data a large number of degrees of freedom are lost, and that makes the test on the means less able to detect a significant trend.

Teams as Cases

Dependent variable is: %W
No Selector
R squared = 24.1%   R squared (adjusted) = 21.4%
s = 71.39 with 30 - 2 = 28 degrees of freedom

Source	Sum of Squares	df	Mean Square	F-ratio
Regression	45239.6	1	45239.6	8.88
Residual	142684	28	5095.86	

Variable	Coefficient	s.e. of Coeff	t-ratio	prob
Constant	-482.222	329.9	-1.46	0.1550
Batting	3.72361	1.250	2.98	0.0059

Divisions as Cases

Dependent variable is: %W/Dvn
No Selector
R squared = 46.2%   R squared (adjusted) = 32.7%
s = 28.07 with 6 - 2 = 4 degrees of freedom

Source	Sum of Squares	df	Mean Square	F-ratio
Regression	2702.44	1	2702.44	3.43
Residual	3151.81	4	787.952	

Variable	Coefficient	s.e. of Coeff	t-ratio	prob
Constant	-565.651	577.0	-0.980	0.3825
Bat/Dvn	4.04421	2.184	1.85	0.1377

D12. Using teams as cases, the correlation is about .18. Using divisions as cases, the correlation is about −.22. The scatterplots and regression analyses for teams as cases and for divisions as cases are shown next. Neither analysis shows a significant linear trend, but it is interesting to note that the team correlation is positive (.18) and the division correlation is negative (−.22). The influence of the most influential points for teams (Seattle and Colorado) is muted a bit when using division means. All things considered, it is generally better to use the data set that contains the greater amount of information, and that would be the team data. But the final choice depends, as always, on the question being asked.

Teams as Cases

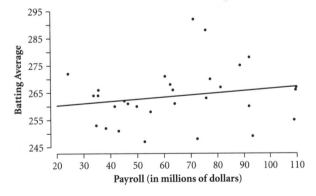

Dependent variable is: Batting
No Selector
R squared = 3.3%   R squared (adjusted) = -0.2%
s = 10.62 with 30 - 2 = 28 degrees of freedom

Source	Sum of Squares	df	Mean Square	F-ratio
Regression	107.168	1	107.168	0.951
Residual	3155.63	28	112.701	

Variable	Coefficient	s.e. of Coeff	t-ratio	prob
Constant	258.784	5.497	47.1	≤0.0001
Pay	0.077814	0.0798	0.975	0.3378

Divisions as Cases

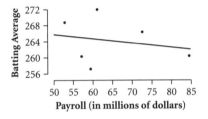

Dependent variable is: Bat/Dvn
No Selector
R squared = 4.8%   R squared (adjusted) = -19.1%
s = 6.272 with 6 - 2 = 4 degrees of freedom

Source	Sum of Squares	df	Mean Square	F-ratio
Regression	7.86357	1	7.86357	0.200
Residual	157.367	4	39.3417	

Variable	Coefficient	s.e. of Coeff	t-ratio	prob
Constant	271.067	15.60	17.4	≤0.0001
Pay/Dvn	-0.106476	0.2382	-0.447	0.6780

D13. Using teams as cases, the relationship between *percent wins* and *payroll* has a correlation of about .34, which is not quite statistically significant at the .05 level (*P*-value = .067). It would be significant at a slightly higher level, so there is borderline evidence of a significant linear trend here.

Using divisions as cases, the plot does not show a linear pattern in the data, and the correlation coefficient (−.11) does not have much meaning as a measure of how well the points fit a straight line. This should not be interpreted as a negative linear relationship because the relationship seems far from linear. This is due mainly to the high percentage of wins in the American West (Seattle, Oakland) with a modest payroll and the relatively low percentage of wins in the American East (New York, Boston) with a high payroll.

Teams as Cases

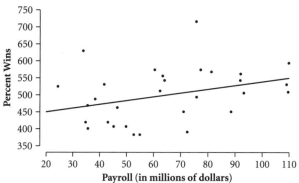

The regression equation is
% Wins = 429 + 1.10 Payroll

Predictor	Coef	Stdev	t-ratio	p
Constant	428.99	39.92	10.75	0.000
Payroll	1.1026	0.5795	1.90	0.067

s = 77.09   R-sq = 11.4%   R-sq(adj) = 8.3%

Analysis of Variance

SOURCE	DF	SS	MS	F	p
Regression	1	21516	21516	3.62	0.067
Error	28	166408	5943		
Total	29	187924			

Divisions as Cases

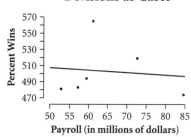

The regression equation is
%WinsDiv = 522 - 0.30 PayDvn

Predictor	Coef	Stdev	t-ratio	p
Constant	522.13	95.02	5.49	0.005
PayDvn	-0.301	1.451	-0.21	0.846

s = 38.22   R-sq = 1.1%   R-sq(adj) = 0.0%

Analysis of Variance

SOURCE	DF	SS	MS	F	p
Regression	1	63	63	0.04	0.846
Error	4	5842	1461		
Total	5	5905			

Histograms and Scatterplots for the Baseball Data

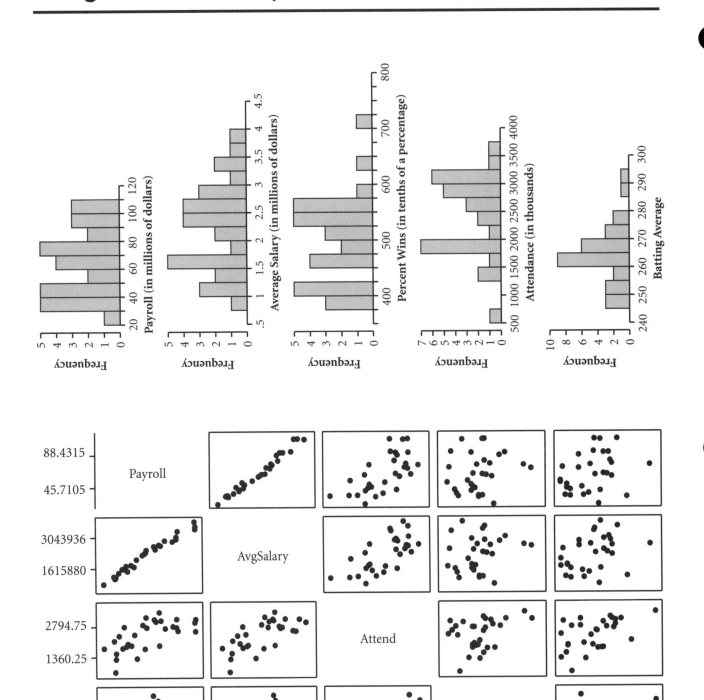

12.3 *Martin v. Westvaco* Revisited: Testing for Employment Discrimination

This case study is based on the *Martin* case, which was introduced in Chapter 1. It can provide considerable closure to your statistics course by bringing together many techniques and by showing students how much more thoroughly they can analyze the data from the *Martin* case now that they've come to the end of their course. This case study is somewhat more involved than the others and introduces several ideas that do not usually appear in an introductory statistics course.

Objectives

Students will review the following topics, which involve methods of significance testing to compare two groups:

- preliminary exploration of a data set using stemplots and boxplots
- two-way tables for summarizing categorical data for two groups
- tests for proportions and checking conditions for their use
- one-sided versus two-sided alternative hypotheses
- shortcomings of dichotomizing a quantitative variable
- Type I and Type II errors
- two-sample *t*-tests and checking conditions for their use
- simulation
- plot over time

Important Terms and Concepts

- categorical data and two-way tables
- significance test for the difference of two proportions
- one-sided versus two-sided alternative hypotheses
- Type I and Type II errors
- two-sample *t*-test for the difference of two means

Lesson Planning

Class Time
Two days

Materials
For D20, several sets of 50 blank cards or slips of paper

Suggested Assignments

Classwork		
Essential	**Recommended**	**Optional**
D14, D16, D17, D19–D23	D18	D15
P13, P18–P20	P14–P17	

Homework		
Essential	**Recommended**	**Optional**
Any of the practice problems can be assigned as homework.		

Lesson Notes: Comparing Termination Rates for Two Age Groups

Practice

P13. **a.** The worst possible case of discrimination against older workers would have been if all of the people laid off were 40 or older.

Terminated?

		No	Yes	Total	Percentage Terminated
	Under 40	14	0	**14**	0
Age	40 or Older	8	28	**36**	77.78
	Total	**22**	**28**	**50**	

b. The numbers in the table that follows illustrate a situation where termination and age are almost independent. However, the numbers don't meet the mathematical definition of independence. If an employee is selected at random, $P(terminated \text{ and } 40+) = \frac{20}{50} = .40$, whereas $P(terminated) = \frac{28}{50} = .56$ and $P(40+) = \frac{36}{50} = .72$. The joint probability of .40 isn't equal to the product of the marginal probabilities ($.56 \cdot .72 = .4032$), although it is close. It is impossible to construct a table with these marginal totals that has independent events because, for example, the number of employees under 40 that weren't terminated would have to be exactly equal to $\frac{(14)(22)}{50} = 6.16$.

Terminated?

		No	Yes	Total	Percentage Terminated
	Under 40	6	8	**14**	57.14
Age	40 or Older	16	20	**36**	55.56
	Total	**22**	**28**	**50**	

c. The following table of actual Westvaco data looks more like the one in part b that illustrates near independence or little association.

Terminated?

		No	Yes	Total	Percentage Terminated
	Under 40	7	7	**14**	50
Age	40 or Older	15	21	**36**	58.33
	Total	**22**	**28**	**50**	

Discussion

D14. **a.** Students might consider three tests: a one-sample z-test of a single proportion, a two-sample z-test for the difference of two proportions, and a chi-square test. The data don't meet the conditions for any of these tests, but students may ignore that for now because they will consider conditions in D16.

A one-sample z-test would test the hypothesis that the proportion of people 40 or older who are laid off is equal to the proportion of people laid off in the population, .56. However, this test is less powerful than a two-sample test because it does not take into consideration the number of people in the *under 40* category. (For example, you also can get an overall layoff rate of .56 if there had been 64 people under 40 and 35 of them [$\approx 54.7\%$] were laid off. The *P*-value for a one-sample test for these data is equal to that of the original data. However, the *P*-value for a two-sample test for these data is different—and smaller—than for the original data.)

This leaves the two equivalent tests (for the two-sided case) of a two-sample *z*-test for the difference of two proportions and a chi-square test.

However, a one-sided alternative makes the most sense because there will be evidence of possible discrimination only if the proportion of older workers who were laid off is greater than the proportion of younger workers who were laid off. The chi-square test is inherently two-sided, so the two-sample *z*-test for the difference of two proportions is the best choice.

b. A one-sided one-sample test of the hypothesis that the "true" percentage of older people who would be laid off equals .56 yields

$$z = \frac{.5833 - .56}{\sqrt{\dfrac{(.56)(.44)}{36}}} \approx 0.2820$$

and a *P*-value of .3890. This test gives no evidence for discrimination.

A one-sided two-sample test of the difference of two proportions gives

$$z = \frac{.5833 - .5}{\sqrt{(.56)(.44)\left(\dfrac{1}{14} + \dfrac{1}{36}\right)}} \approx 0.5330$$

and a *P*-value of .2970. This test also gives no evidence for discrimination.

Why the difference in the two *P*-values? A large majority of employees are 40 or older, so their layoff rate of 58% has a large role in determining the overall layoff rate of 56%. Consequently, the overall rate of 56% is close to the 40 or older group's layoff rate of 58% (and not so close to the under 40 group's layoff rate of 50%.) Thus the *P*-value will be larger in a one-sample test of a proportion and smaller in a two-sample test.

A chi-square test of independence (or homogeneity) will have a *P*-value double that of the one-sided two-sample *t*-test, or .5940.

c. Taking the results from any of the tests at face value, you must conclude that it is quite easy just by chance to get a difference this size in the proportions of workers in the two age groups who were laid off.

D15. In general, the test for Youth Enterprises will be more likely to detect the discrimination. To see this, consider how the standard errors used in the two tests will compare. Each will contain a factor of the form

$$\sqrt{\frac{1}{n_1} + \frac{1}{n_2}}$$

where n_1 is the number of younger workers and n_2 is the number of older workers. Because the total number of workers is fixed at 50, you can check by trial and error that the standard error will be smallest when the numbers of older and younger workers are equal. Alternatively, graph

$$y = \frac{1}{x} + \frac{1}{50 - x}$$

and note that $x = 25$ gives the smallest value of *y*. To use calculus, minimize

$$\frac{1}{n_1} + \frac{1}{50 - n_1}$$

by setting the derivative equal to 0,

$$0 = \frac{-1}{n_1^2} + \frac{1}{(50 - n_1)^2}$$

and solve to get $n_1 = 25$.

Lesson Notes: Checking Conditions

Discussion

D16. The conditions for a two-sample test for the difference of two proportions are listed on page 468 of the student text. The only condition that is met is that the expected frequencies are all at least 5. You do not even have two separate populations, let alone two independent random samples.

However, it does seem reasonable to conclude that if Westvaco picked 28 of its 50 employees completely at random for layoff, it is reasonably likely to get 21 or more in the 40 or older age group. The statistical evidence so far does not provide evidence for Martin's case for discrimination.

As will be discussed later, the situation actually calls for a randomization test (as in Chapter 1) or Fisher's exact test. However, a two-sample test works well as an approximation of those methods.

D17. It is true that the test is based on a probability model, that the model assumes that outcomes are randomly selected, and that in reality the outcomes were not random. This does not make use of the significance test invalid, however. The test can be used to answer this question: "If the process of selecting workers for layoff had been random, how likely would it be to get a difference in proportions laid off as big as Westvaco got between older and younger workers?" As long as it is made clear that this is the question being answered, the test is quite valid.

Thus, this is not a reason to suspect the validity of a significance test. Often, the null hypothesis in a significance test is that the data look like a random sample from some population. We are testing to see whether the data production process was equivalent to selecting people for layoff at random, at least with respect to age.

Lesson Notes: Cutoff Age

Practice

P14. Here's the five-number summary and the boxplot.

$$\text{Min} = 22 \qquad Q_1 = 37 \qquad \text{Median} = 53$$
$$Q_3 = 56 \qquad \text{Max} = 69$$

There are no outliers because there are no observations beyond $1.5 \cdot IQR = (1.5 \cdot 19)$ from the nearest quartile.

Two aspects of the shape stand out. First, the distribution is bimodal, with one peak

in the low 30s and a second, higher peak in the upper 50s. (Various explanations are possible. Perhaps the two peaks represent major recruiting and hiring efforts at two different times, one recent and the other quite far in the past. Alternatively, perhaps the two peaks were caused by a large number of resignations, terminations, and transfers of workers whose ages put them in the gap between the two peaks.) Note that the boxplot can't show the bimodality.

A second important feature of the shape is that the distribution is skewed toward the low values. (Compared to many departments and companies, the work force in the engineering department tended to have more older workers than younger ones.)

P15. With 40 as the cutoff, 36 of 50, or 72%, of the workers are in the older age group. With 50 as the cutoff, 28 of 50, or 56%, are in the older age group.

P16.

| | | **Terminated?** | | | |
		No	Yes	Total	Percentage Terminated
Age	**Under 50**	13	9	22	40.91
	50 or Older	9	19	28	67.86
	Total	22	28	50	

P17. *Check conditions.* The conditions for a test of the difference of two proportions are not met because you do not have two independent random samples from two large populations. However, using this test as an approximation is justified with hypotheses as stated next.

State your hypotheses.

H_0: The difference in the proportion of workers laid off who were under 50 and the proportion of workers laid off who were 50 or older is no larger than you would expect if Westvaco were picking 28 people at random for layoff.

H_a: The difference is larger than reasonably can be explained by chance alone.

Compute the test statistic and draw a sketch.
The *z*-statistic is

$$z = \frac{\frac{19}{28} - \frac{9}{22}}{\sqrt{(.56)(.44)\left(\frac{1}{28} + \frac{1}{22}\right)}} \approx 1.9055$$

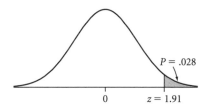

P = .028

0   *z* = 1.91

This has a one-tailed *P*-value of .02836. A difference in proportions of .270 or larger would occur by chance less than 3 times out of 100.

Write a conclusion in context. Reject the null hypothesis. If Westvaco were picking people at random to lay off, a difference of .270 between the proportion of people 50 or older who were laid off and the proportion of people under 50 who were laid off is not reasonably likely to occur. This doesn't prove Westvaco was discriminating, but it gives reasonable cause to ask them to justify their process for deciding who got laid off.

Discussion

D18. Using 50 as a cutoff leads to much stronger evidence in support of a claim of discrimination. Students may not agree about which choice, 40 or 50, is more informative, but this much is clear: The test using 50 as the cutoff age reveals a very clear-cut pattern that is not detected by the test using 40.

Note: Students often ask whether the fact that age 40 or older is the protected class means that that is where the cutoff must be made. The answer is no. For example, suppose there is a company that has 100 40-year-olds and 100 60-year-olds doing exactly the same job and they lay off all of the 60-year-olds and none of the 40-year-olds. A 60-year-old is in the protected class and would be able to make a very good case of age discrimination.

D19. a. Neither test so far meets the criterion established by the Supreme Court, although

the second test (in P17) comes very close with a one-sided *P*-value of .028.

b. Option I is true.

c. A Type I error, if the null hypothesis is true.

d. A Type II error would be deciding that a company does not discriminate on the basis of age when, in fact, it does.

Note that the probability of a Type II error depends on how virulent the discrimination at a guilty company happens to be. Even for the most extreme forms of discrimination, in which employees are automatically laid off in order of age, starting with the oldest, the chance of a Type II error can be nearly 100%, if the number of employees is small or if the number laid off is small.

Lesson Notes: Looking for a Better Approach

Practice

P18. The shapes of the distributions of ages are similar: somewhat skewed toward the smaller ages. The spread of the ages of those terminated is slightly greater than for those retained. What the plot makes clear, however, is that the average age of those terminated is higher than the average age of those retained.

```
       Retained |   | Terminated
                | 2 | 2  3
           9  5 | · |
        4  2  1 | 3 | 0  1  2  3
           8  7 | · | 5
              2 | 4 | 2
  8  8  8  8  7 | · | 9
        4  4  3 | 5 | 0  2  3  3  4
     9  7  6  5 | · | 5  5  5  5  6  6  9  9
           1  0 | 6 | 1  3  4  4
                | · | 6  9
```

P19. Here are the five-number summaries needed to make the boxplots.

	Min	Q_1	Median	Q_3	Max
Terminated	22	38.5	54.5	59	69
Retained	25	37	48	55	61

There are no outliers because there are no values more than 1.5 *IQR*s beyond the nearest quartile. The impression of the shapes, centers, and spreads of the two distributions is the same as that from the back-to-back stemplot.

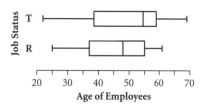

T = Terminated
R = Retained

P20. Students will discuss how to state the hypotheses and conclusion in D21. For now, they should understand that the difference in the mean ages is not statistically significant but they may not be sure what hypotheses and conclusion in context are appropriate.

State your hypotheses. The null hypothesis is that the difference in the mean age of workers laid off and the mean age of workers retained is no larger than you would expect if Westvaco were picking the 28 people at random for layoff. This should be a one-sided test, so the alternate hypothesis is that the difference in the mean age of workers laid off and the mean age of those retained is larger than you would expect if people were selected at random for layoff.

Compute the test statistic and draw a sketch. The test statistic is

$$t = \frac{\bar{x}_1 - \bar{x}_2}{\sqrt{\dfrac{s_1^2}{n_1} + \dfrac{s_2^2}{n_2}}} = \frac{49.86 - 46.18}{\sqrt{\dfrac{13.40^2}{28} + \dfrac{11.00^2}{22}}} \approx 1.066$$

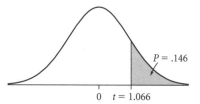

The approximate *df* is 47.89, which gives a *P*-value of .146.

Write a conclusion in context. Do not reject the null hypothesis. If 28 workers were selected totally at random to be laid off, then it is reasonably likely to get a difference of $49.86 - 46.18 = 3.68$ years or more in the average age of employees laid off minus the average age of the employees retained. Taking the results of the test at face value, the

conclusion is that although the pattern is consistent with what you would expect to see if discrimination were present, the *P*-value is not small enough to satisfy the criterion (.025) set by the Supreme Court.

Lesson Notes: Conditions for a *t*-Test

Discussion

D20. Make up a deck of 50 cards with the ages of all Westvaco employees. Shuffle the deck and draw out 28 cards to represent the ages of employees laid off under the null hypothesis of no age discrimination. Repeat this process many times. The average age of those laid off was 49.89. It will tend to fall among the larger values in the distribution of average age of those selected by chance alone.

D21. ***State your hypotheses.*** The null hypothesis is that the difference in the ages of those terminated and those retained is similar to what you would get by writing the names of all 50 employees on cards and drawing 28 of them to terminate. The alternate hypothesis is that the difference (average age of those terminated minus average age of those retained) is too large to reasonably attribute to a random process like that described.

Write a conclusion in context. If Westvaco were selecting 28 employees entirely at random out of the 50 employed for termination, the probability of getting a difference of 3.68 years in the average age of those terminated minus the average age of those retained is about .146. (Note that seeing a difference greater than 3.68 years in the difference of means has the same probability as seeing a mean age of those laid off greater than 49.86.) Therefore, you can't reject the hypothesis that the selection process was equivalent to drawing names at random.

D22. As noted in the answer to P14, the shape clearly departs from normal in two ways: it is bimodal, and it is skewed toward low values. Because the *t*-test depends on averages, the bimodality will not be a problem: The *average* for random samples of size 22 or 28 from a bimodal population like the one here will not itself have a markedly bimodal distribution. (Some ages used to compute the sample average will come from the lower cluster of ages, others will come from the upper cluster, and the averaging process will fill in the gap.) Skewness is potentially a bit more of a problem, although the fact that here both sample sizes are above 20 and are roughly equal is reassuring. On balance, the departures from normality seem comparatively mild.

Lesson Notes: Reduction over Time

Discussion

D23. Here's what may be the simplest explanation: The steep drops in Rounds 1 and 2 for workers aged 50 or older are consistent with a decision process that shows strongest bias against older workers in the early rounds. In later rounds, very few older workers remain (those in key positions, say, or those with unusual ability or particularly valuable knowledge based on years of experience). Thus, it has become difficult to find other older workers to lay off, so younger workers become more likely (than previously) to be targeted for layoff. This logic suggests that earlier rounds are more informative because there are fewer constraints when there are more employees to choose from. Therefore, the analysis that treats each round separately is better—more informative—than one that lumps all five rounds together.

Notes

Notes

Key Curriculum Press

Innovators in Mathematics Education

Comment Form

Please take a moment to provide us with feedback about this book. We are eager to read any comments or suggestions you may have. Once you've filled out this form, simply fold it along the dotted lines and drop it in the mail. We'll pay the postage. Thank you!

Your Name _____

School _____

School Address _____

City/State/Zip _____

Phone _____

Book Title _____

Please list any comments you have about this book.

_____
_____
_____
_____
_____
_____
_____
_____
_____
_____
_____

Do you have any suggestions for improving the student or teacher material?

_____
_____
_____
_____
_____
_____
_____
_____

To request a catalog, or place an order, call us toll free at 800-995-MATH, or send a fax to 800-541-2242. For more information, visit Key's website at www.keypress.com.

Please detach page, fold on lines and tape edge.